Integers

The system of integers can be viewed as an enlargement of the set of whole numbers.

Set of Integers
..., −4, −3, −2, −1, 0, 1, 2, 3, 4, 5, ...
Negative integers   Zero   Positive integers

Extending the number system to include integers provides a solution to equations such as $3 + \Box = 1$ and $6 - 8 = \Box$. Also, the negative integers provide an *additive inverse*. That is, $4 + \Box = 0$; the number -4 is the additive inverse of $+4$ since $+4 + -4 = 0$ and zero is the identity element for addition.

An integer must fit into one and only one of the following classifications. Integer (m) equals zero; or (m) is positive; or $(-m)$ is positive.

The properties for whole numbers also hold true for integers. In addition to the properties, the system of integers has closure for the operation of subtraction. That is, when an integer is subtracted from another integer, the difference is an integer.

Rational numbers

Rational numbers have the same properties as whole numbers. There are several other ideas that are important to thinking concerning rational numbers.

(1) The denominator may never be 0 because $\frac{5}{0}$ can be interpreted as 5 divided by 0, and division with zero as a divisor is undefined since if $\frac{5}{0} = \Box$ then $\Box \times 0 = 5$ and there is no unique number which will fulfill this necessary limitation.

(2) The rational numbers are *closed* with respect to division. The system of integers does not provide an answer to $3 \times \Box = 2$ or $2 \div 3 = \Box$. Development of rational numbers allows an answer to these types of mathematical sentences because $3 \times \frac{2}{3} = 2$ and $2 \div 3 = \frac{2}{3}$.

(3) If the cross-products of two fractions are equal, they are equivalent fractions (they name the same rational number). Thus, $\frac{3}{4} = \frac{6}{8}$ because $24 = 24$.

(4) Fractions can be renamed by multiplying the numerator and the denominator by the same whole number. Thus, $\frac{5}{5} \times \frac{3}{5} = \frac{15}{25}$; $\frac{15}{25} = \frac{3}{5}$. This is because $\frac{5}{5}$ is another name for $\frac{1}{1}$ which is the identity element of multiplication.

(5) The identity element for addition of rational numbers is zero. Zero can be named by any of the set of fractions $\left\{ \frac{0}{1}, \frac{0}{2}, \frac{0}{3}, \frac{0}{4}, ..., \frac{0}{N} \right\}$.

(6) The rationals provide a *multiplicative inverse*. That is, $\frac{2}{3} \times \Box = 1$; the number $\frac{3}{2}$ is the multiplicative inverse for $\frac{2}{3}$ since $\frac{2}{3} \times \frac{3}{2} = 1$ and one is the identity element for multiplication.

372.7   69027
R44g

DATE DUE		
Apr 8 70		
Mar21'73		
Apr 19'80		
GAYLORD M-2		PRINTED IN U.S.A.

DISCARDED

Guiding discovery in
elementary school mathematics

Guiding discovery in elementary school mathematics

C. ALAN RIEDESEL

The Pennsylvania State University

APPLETON - CENTURY - CROFTS

Division of Meredith Corporation

New York

To Ardeth and Our Five

PREFACE

The recent "revolution" in the mathematical content offered to pupils in the elementary school and the continued "evolution" of teaching procedures for developing mathematical understandings pose a real challenge to the elementary school teacher. Two major goals—the improvement of the mathematical background of teachers and the improvement of teaching procedures used by teachers—must be attained if curricular improvement in elementary school mathematics is to become a reality.

Numerous books have recently been published which focus on the improvement of the background of pre-service and in-service elementary school teachers. Also, there is a trend for colleges and universities throughout the nation to require from three to twelve semester hours of content mathematics which is designed especially for the prospective elementary school teacher.

As the gap in the mathematical background of the elementary teacher is closed, it becomes increasingly important that close attention be directed to the approach to teaching used with modern mathematics. At present there is a lack of materials which give the teacher specific help in facilitating pupil discovery while teaching topics in modern mathematics.

The purpose of this book is to provide prospective and in-service elementary school teachers with illustrative situations that make use of modern mathematical content and ideas to develop a guided discovery approach to teaching mathematics in the elementary school.

Many decisions had to be made concerning the blending of mathematical preciseness with readability. Thus, on occasions when the meaning is clear, a term such as "multi-digit multiplication" is used rather than "multiplication of numbers represented by multi-digit numerals." The writer is grateful to Frank Kocher and Ward Bouwsma of the Mathematics Department of The Pennsylvania State University for their reading of the manuscript from a mathematical standpoint and for the suggestions they gave.

The author is indebted to many other persons for their aid during various stages of the development. Marilyn Suydam and Cecil Trueblood, in addition to undergraduate and graduate class members, gave helpful suggestions on presentation. Special thanks are due members of undergraduate and graduate classes for their pertinent comments. Aid in indexing was given by Marion Baxter and Mark Riedesel. Mrs. Kathryn Little gave valuable editorial assistance.

Finally, the writer wishes to thank Herbert F. Spitzer of the University of Iowa for arousing the writer's interest in inductive approaches to teaching elementary school mathematics.

C. A. R.

CONTENTS

*Guiding discovery in
elementary school mathematics*

1

The changing elementary school mathematics curriculum

Each generation of pupils and teachers has experienced changes in the content of school courses and in the approaches used to teach those courses. The present generation is no different, and some of the greatest changes are occurring in the mathematics curriculum. As recently as 1956 it would have been possible to say, "The curriculum in elementary school mathematics has not changed notably in the past twenty years. The major changes since 1936 have been in the *approach* to teaching the subject." Today this is not true. Since 1956 the grade level at which topics are introduced has been modified, and new subject matter has been included in the curriculum. Also, changes in teaching procedures, which have been steadily evolving since the early 1930's, are now more widely accepted.

A VISIT TO TWO CLASSROOMS

A picture of the change in teaching procedures can be developed by visiting two elementary school classrooms of today. The pupils are studying a topic that is new to the elementary school. One teacher makes use of an explanatory approach to teaching, while the other uses a form of "guided discovery" approach. The topic selected as an illustration is "clock" or "modular" arithmetic. This topic was not selected because of its cruciality to the elementary school mathematics program, but rather because a topic that is not "standard" may better lend itself to analysis and comparison.

Explanatory pattern

The teacher gave each class member a dittoed table of the addition combinations in modulo 12. She said, "Notice that this addition table differs from the regular addition table. It corresponds to addition on the clock. You can see from the table that $5 + 8 = 1$. This is because with a clock when you

1

+	1	2	3	4	5	6	7	8	9	10	11	12
1	2	3	4	5	6	7	8	9	10	11	12	1
2	3	4	5	6	7	8	9	10	11	12	1	2
3	4	5	6	7	8	9	10	11	12	1	2	3
4	5	6	7	8	9	10	11	12	1	2	3	4
5	6	7	8	9	10	11	12	1	2	3	4	5
6	7	8	9	10	11	12	1	2	3	4	5	6
7	8	9	10	11	12	1	2	3	4	5	6	7
8	9	10	11	12	1	2	3	4	5	6	7	8
9	10	11	12	1	2	3	4	5	6	7	8	9
10	11	12	1	2	3	4	5	6	7	8	9	10
11	12	1	2	3	4	5	6	7	8	9	10	11
12	1	2	3	4	5	6	7	8	9	10	11	12

count 8 hours from 5 o'clock you arrive at 1 o'clock." The teacher then demonstrated this on a model clock. She also explained several addition combinations on this clock.

Next the teacher drew a number line on the chalkboard and stated, "You can use a modification of the number line to solve clock arithmetic problems. I'll show you. If you wanted to find 6 + 8 in clock arithmetic you would start at 6 and then move ahead 8 spaces (demonstrates on number line). Today

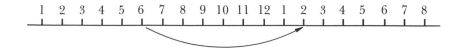

we are going to work with this system. Make use of the table or number line to work the material on the practice sheet."

PRACTICE SHEET

Clock Arithmetic: Make use of the table to find your answer. You may also use the number line or the clock pictured below.

$$5 + 9 = \square$$
$$7 + 10 = \square$$
$$9 + 8 = \square$$
$$4 + 3 = \square$$

On the second day the teacher said, "You can see that in clock arithmetic we do not have a zero symbol. Notice that even though we don't have a 0, the 12 acts in the same way as 0. For example, $8 + 12$ in clock arithmetic equals 8. Thus, 12 acts in the same way 0 does in our system. You could exchange 0 for 12 and still use the clock arithmetic system. In this case 0 would be at the top of the clock.

After the class had corrected the previous day's assignment, the teacher said, "It is important to see mathematical relationships. Look at your addition table while I explain several of the more important relationships.

"First, addition using clock arithmetic is commutative. The order of the addends does not affect the sum. Notice that when we add $8 + 4$ we get the same answer as when we add $4 + 8$. Also, notice that when the table is folded from the upper left-hand corner to the lower right-hand corner, both sides match. This is typical of the table for an operation that is commutative. Look at each of the rows. You should see that the numerals follow a "one-more" sequence across each row. Now look down each column. You should be able to see that there is a one-more sequence down each column.

"On occasions we may want to subtract using clock arithmetic. Watch as I work a subtraction example using the demonstration clock and then show you how to use the table when subtracting. Using the demonstration clock, you can see that to subtract I move the hand counterclockwise. Watch as I take $8 - 4$.

"Now on the table—you should think of finding an addition sentence to replace your subtraction sentence. We can write $8 - 4 = \square$ as the addition

+	1	2	3	4	5	6	7	8	9	10	11	12
1	2	3	4	5	6	7	8	9	10	11	12	1
2	3	4	5	6	7	8	9	10	11	12	1	2
3	4	5	6	7	8	9	10	11	12	1	2	3
4	5	6	7	8	9	10	11	12	1	2	3	4
5	6	7	8	9	10	11	12	1	2	3	4	5
6	7	8	9	10	11	12	1	2	3	4	5	6
7	8	9	10	11	12	1	2	3	4	5	6	7
8	9	10	11	12	1	2	3	4	5	6	7	8
9	10	11	12	1	2	3	4	5	6	7	8	9
10	11	12	1	2	3	4	5	6	7	8	9	10
11	12	1	2	3	4	5	6	7	8	9	10	11
12	1	2	3	4	5	6	7	8	9	10	11	12

situation $4 + \square = 8$. Now if you look for the 4 in the left-hand column and then move over to the 8, you can see that directly above the 8 is 4. Thus $8 - 4 = 4$."

During the remaining portion of the period the teacher directed her pupils to prove that the commutative property for addition was true for clock arithmetic and gave the class members several examples to verify the associative property.

The time spent on a topic such as modular arithmetic will vary with the local instructional program, the mathematical level of the class, and enthusiasm. Further work on subtraction, development of multiplication and division, and work on modular systems other than 12 could be continued. A modulo 7 or "everyday arithmetic" might be used, as might modulo 2 or modulo 4. The teacher using an explanatory approach would continue to explain each step to the pupils before giving them an opportunity to work problems and exercises. Wide use would be made of the chalkboard, number line, and flannel board for the teacher's demonstrations and explanations.

Guided discovery pattern

The teacher who used the guided discovery pattern began the study of clock arithmetic by giving each pupil a duplicated sheet containing the following verbal problems:

1. A 10-hour countdown is planned for a rocket launching. If the countdown begins at 5 in the morning and there are no delays, at what time will the rocket be launched?

2. The Martin family is planning a Labor Day weekend trip to Washington, D.C. They plan to leave at 9 in the evening to avoid the holiday traffic. At what time will they arrive in Washington if the trip takes them 5 hours?

The first problem was read orally by the teacher; then she said, "Solve the problem and then show that your answer is correct by solving it in another manner. If you finish early, try to develop a diagram or explanation that you think would help someone having trouble with the problem." After the pupils had started to work, the teacher moved about the room noting various techniques used to solve the problem. She gave aid to individuals having difficulty getting started by asking questions such as "Can you think of a mathematical sentence you could use to solve the problem?" "What type of diagram could you use?"

When the majority of the class had finished the first problem and started on the second, the teacher asked several individuals to put their solutions on the chalkboard. When they had finished writing on the board she said, "Let's stop for a minute and discuss the first problem. Larry, please tell us how you worked it."

Larry: I knew that I had to add 10 hours to 5. The answers was 15. We don't usually say 15 o'clock, so I thought 5 plus 7 equals 12, and there are 3 hours beyond 12. The answer would be 3 in the afternoon.

$$\text{Mathematical Sentence: } 5 + 10 = \square$$
$$5 + (7 + 3) = (5 + 7) + 3 = \square$$
$$12 + 3 = 3$$

Nancy: At first I added $5 + 10$ and got an answer of 15. We don't express time this way so I tried drawing a clock face with an hour hand. (I didn't need the minute hand because we were dealing only with hours.) Then I began at 5 and counted 10 hours. My answer came out 3. The rocket would be launched at 3 in the afternoon.

Jim: I followed about the same thinking as Larry and Nancy, but I didn't want to draw a circle. Instead, I made a "clock number line" and started over with 1 when I moved beyond 12.

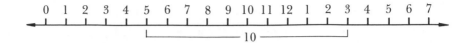

Following class discussion of the problem-solving methods used, the teacher asked, "How does the addition we're doing using the clock compare with regular addition?" The pupils offered several suggestions such as "We only use 12 numerals." "We get an answer that is between 1 and 12." "It's the same until we get an answer larger than 12; then we start over." Next the teacher asked, "What could we use to help us quickly find an answer to an addition or subtraction combination using clock arithmetic?" The students

+	1	2	3	4	5	6	7	8	9	10	11	12
1												
2												
3												
4												
5									2	3		
6												
7												
8												
9					2							
10												
11												11
12												

suggested that a table might be constructed or that they might write down all of the combinations and learn them. After a short discussion it was agreed that the first suggestion was the more feasible since this type of computation is not used often enough to justify memorizing the facts. The pupils were each given a copy of the table on page 6 with instructions to fill in the missing numerals.

The class was directed to work on the table during study time. The teacher also suggested that they try to find ways of saving time in developing the table, that they compare the completed table with the regular addition table, and that they try to find a means of using the table for subtraction by looking for patterns.

On the second day, a completed table was projected on the wall with an overhead projector. (It could have been drawn on the chalkboard.) The teacher asked, "Did you find any differences between this table and the regular addition table other than those we mentioned yesterday?" One student said, "Yes, I noticed that we don't have 0 in this table. That seemed funny to me." Several other pupils stated that they also had noticed the absence of 0.

The teacher asked, "How did we get along without 0? Think out your explanation clearly while we give the others a chance to get an answer." After a short pause several class members gave their ideas concerning the lack of a zero symbol. They explained that while the numeral 0 did not appear in the table, 12 acted in the same way as 0. It was also suggested (and demonstrated by one pupil) that it would be possible to exchange 0 for 12 and still use the system. The other questions posed on the previous day by the teacher were discussed. Pupils made the following remarks:

John: I saved time in filling out the table when I noticed the diagonal pattern running from the lower left-hand side to the upper right-hand side. The numerals in each line are the same.

Ann: I noticed that if a diagonal line were drawn from the upper left-hand corner to the bottom right-hand corner and the paper folded along that line, both sides would match.

Jill: Each numeral appears once and only once in each row across and up and down.

Mike: The numerals follow a one-more sequence across each row and down each column.

Chris: It doesn't make any difference; start at 6 and add 3, or start at 3 and add 6.

Kim: The number value jumps by 2's down the diagonals.

Carl: On any diagonal drawn from the lower left to the upper right the same numeral repeats.

+	1	2	3	4	5	6	7	8	9	10	11	12
1	2	3	4	5	6	7	8	9	10	11	12	1
2	3	4	5	6	7	8	9	10	11	12	1	2
3	4	5	6	7	8	9	10	11	12	1	2	3
4	5	6	7	8	9	10	11	12	1	2	3	4
5	6	7	8	9	10	11	12	1	2	3	4	5
6	7	8	9	10	11	12	1	2	3	4	5	6
7	8	9	10	11	12	1	2	3	4	5	6	7
8	9	10	11	12	1	2	3	4	5	6	7	8
9	10	11	12	1	2	3	4	5	6	7	8	9
10	11	12	1	2	3	4	5	6	7	8	9	10
11	12	1	2	3	4	5	6	7	8	9	10	11
12	1	2	3	4	5	6	7	8	9	10	11	12

Paul: You asked if we could subtract with the table. We can think of subtraction as finding the answer to a mathematical sentence such as $9 - 5 = \square$ and $5 + \square = 9$. If you start at 5 on the left and move over to the 9, the answer is the number on the top row above the 9. This is true because subtraction is undoing addition.

The teacher encouraged the pupils to continue to look for patterns. Then she asked, "What properties do we know to hold true in whole number addition?" The pupils stated that (1) a change in the order of the addends does not change the sum: $6 + 7 = 7 + 6$ (the commutative property of addition); and (2) that when adding more than two numbers (for example, three numbers), the first two could be grouped and added and this sum added to the third, or the second and the third could be grouped and added and this sum added to the first: $5 + 6 + 9 = (5 + 6) + 9 = 5 + (6 + 9)$ (the associative property of addition).

The next question posed was, "Will these properties always hold true for clock arithmetic? Can you prove this?" The work that followed gave the pupils an opportunity to prove by checking all cases that the commutative property held true. This was demonstrated by folding the table from the upper left-hand corner to the lower right-hand corner. The class decided that while all cases of the associative property could be checked in clock arithmetic, the time to do so would exceed the value derived. The remainder of the period was spent in continuing the search for patterns and in working several verbal problems and exercises provided on a worksheet.

The teacher developed the same content as that of the explanatory approach for the remaining days. However, she continued to pose questions and to draw out the thinking of the pupils.

Analysis

It is obvious that no one teacher makes exclusive use of explanatory procedures while another uses only discovery procedures. By the very nature of teaching, some aspects of each approach are used. However, it should be noted that many teachers tend to emphasize one of the two approaches. Also, not all superior teaching procedures are related to the issues of "teacher telling" as opposed to "pupil discovery." The comments that follow attempt to accomplish two things: (1) to point out differences between the "explanatory" and "discovery" procedures used in the preceding lessons and/or other lessons to follow; and (2) to point out several suggestions for teaching arithmetic which are considered effective but are not tied to either method.

The guided discovery pattern is one of active learning. Rather than waiting for the teacher to tell them "what" and "how," the students attempt to "discover" a solution by themselves. If a pupil is not able to solve a problem for himself, the teacher comes to his aid with a question or a comment designed to provide insight. Actively involved in the learning process, the student is more likely to be attentive. The pupil's role in the explanatory approach requires that he listen rather than act. Often the pupil is not sure whether or not he needs to listen to what the teacher is saying. Thus, he may give the teacher's explanation half-hearted attention.

The guided discovery approach stresses building new knowledge on the foundations of past experience. This approach is of value to students in social situations as well as in academic endeavors. It also closely resembles the approach taken by mathematicians and scientists. Pupils taught by the explanatory method have a tendency to see if they can find a teacher or a book that will answer any questions they have. Thus, they are much more intellectually dependent in problem-solving situations.

Because the guided discovery method stresses pupil thinking, the classroom is pupil-centered. The teacher must ask the right question at the right time; to do this she must understand the pupils. The explanatory approach fosters a classroom climate in which the teacher is the font of all wisdom.

Pupils wait for the teacher to "say" what *she* thinks before they think or form opinions.

The discovery approach stresses a search for relationships and patterns and leads to an understanding of mathematical structure. Such insight is valuable at all levels of mathematics. Patterns pointed out by the teacher tend to be sensed rather than understood.

As was previously stated, no teacher uses one approach exclusively. Thus, there are several procedures which can be used with either a discovery or an explanatory approach. Some of the best include:

Verbal problems.   Such problem situations are effective for introducing new topics, for they provide the student with a physical world model from which he is to abstract mathematical ideas. They also identify a use of the material. When a student sees a need or use for the phase of mathematics being taught, his motivation to learn is heightened.

Multiple methods of solution.   The use of several methods of solving a problem or an exercise is helpful in several ways. (a) It allows for individual differences in approach and level of abstract thinking; one child can count to find the answer to an addition problem, while a more advanced pupil can think the answer. (b) It develops self-confidence; pupils are better able to attack new material when they have developed several methods of approaching mathematical situations. (c) It leads to several solutions, encouraging the kind of pupil discussion and debate valuable for developing mathematical thinking.

Comparisons.   Both teaching patterns described above emphasized making comparisons between the modular system and whole number addition. Such comparisons aid the pupils to gain deeper insight into the number system.

In addition, the teacher may use materials such as the number line and the abacus to develop mathematical understanding.

The preceding vignette and analysis touched briefly upon two approaches to the teaching of elementary school mathematics which are in use today. Certainly these short summaries are not exhaustive. In the chapters that follow, an attempt will be made to highlight a guided discovery approach to other areas of the mathematics curriculum. Also, procedures and materials which may be incorporated into other instructional plans will be suggested.

DEVELOPMENT OF THE CONTEMPORARY ELEMENTARY SCHOOL MATHEMATICS CURRICULUM

In early colonial days schools existed only in towns and in the more densely settled districts. Even in the communities where school was held, the study of mathematics was often not pursued. If taught, mathematics usually consisted simply of learning to count and to perform the fundamental operations with whole numbers. "Ciphering" was the principal mathematics taught in schools during colonial times, and the freshman mathematics course at Harvard College went no further than an eighth- or ninth-grade course of today. Very seldom was arithmetic taught to girls.

The early textbooks, which were imported from England, were single copies for the "master"; the students copied problems and exercises from the master's book into copy books. The first arithmetic written by an American author and printed in the United States is believed to have been *Arithmetic, Vulgar and Decimal,* 1729, by Isaac Greenwood of Harvard College. Greenwood's book received little publicity, and consequently the first influential book published in this country was the arithmetic of Nicholas Pike, published in 1788. This book was very popular during the late 1700's and early 1800's. Its major competition was a book written in England by Thomas Dilworth and first published in 1744. During the early 1800's two American arithmetic books, *The School Master's Assistant* by Nathan Daboll and *The Scholar's Arithmetic* by Daniel Adams, were introduced. These, along with Pike's book, dominated the field.

The approach taken by these early authors was (1) to state a rule, and (2) to give several examples with explanation (steps in computation, not meaning). Their works dealt extensively with changing English money to Federal money, since the transition from the old to the new currency caused merchants many problems. Study of verbal problems in such textbooks reveal much concerning the activities of the day. The following problems are typical.[1]

Supposing a man's income to be 2555 dollars a year; how much is that per day, there being 365 days in a year? Ans. 7 dollars.

In 671 eagles, at 10 dollars each, how many shillings, three-pences, pence and farthings? Ans. 40260 shill, 161040 three-pences, and 1932480 qrs.[2]

At the late Census, taken A.D. 1800, the number of Inhabitants in the New-England States was as follows, viz. Newhampshire 183858; Massachusetts, 422845; Maine, 151719; Rhode Island, 69122; Connecticut, 251002; Vermont, 154465; what was the number of inhabitants at that time in New England? Ans. 1233011 inhabitants.

In the period between 1815 and 1820 American educators began to revise their methods of teaching arithmetic. This reform was based on the philosophy of Joseph Pestalozzi, a Swiss educational reformer whose ideas were gaining great popularity in Europe and whose works in translation were beginning to appear in America. One of the first to adopt the ideas of Pestalozzi was Warren Colburn in his *First Lessons in Intellectual Arithmetic,* published in 1821. Rather than follow the then typical question-and-answer

---

[1] Daniel Adams, *The Scholar's Arithmetic of Federal Accounting* (Montpelier, Vermont: Printed by Wright & Sibley for John Prentiss, 1812).
[2] Note that the comma was not used in expressions such as 183858.

approach in which a question such as "What is arithmetic?" was asked and
an answer such as "Arithmetic is the art or science of computing by numbers,
either whole or in fraction" was given, Colburn asked questions such as
"How many thumbs have you on your right hand?" "How many on your
left?" "How many on both together?" The explanation was left up to the
student. The preface to Colburn's first book contains the following suggestions for teaching arithmetic:[3]

> Every combination commences with practical examples. Care has been taken to
> select such as will aptly illustrate the combination and assist the imagination of the
> pupil in performing it. In most instances, immediately after the practical, abstract
> examples are placed. . . . The examples are to be performed in the mind, or by means
> of sensible objects, such as beans, nuts, etc. The pupil should first perform the
> examples in his own way and then be made to observe and tell how he did them,
> and why he did them so.

Colburn's inductive approach influenced the later writings of Adams, who
included both reasoning and rules.

A. W. Grube of Germany, another follower of Pestalozzi, developed a
program which became popular in the eastern United States in the middle
1800's. He made use of objects in his approach but did not teach addition,
subtraction, multiplication, and division in order. Grube, instead, worked
with all four processes on very small numbers (usually 1 to 10) before proceeding on to larger numbers. Under the Grube system 3×3 was developed before $9 + 2$.[4] An inductive approach to teaching was advocated by followers of
Grube. In light of the curriculum changes today, it is interesting to note that
Grube suggested that geometry be a part of the mathematics program at all
grade levels.

Until the middle 1800's one book often served as the text for the entire
arithmetic program. During the late 1800's the number of books required to
cover the curriculum increased from one or two to four or five. Often the
entire grade school program was incorporated in two books on mental arithmetic (non-pencil and paper) and three books on written arithmetic. The
majority of books at this time did not systematically introduce topics at the
appropriate grade level.

Because many of the teachers of this period were unable to capture the
spirit of either Colburn's or Grube's approach, these two reformers exerted
far less influence than their ideas warranted. The majority of writers and
teachers of the middle and late 1800's believed mathematics helped to train
the mind (mental discipline), just as they believed Latin trained the mind.
In his arithmetic books, which were very popular during this era, Joseph

---

[3] Warren Colburn, *First Lessons* (Boston: Houghton Mifflin, 1884), pp. 209–210. Quote taken
from the reprint of the preface to the 1821 edition.
[4] For an example of programmed materials that teach all four operations with the
numbers 1 to 10 before dealing with larger numbers, see S. R. Meyer, "A Program
in Elementary Arithmetic: Present and Future," *Automatic Teaching: The State of
the Art,* E. H. Galanter, ed. (New York: Wiley, 1959), pp. 83–84.

Ray took this view. Ray[5] states, "Two objects are to be accomplished in the study of arithmetic, viz., the acquisition of a science necessary to the business of life, and a thorough course of mental discipline." While there were a few mathematicians who argued against "mental discipline," it was not rejected by the majority of mathematics educators until the early 1900's.

The first book specifically on the teaching of arithmetic was written by Edward Brooks. The book is well written and worth several hours of study by the student of elementary school mathematics. The reader may observe from the preface reprinted below that had the suggestions of Brooks been adopted in 1880, the teaching of mathematics would have improved at a more rapid rate. Brooks states:[6]

Progress in education is one of the most striking characteristics of this remarkable age. Never before was there so general an interest in the education of the people. The development of the intellectual resources of the nation has become an object of transcendent interest. Schools of all kinds and grades are multiplying in every section of the country; improved methods of training have been adopted; dull routine has given way to a healthy intellectual activity; instruction has become a science and teaching a profession.

This advance is reflected in, and, to a certain extent, has been pioneered by, the improvements in the teaching of arithmetic. Fifty years ago, arithmetic was taught as a mere collection of rules to be committed to memory and applied mechanically to the solution of problems. No reason for operation was given, none were required; and it was the privilege of only the favored few even to realize that there is any thought in the processes. Amidst this darkness a star arose in the East; that star was the mental arithmetic of Warren Colburn. It caught the eyes of a few of the wise men of the schools, and led them to the adoption of methods of teaching that have lifted the mind from the slavery of dull routine to the freedom of independent thought. Through the influence of this little book, arithmetic was transformed from a dry collection of mechanical processes into a subject full of life and interest. The spirit of analysis, suggested and developed in it, runs today like a golden thread through the whole science, giving simplicity and beauty to all its various parts. . . .

As can be noted, the spirit of Brooks approach is in keeping with many ideas proposed today.

The turn of the century ushered in the practices of using different textbooks for every two grades and then different textbooks for every grade. Probably the most influential writer on mathematics education in the early 1900's was David Eugene Smith, an exceptionally prolific writer. He authored elementary, secondary, and college textbooks for students; books on the teaching of elementary school and secondary school mathematics; and standard works on the history of mathematics. In 1913 Smith made the following suggestions concerning content and method in arithmetic:[7]

[5] Joseph Ray, *Practical Arithmetic, Ray's Arithmetic, Part Third*, rev. ed. (Cincinnati: Winthrop B. Smith & Co., 1853), p. iii.
[6] Edward Brooks, *The Philosophy of Arithmetic* (Lancaster, Pa.: Normal Publishing Co., 1880), preface.
[7] David Eugene Smith, *The Teaching of Arithmetic* (Boston: Ginn, 1913), p. 51. Quoting W. W. Hart.

. . . (1) that pupils begin with content (having first felt some sensible reason for approaching the subject); (2) that they then pass to a use of symbols, to be handled automatically when expediency demands it, employing a particular form of expression only because that form best expresses the thought held; (3) that they be encouraged in flexibility of expression as well as of thinking, the former, however, always being controlled by the latter; and (4) that they be given many opportunities to exercise choice and judgment in applying the knowledge gained in life situations.

Following the demise of "mental discipline," the stimulus-response explanation of learning, often called connectionism and usually credited to Edward Thorndike, was in vogue. Drill procedures were strongly emphasized. An example of the thinking of writers of the connectionist school in the field of elementary school mathematics is F. B. Knight's comments:[8] "Theoretically, the main psychological basis is a behavioristic one, viewing skills and habits as fabrics of connection." E. P. Cubberley states:[9]

In the field of methods, the new psychology has thrown much light on our teaching procedures. We know now the importance of learning of the formation of the right kind of mental connections, or bonds, and that right habit-formation is as important in the teaching of arithmetic as in action and conduct. We also have worked out definite procedures for the best types of practice and drill, and improvement can now proceed according to established rules.

Extreme and often faulty application of connectionism caused many arithmetic programs to be little more than endless drill exercises. Pupils knew that $7 \times 5 = 35$ because their teacher and their textbook had told them so. They had little idea of why this was true.

Along with the S-R approach, writers such as Knight and L. J. Brueckner placed much emphasis upon the study of the relative difficulty of various computational materials and the identification of unit skills to be mastered. These studies lead to practices such as introducing 7×3 a year before the introduction of 3×7. Such procedures vary greatly from the current emphasis upon the study of number relationships.

Social utility

From the 1920's through the middle 1950's many educators advocated that the topics in arithmetic be selected only from material used in daily life. Prominent in the social-utility movement were such writers as Wilson, Brueckner, and F. E. Grossnickle. Wilson states:[10] "Limiting grade work in arithmetic to the mastery of the socially useful not only will remove a great burden from the backs of children but will contribute to better

[8] National Society for the Study of Education, Part I, *Some Aspects of Modern Thought in Arithmetic*, Part II, *Research in Arithmetic*, Twenty-ninth Yearbook (Chicago: Distributed by the University of Chicago Press, 1930), p. 5.
[9] Ralph S. Newcomb, *Modern Methods of Teaching Arithmetic* (Boston: Houghton Mifflin, 1926), p. vii.
[10] From *Teaching the New Arithmetic,* 2nd. ed., by Guy Wilson and others, p. 12. Copyright © 1951. Used by permission of McGraw-Hill Book Company.

teaching and a better mental-hygiene program in the schoolroom." The students of Wilson conducted extensive studies upon the use of arithmetic in the lives of children and adults. From these studies Wilson made recommendations such as: the only fractions to be taught are the halves, fourths, thirds, eights, and sixteenths; and only operations on whole numbers should be mastered. The emphasis was upon use, with little thought given to the understanding of mathematics.

Meaning theory

In the middle 1930's many mathematics educators placed less stress on the S-R theory and adopted the Gestalt theory. The Gestaltists placed greater emphasis upon insight, relationships, interpretations, and principles than did the connectionists. One of the chief spokesmen for the "meaning theory," a field orientation, was William Brownell. He conducted significant studies which helped to establish the principle that pupil achievement in mathematics is better when the children understand the mathematical principles than when they learn only meaningless computational procedures. Over the years, evidence collected from further research has borne this out.

Discovery methods

Since the time of Socrates, some educators have advocated the use of provocative questions accompanied by pupil thinking and "discovery." The thread of inductive procedures has appeared, disappeared, and reappeared in mathematics teaching. It can be noted from the previous material that Warren Colburn advocated an approach that somewhat resembled the current discovery approach, but the thread was lost again until the middle 1930's when studies by McConnell[11] and Thiele[12] once again brought attention to inductive or discovery procedures in elementary school mathematics. Since 1938 Spitzer has worked on procedures which emphasize pupil discovery. His book on teaching arithmetic probably was the first to give practical procedures for the use of an inductive approach.[13]

The mathematics curriculum in ferment

The scientific advances of the twentieth century were heightened by the extensive governmental effort during World War II. During that time the layman became somewhat familiar with the large role that mathematics played in the development of the atomic bomb and of modern computer

[11] T. R. McConnell, *Discovery Versus Authoritative Identification in the Learning of Children,* University of Iowa Studies in Education (Iowa City: State University of Iowa, 1934), Vol. IX, No. 5.
[12] C. L. Thiele, "The Contribution of Generalization to the Learning of Addition Facts," Teachers College Contributions to Education, No. 763 (New York: Bureau of Publications, Teachers College, Columbia University, 1938).
[13] Herbert F. Spitzer, *The Teaching of Arithmetic,* 1st ed. (Boston: Houghton Mifflin, 1948).

Table 1-1.

PROJECT	ORIGIN	SPONSOR	DIRECTOR	PURPOSES OR OBJECTIVES	CONTENT	SPECIAL NOTES
SCHOOL MATHEMATICS STUDY GROUP (SMSG)	1958 (Jr. H.) 1960 (4-6) 1963 (K-3)	National Science Foundation (NSF)	Edwin Begle	Improvement of curriculum; skills plus deeper understanding of basic mathematical concepts and structure; provide better mathematical motivation; develop material for both pupils and teachers.	Sets; basic number properties; number operations and number theory including factors and primes; notation including exponents and numeration systems relationships; geometry: non-metric, measurement, and co-ordinate.	Designed to stimulate publishers and serve as a basis for developing criteria; a very influential program.
GREATER CLEVELAND MATHEMATICS PROGRAM (GCMP)	1959 (K-6)	Educational Research Council of Greater Cleveland	B. H. Gundlach (original) G. S. Cunningham	Development of a new mathematics curriculum for all children; emphasis is upon mathematical correctness and pedagogical soundness; logical structure through discovery approach; teaching sequence of problems followed by structural principles followed by symbolism.	Sets; basic number properties; number operations; number theory including factors and primes; notation including exponents and numeration systems relationships; geometry: non-metric, measurement, and co-ordinate.	Noteworthy for the in-service program; program places stress on continuity K-12.

Project	Year	Funding	Director	Objectives	Content	Notes
MINNESOTA SCHOOL MATHEMATICS CENTER (Minnemath)	1962	NSF	Paul Rosenbloom	To teach arithmetic geometrically; to make children familiar with algebra early; stress on inductive techniques and scientific applications.	Number line work; functions; numbers in frames; estimation; lattices; geometry.	A complete elementary school program is planned; stress placed on uses of mathematics in science.
UNIVERSITY OF ILLINOIS ARITHMETIC PROJECT	1958	Carnegie Corporation NSF	David Page	To find more and better content for elementary school mathematics; intuitive" approach to teaching; to develop in-service films.	Geometry: non-metric, measurement, co-ordinate; algebraic arithmetic; relationships.	Supplementary for children; enrichment program stressed; little stress on physical world settings.
MADISON PROJECT	1957	Sloan Fnd. Holzer Fnd. NSF Ford Fnd. U.S. Office of Educ.	Robert Davis	To improve the content of elementary school mathematics; to use an "intuitive" approach; to develop a theory of instruction; to provide in-service help for teachers.	Algebra (frame arithmetic); geometry; heavy emphasis upon co-ordinate geometry and graphing.	Supplemental and enrichment.
STANFORD PROJECTS Sets Geometry Logic	1959	NSF	Patrick Suppes Newton Hawley (geometry)	To develop basic concepts through the use of sets, geometry, and logic; to teach more mathematics; emphasis upon explanatory approach to teaching.	Sets and numbers; geometry for primary grades (non-metric and geometric construction); logic (for superior intermediate grade pupil).	Curriculum K-6 in progress; heavy emphasis is upon sets and set notation; logic program very formal.

technology. Postwar interest in science and mathematics has been heightened by the "Space Race." With the emphasis upon continuing as the world's scientific leader, the United States government and various private foundations have become interested in aiding mathematicians and mathematics educators in the improvement of mathematics programs in the schools. Many experimental programs have been developed and are now being developed. Some of the earliest and most significant projects dealing with elementary school mathematics are described in Table 1-1.[14]

The report of the Cambridge Conference on School Mathematics

During the summer of 1963 twenty-nine mathematicians met in Cambridge, Massachusetts, to view the future of school mathematics. The conference was organized and administered by Educational Services Incorporated under a grant from the National Science Foundation. The participants expressed their purposes in the Caveat as follows:[15]

The reader is urged to recognize the report that follows for what it is and for nothing more. A small number of professional mathematicians have attempted to express their tentative views upon the shape and content of a pre-college mathematics curriculum that might be brought into being over the new few decades. These views are intended to serve as a basis for widespread further discussion and above all, experimentation by mathematicians, teachers, and all others who share the responsibility for the processes and goals of American education. At this stage of their development they cannot be pretending to represent guidelines for school administrators or mathematics teachers, and they should not be read as such. If this report, however, fulfills its purposes by provoking general debate and bold experimentation, those guidelines may ultimately emerge.

Much discussion has occurred since the Cambridge conference. To some, the report represents the ultimate limit to which the elementary school mathematics curriculum might be "mathematized." To others, it represents the next logical step in the development of the mathematics curriculum. The report contains suggestions for a very strong mathematical treatment at the elementary school level and advocates applications of physical word situations.

The suggestions for elementary school (K-6) are ambitious and would require a high level of teacher preparation and, perhaps, a high level of student preparation. Since this report is of importance to the students of elementary school mathematics, the outline for grades K-6 is found in Appendix A.

[14] Note: There are a number of other experimental projects on a smaller scale. Also, current commercial textbooks and courses of study reflect the flavor of many of the experimental programs.
[15] *Goals for School Mathematics,* The Report of the Cambridge Conference on School Mathematics (Boston: Published for Educational Services Inc. by Houghton Mifflin, 1963).

Modern content and modern teaching

Each of the new programs in elementary school mathematics has features unique to it. Some of the programs place a heavy reliance on "set" terminology from early in the program; at least one does not mention "set." One program makes use of a very precise vocabulary from kindergarten on; another avoids using mathematical terminology. Some introduce multiplication as a series of additions; others introduce multiplication by the cross-product (Cartesian product) of sets. Most programs advocate a discovery approach, while a few emphasize the teaching procedure present in a "show-and-tell" approach. With such differences in modern programs how can one answer questions such as "What is modern mathematics?" "Isn't modern mathematics the same old things, but with new terminology?" "Isn't modern mathematics just teaching for understanding?" "Aren't sets and number sentences the essence of modern mathematics?" "We're putting in 'new mathematics' in our school—what do you think of it?"

The careful student of elementary school mathematics is hard pressed to give a precise definition of modern mathematics. While it would be difficult for a thoughtful student to find complete agreement between any two programs, the following elements are common to the majority of new curriculums.

1. An increased emphasis upon the structure of mathematics, its laws, and principles. A search for patterns to find sequences and order. Insight into the logical and expanding development of mathematics.

2. An increased emphasis upon letting the pupil figure things out for himself. Such an approach has many names. It may be called discovery, guided discovery, developmental, or inductive, all of which emphasize the same basic goals.

3. An increased emphasis upon correct terminology. Correct names are used to identify mathematical ideas. If it appears unwise to use a particular vocabulary word, none would be used rather than to substitute an imprecise term.

4. A readjustment of grade placement of topics. (The grade placement of most standard topics has gone back to what it was early in the century. During the 1930's many topics were moved to higher grades.) There is a spirit of let's see what the child can learn.

Source: United Feature Syndicate.

Has Linus' teacher adopted a modern approach to teaching the "new math"?

5. The inclusion of topics not typically taught in the elementary school. While until 1955 the majority of the first six grades was spent on arithmetic and some simple algebra, many new programs have added such topics as non-metric geometry, numeration systems with bases other than ten, exponents, and logic.

Any movement that gains momentum as rapidly as that of the "new mathematics" is bound to have weaknesses. Persons anxious to jump on the bandwagon before it passes them by may go to extremes that often cause the originators of new programs to shudder.

Establishing a balance

A number of factors interact to create curricular change. Glennon suggests that decisions on selection of content for inclusion in the elementary school mathematics program may be arrived at from three sources: (1) social theory (needs of society, sociological theory, or social-utility theory); (2) the needs of the subject theory (logical organization theory and meaning theory); and (3) psychological theory (needs of the individual, felt-needs theory, or expressed-needs theory).[16] He further suggests that any time these three theories are not well balanced, the curriculum suffers. In schools of the Summerhill [17] variety, the mental health approach, which results in mathematical instruction only when the child expresses a need for it, may weaken the program. We have noted how extreme application of the social-utility theory may have weakened the mathematics program for the thirty years prior to 1950. At the present time, the movement is in the direction of the needs of the subject approach. Too extreme a position by followers of this theory could also damage the curriculum.

Social and emotional climate

The following four suggestions for the selection of topics to be taught in elementary school mathematics are offered with the belief that their use will produce a healthy balance in the curriculum.

1. The topics taught should be mathematically sound.

2. The topics should be a kind that, when presented, "makes sense" to the student. The student should be able to see a reason for the study of a topic.

3. The topics should be teachable; that is, the difficulty should be such that, with effort, the student can understand the material.

4. The topics should lend themselves to mathematical exploration and pupil discovery.

The chapters that follow offer a blending of modern content and modern teaching which the author believes to be reasonable and forward looking.

---

[16] V. J. Glennon, "Some Perspective in Education," *Enrichment Mathematics for the Grades.* The Twenty-seventh Yearbook of the National Council of Teachers of Mathematics (Washington, D. C.: The Council, 1963).
[17] A. S. Neill, *Summerhill* (New York: Hart Publishing Company, 1960).

1. Compare the introduction of a topic in a current commercially prepared textbook with materials from one of the programs discussed in the chapter. Note such things as grade placement, approach to teaching, use of vocabulary, and use of problem situations to introduce new material.
2. Obtain a commercial textbook published before 1960. Compare the grade placement and topics included with one of the programs.
3. Write a lesson illustrating the way that you could use a guided discovery approach to introduce a topic new to the elementary school curriculum.
4. Compare the items of a current standardized test with the content of a textbook published after 1963.
5. Try to teach a friend a topic in mathematics new to him using a discovery approach. Think out carefully the questions you could use to guide the friend.
6. Trace the history of the teaching of some topic as far back as you can. Note differences in terminology, computational procedures, and emphasis upon understanding.
7. Observe an elementary school mathematics lesson. Try to determine the philosophy of teaching used by the teacher.
8. Write a one-page answer to a parent's question, "What is modern mathematics?"

SUGGESTED REFERENCES

Ausubel, David P., "Some Psychological and Educational Limitations of Learning by Discovery," *The Arithmetic Teacher,* Vol. 11, No. 5 (May 1964), pp. 297–302.

Banks, J. Houston, *Learning and Teaching Arithmetic* (Boston: Allyn & Bacon, 1964), pp. 1–22.

Brownell, William A., "The Place of Meaning in the Teaching of Arithmetic," *Elementary School Journal,* Vol. 47 (January 1947), pp. 256–265.

Bruner, Jerome S., *Toward a Theory of Instruction* (Cambridge: The Belknap Press of Harvard University Press, 1966), Chap. 3.

Deans, Edwina, *Elementary School Mathematics, New Directions* (Washington, D. C.: U. S. Department of Health, Education and Welfare, U. S. Government Printing Office, 1963).

Fehr, Howard F., "Sense and Nonsense in a Modern School Mathematics Program," *The Arithmetic Teacher,* Vol. 13, No. 2 (February 1966), pp. 83–91.

Flavell, John H., *The Developmental Psychology of Jean Piaget* (Princeton: Van Nostrand, 1963).

Grossnickle, Foster E., and Brueckner, Leo J., *Discovering Meanings in Elementary School Mathematics* (New York: Holt, Rinehart and Winston, 1963), pp. 30–49.

Lankford, Francis G., Jr., "Implications of the Psychology of Learning for the Teaching of Mathematics," *The Growth of Mathematical Ideas, Grades K-12,* Twenty-fourth Yearbook of the National Council of Teachers of Mathematics (Washington, D. C.: The Council, 1959), pp. 405–430.

Spitzer, Herbert F., *What Research Says to the Teacher: Teaching Arithmetic* (Washington, D. C.: National Education Association, 1962).

Smith, H. L., "One Hundred Fifty Years of Arithmetic Textbooks," *Bulletin of School of Education,* XXI (Bloomington, Indiana, 1945).

Swain, Robert L., "Modern Mathematics and School Arithmetic," *Instruction in Arithmetic,* Twenty-fifth Yearbook of the National Council of Teachers of Mathematics (Washington, D. C.: The Council, 1960), pp. 270–295.

Welmers, Everett T., "Arithmetic in Today's Culture," *Instruction in Arithmetic,* Twenty-fifth Yearbook of the National Council of Teachers of Mathematics (Washington, D. C.: The Council, 1960), pp. 10–33.

USE OF SUGGESTED REFERENCES

1. Compare Ausubel's discussion of discovery with this chapter.
2. Study the check list of the Post-War Plans of the National Council of Teachers of Mathematics listed by Banks. Are they still appropriate today?
3. Read Brownell's suggestions concerning meaning. Do they still hold today?
4. This chapter and the chapters that follow focus on strategies for teaching elementary school mathematics. Focus on specific issues in the teaching of mathematics in light of Bruner's writings.
5. Look at the portions of experimental projects presented by Deans. Compare the material in two projects.
6. How do the comments made by Fehr compare with the Cambridge Report?

What areas of a modern mathematics curriculum does he view as "sense"? As "nonsense"?

7. How could Piaget's findings on children's mathematical thinking be used as a base of curriculum experimentation? How could his findings be developed into teaching strategies?

8. Read Grossnickle and Brueckner's suggestions concerning the use of the mathematics classroom as a learning laboratory. What laboratory materials would you use to teach an introductory lesson on division of whole numbers?

9. Study Lankford's chapter on learning theory and teaching mathematics. Become familiar with the principles suggested in the chapter.

10. Analyze Spitzer's review of research findings. What do they suggest concerning teaching method?

11. Compare the material in the old textbooks described by Smith with the S.M.S.G. materials.

12. After reading Swain's chapter, list the ideas which Swain suggests as being important to modern mathematics in the elementary school.

13. From Welmers' chapter develop a list of several cultural goals that elementary school mathematics should fulfill.

2

*Early school contacts
with mathematics*

"Bill has more candy than I do."

"How many more pennies do I need to buy a candy bar?"

"Aunt Nancy gave Tom a nickel and me a penny. Who can buy the most?"

"I can count to ten. Want to hear me?"

"Jack is bigger than I am. Mother is bigger than Jack. Dad is the biggest one in our family."

Early in the life of a child his parents or brothers and sisters begin to acquaint him with mathematics. Many times each day he hears references to time, temperature, the number of objects, days of the week, shapes of objects, and other mathematical situations.

Preschool children vary in the contacts they have with mathematics. Studies such as those by Bjonerud,[1] Davis,[2] and MacLatchy[3] reveal that the average beginning kindergarten child recognizes or is able to understand to at least some extent (1) rational counting (counting with meaning) beyond ten by ones, (2) sets of one, two, three, and four objects, (3) situations requiring use of largest, smallest, tallest, longest, inside, beside, most, closest, and farthest, (4) the calendar, foot rule, and quarts, (5) the telling of time on the full hour, (6) the geometric figures of a circle and a square, (7) the solution of simple, orally presented problems involving addition and subtraction, and (8) an object cut into halves or thirds.

It should be remembered that while many beginning kindergarten children possess fewer skills than those listed, many possess a greater number. The teacher of young children should enrich the pupils' backgrounds, as well as correct any mathematical misconceptions they possess.

[1] Corwin E. Bjonerud, "Arithmetic Concepts Possessed by the Preschool Child," *The Arithmetic Teacher*, Vol. 7, No. 7 (November 1960), pp. 347–350.

[2] O. L. Davis, Barbara Carber, and Carolyn Crigler, "The Growth of Pre-School Children's Familiarity with Measurement," *The Arithmetic Teacher*, Vol. 6, No. 4 (October 1959), pp. 186–190.

[3] Josephine H. MacLatchy, "The Pre-School Child's Familiarity with Measurement," *Education*, Vol. LXXI, No. 8 (April 1951), pp. 479–482.

STRUCTURE VERSUS INCIDENTAL LEARNING

Great variation in mathematical content and mathematical emphasis can be found at the kindergarten level. An observer visiting kindergartens throughout the nation would find some situations where the teacher carefully avoids any reference to numbers, others where the program consists of rote counting and an occasional use of the classroom store, and still others where the instruction in mathematics is very systematic and rather abstract.

The content of mathematics for the kindergarten should meet the same criteria demanded for the grades, but have a somewhat different emphasis. At the kindergarten level the pupils should be given wide opportunities to learn mathematics, but without extensive study for mastery. The kindergarten program should provide the pupils with ideas and experiences upon which they can build. Thus, it should be (1) understandable, (2) accurate, (3) motivated to make sense to the learner, and (4) geared to give the pupils many opportunities to explore ideas without a pressure for mastery.

A SUGGESTED KINDERGARTEN PROGRAM[4]

Current courses of study and professional books on the kindergarten are usually rather vague as to the content of the program. There is general agreement that some "number work" should be offered, but few specific suggestions. In light of the importance of mathematics in the total school program, the background which most kindergarten children bring to school, and the interest of young children in numbers, mathematics should be an important part of the kindergarten program.

The topics and the suggestions for teaching which follow are designed to give the reader a look at the type of experiences which can provide a useful mathematical background to the early primary school child. Because classes vary in the mathematical abilities they possess, many of the suggested experiences will be appropriate for kindergarten, while others will be more appropriate later in the primary grades. Also, several suggestions are made for mathematical experiences that continue at higher grade levels. These mathematical experiences involve counting, writing numerals, and place value.

Sets[5]

For most children, an intuitive idea of sets is developed before they begin kindergarten. Some may have matched sets in one-to-one correspondence; others may have learned to give number names to various sets.

---

[4] The suggestions are appropriate for the early work in grade one in schools which do not have a kindergarten program.
[5] A review of set concepts is presented in Appendix B.

In fact, almost all of the beginning kindergarteners will be able to give the cardinal number of the set to sets containing less than five objects. Because most children possess some knowledge concerning sets, the teacher should exercise care in selecting content and procedures which present a challenge to the children and clarify the situation.

Introducing sets.   An alert teacher can use a natural situation to introduce a new term to her kindergarten class. For example, early in the year a teacher who observed class members putting a set of dishes into the cupboard of the playhouse asked, "What do you call those dishes?"

The children responded with, "Just dishes." "A group of dishes." "A set of dishes." The majority of the class agreed that their mothers normally talked about a set of dishes. The teacher asked the class if they could have sets of other things. The pupils suggested sets of blocks, sets of crayons, sets of silverware, sets of books, sets of furniture, and sets of marbles. After a short discussion and some argument, the class members agreed that any collection of things could be called a set.

During the days that followed, the teacher used the terms "set" and "member of a set" informally in situations such as "Jim, put the set of blocks on the table." "Alice, it's your turn to put the set of dishes on the table for our lunch." "Mark, how will the set of spoons you put on the table compare with Alice's set of dishes?" "Which set—boys or girls—have more members?" "What set is Jean a member of—team 1 or team 2?"

The teacher also pointed out casually the members of sets that were in some of the stories which she read to the class. She asked, for example, "To which set did Tim belong, the Jones family or the White family?" "To which set did Puff belong, the set of cats or the set of dogs?" "To what set does the pet in our last story belong?"

Comparing sets.   The comparison of sets provides an opportunity to make use of orally presented problem situations. One morning the teacher began by saying, "I overheard two little neighbor children arguing about the size of their sets of trucks. Bill said he had more and Ken said that he had more. I've placed some pictures of trucks on the flannel board. The black are

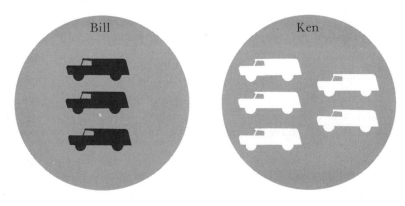

those that Bill had and the white trucks are those that Ken had. Does Bill have more than or fewer than Ken?"

After a momentary pause, the majority of the children raised their hands. The teacher selected one of the average pupils to answer the question. The pupil said, "I believe that Ken has more trucks than Bill. I'll show you." She then went to the flannel board, matched Bill's three trucks with Ken's three, and said, "See, Ken still has trucks left over."

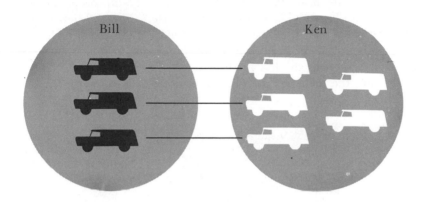

Other pupils were asked to tell how they found an answer. Several said that they had counted the trucks and knew that Ken had 5 trucks and Bill 3. Five is more than 3, so Ken had more trucks. Others said that they just knew Ken had more but weren't quite sure why they knew.

Class discussion brought out the point that matching[6] could be used either to determine which set had more trucks in it or as a good check to counting, if the pupil knew how to count.

During the remainder of the lesson and periodically thereafter, problem situations requiring the group to decide which was more than, less than, or equal to were used. These problems involved materials such as pennies, soda straws, milk cartons, and the set of postcards collected on a trip by one child. Throughout the kindergarten year, pupils should be provided with many opportunities to compare sets.

Subsets. The concept of subsets was introduced by the teacher through the use of the following problem. "Jane has this set of dolls (three baby dolls and two rag dolls) on the table. Her friend asks her to bring along only her rag dolls. Which of the dolls would she take? Would you pick them up, Jill?" (Pause while Jill picks up the rag dolls.) "Does Jill have the set of rag dolls? Does she have the entire set of dolls? No, we call the set of rag dolls a subset of the set of dolls because every member of the set of rag dolls is a member of the entire set of dolls. Can you give me other examples of subsets?"

---

[6] Mathematically this procedure is usually referred to as placing sets in one-to-one correspondence.

The pupils gave examples such as "The boys are a subset of the children in our class." "Bob is a subset of the boys." "The red truck is a subset of our toys." Reference was also made to members of a set who would not be members of a particular subset. For example, blocks are members of the set of toys, but are not members of the subset of toys that have wheels.

The empty set.   During a play period the teacher drew a ring on the floor and gave several pupils bean bags. Then she said, "Stand back and see how many of the bean bags you can toss into the circle." The children were moved back a good distance. The teacher continued, "Let's record their success on the chalkboard. Go ahead. I'll write Jane's name and draw a picture of the set of bean bags she has in the circle; now Tom's, now Nancy's, now Joe's. What are the members of Nancy's set of bean bags in the circle?"

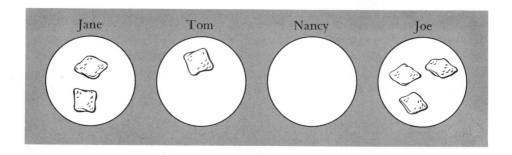

Nancy said, "There aren't any members in the set of bean bags I tossed into the circle."

The teacher then asked if the class could think of sets that had no members. The pupils were not sure for a short time whether or not a set could be a set if it had no members. Ken partially resolved the question with the comment, "You'd have to have sets that have no members. I could tell someone that I would spend the set of pennies in my bank and then get home to find that my little brother had lost them for me. So my set of pennies would contain no members." After further discussion, the class agreed that it would be possible to have a set that had no members. The pupils gave examples such as "The set of fish my father caught when he went fishing last week." "The set of bicycles that I own." "The set of millionaires on our block." As the discussion continued, the children enjoyed thinking of rather wild examples of the empty set such as "The set of elephants in the room." "The set of persons under one foot high in the room." "The set of movie stars in the room." "The set of persons higher than the school house." "The set of Martians in our classroom."

Using numbers with sets.   "How many pictures of animals did George bring?" "How many of our kindergarten class ride on Bus 3?" "How many napkins do we need for Mary's table?" Pupils need many experiences, with or without counting, for developing the ability to recognize the number of members in a set. These and many other experiences which arise in the kindergarten provide an opportunity for pupils to determine "how many." Pupils can first work with actual sets of objects and then move to work with perception cards (cards containing a number of geometric designs).

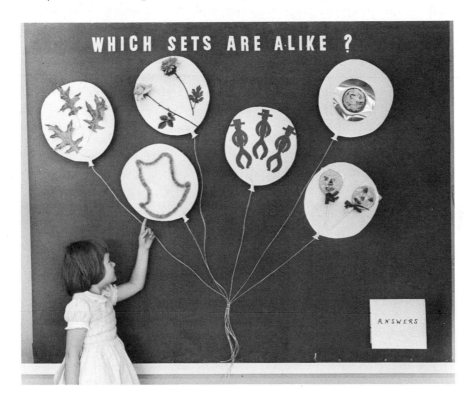

Source: Still Photo Services U. D. I. S., Pennsylvania State University.

Phyllis is trying to determine which sets have the same cardinal number.

Comparing numbers

After pupils understand the relationship of "more than" and "less than" between two sets and are able to associate numbers to sets, the teacher can begin to develop the pupils' ability to compare numbers. Comparing the number of sets of varying sizes is not only a valuable mathematical endeavor but is also of great social application. The teacher may begin work with comparing numbers by saying, "I've placed some figures on the flannel board which represent the set of baseball cards which Jeff brought to school and the set of baseball cards which Alice brought to school. Is Jeff's set larger or smaller than Alice's?"

The pupils agreed that Jeff's set contained fewer cards than Alice's. The class then identified the number that would be associated with Jeff's set of cards (4) and the number that would be associated with Alice's set of cards (5). The teacher said, "I have a symbol that I can place between the two numbers which will tell us that Jeff's set has fewer cards than Alice's set." (Holds up a flannel < and then turns it to >.) "Which way do you think this symbol should point?" A short discussion followed in which most pupils expressed the view that the smaller end (the pointed end) should be next to the 4, while the open end should be next to the number 5.

The teacher informed the pupils that they were correct and then added, "We couldn't actually decide about this symbol because mathematicians had already developed this symbol and its meaning. However, you can see why they did."

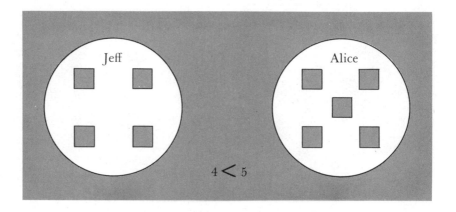

Equality and equivalence. When you deal with sets and numbers, the ideas of equality and equivalence become important. In traditional mathematics programs the difference between equality and equivalence was often hazy. Occasionally a teacher said, "Although $4 + 5$ is equivalent to 9, not equal to 9, we write the sign of equality ($=$) rather than the sign of equivalence ($\sim$) to save time." In this case the teacher was experiencing difficulty in making a distinction between sets and numbers. Two sets may only be equivalent, but the number property of the two sets is the same; therefore, they represent equal numbers. Thus, {Tom, Mike, Alice} and {Bob, John, Harry} are equivalent sets since they can be matched in one-to-one correspondence. However, N {Tom, Mike, Alice} = N {Bob, John, Harry} = 3 because the number idea of threeness is conveyed by both sets. It should be remembered that two sets are equal if they have the same elements; that two sets are equivalent if their elements may be matched in one-to-one correspondence; and that numbers have many names (6, $3 + 3$, $8 - 2$, and $5 + 1$ are all different names for the same numbers).

Source: United Feature Syndicate.

Sally may be puzzled because the teacher has failed to tie "set terminology" to a problem situation or has overemphasized terminology to the exclusion of the basic mathematical ideas.

Counting

Many beginning school children possess a background of counting, both rote (calling of the number names in order, but without meaning) and rational (identifying the "how many" or "which one" aspect of numbers). The beginning use of numbers should be developed in a manner that makes use of the background of these students without causing those without counting background to flounder.

Some teachers of modern programs have become confused concerning the role of counting in the early school program and have placed almost total reliance upon the recognition of the number of objects in a set without counting. This practice is to be questioned. Not only do children have difficulty identifying the number of objects in a set larger than 5 (unless a definite pattern is shown) but also the procedure greatly limits the use of large numbers. Experience has shown that first-grade pupils greatly enjoy counting large numbers of objects in a set. In fact, the majority can learn to count and to understand the meanings of numbers up to at least one thousand. The role of counting in the kindergarten and first-grade programs can not be overemphasized. The Cambridge Report contains the following suggestion which supports this contention:

One general principle appears to be this: Whenever possible, the child should have some intrinsic criterion for deciding the correctness of answers, without recourse to authority. In the present work [kindergarten through second grade] this bed-rock foundation is generally provided by the fundamental operation of *counting*. The child's slogan might well be: when in doubt, *count!*

Counting experiences for children. In developing counting experiences one teacher began by asking, "Will those of you who have birthdays this week (or today and tomorrow if there are a great number in a given week) raise your hands." Three children raised their hands. The teacher asked, "How many birthday hats will we have to make?" A large number of children raised their hands. When called upon one child said, "We'll have to make three hats." The teacher questioned the group as to how they knew the number of hats was three. Explanations included: "I counted one, two, three." "My sister is three-years old and we hold up three fingers to tell how old she is." "You can match three fingers with the children that stood up."

During the next few days the teacher used a number of questions that required the determination of the number of objects in a set. The class engaged in experiences such as counting the numbers of persons who needed milk at each table (usually somewhere between 5 and 8); chairs needed to seat some of the class; dogs in a picture on the bulletin board; pennies brought by each pupil for a charity drive.

The chart depicted below was used as a reference set to give the number name to another set. The development of the chart was a total class project that was directed by the teacher's questions. At this time no attempt was made to identify the numerals. Children who could read the numerals were free to refer to their names.

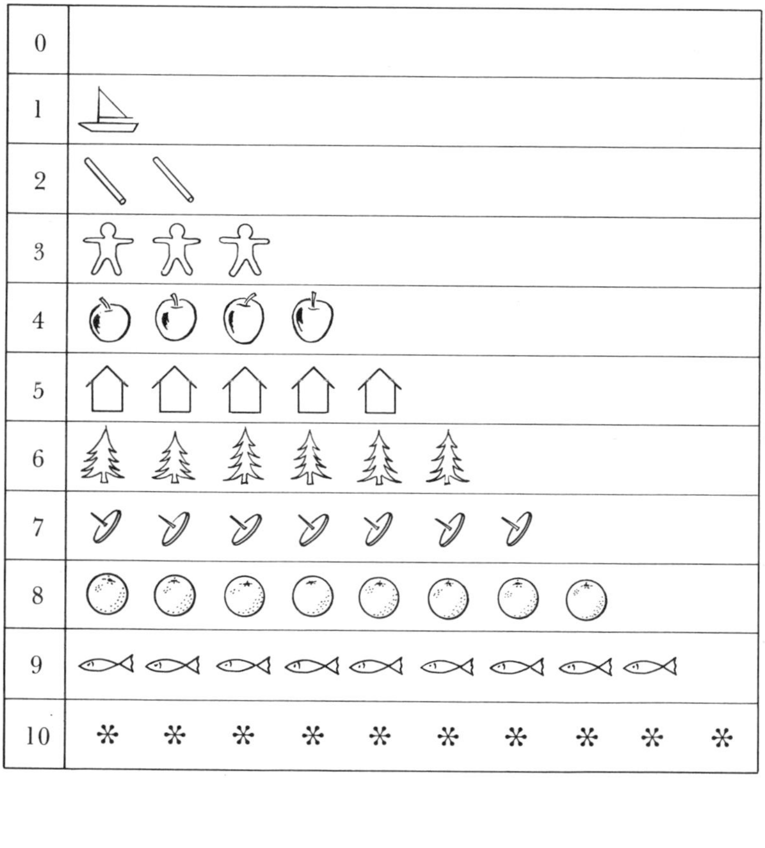

As the children continued to develop their understanding of the number of objects in the set, the teacher made use of songs, problems, games, and finger play to provide further experience with using the number names. The following list represents some of the situations used by the teacher:

1. How long do you think it is until Valentine's Day? Let's look on the calendar and count the number of days.

2. I noticed that many of you have picked beautifully colored leaves on the way to school. Let's count to see how many we have.

3. Bob has built a very nice train with the blocks. Count to find the number of cars in the train.

4. Let's see how many minutes it will take all of us to get our boots on to go outside for recess. Count along with me. I'll write the numeral on the board and then tomorrow we can see if we can beat today's record.

5. As we sing "This Old Man," hold up your fingers to designate the number we're singing about. Let's start: "This old man, he played one, he played nic nac on my thumb, etc."

6. As I read *One Fish, Two Fish, Red Fish, Blue Fish,*[7] hold up the number of fingers that indicate the number of fish talked about in the story.

7. Simon says clap your hands four times; Simon says jump-up-and-down six times; etc.

Counting beyond ten.   Because many pupils who are starting to school can count beyond ten either by rote or rationally (with understanding), the teacher's main concern may be one of emphasizing the idea of "Eleven is the word we use to mean ten and one more"; "twelve means ten and two more"; "thirteen means ten and three more"; etc. Pupils often experience greater difficulty with the "teens" than with larger values. This is probably because of the inconsistency of eleven and twelve, compared to the rest of the "teen" values, and the reverse sequences as compared with the number names beyond. For example, we call 36 "thirty-six"; but call 16 "sixteen," not teen six. Also, if a pupil learns the names of the even tens (twenty, thirty, forty, etc.), he can be led to discover the pattern of reading the tens value and the ones value. For example, if the pupil knows that 22 is read "twenty-two," and he knows that 40 is "forty," he can reason that 42 would be read as "forty-two."

Because of the inconsistency of the names for numbers between ten and twenty, it is advantageous for pupils to first learn to count to ten and then learn to count to 100 by tens. With such a procedure, the pupil would count ten, two tens, three tens, four tens, . . . one hundred. This procedure has merit for the pupil who does not count beyond ten when he starts school.

[7] Theodore Seuss Geisel (pseud. Dr. Seuss), *One Fish, Two Fish, Red Fish, Blue Fish* (New York: Random House, 1960).

This emphasis on the base of ten also develops the concept of grouping by tens which is of major importance in developing place-value concepts.

Ordinal usage in counting.   Children have many early uses for the position of an object in a linear sequence. For example, they discuss such things as "Who is first in line?" "I'm the third person to bat." "We're going on our vacation on the twenty-first of the month." "I finished fourth in the race." The teacher can make use of ordinals in situations involving the location of pages in a book, the daily use of calendars, and the line pupils form for games. Pupils experience little difficulty with this "which one?" aspect of numbers, when it is used naturally.

Counting in the upper grades.   Counting is one of the best background experiences for addition, subtraction, multiplication, and division. It is also one of the best means of checking the accuracy of an answer to a computational exercise. Because of its many uses, pupils who have very good facility in counting usually experience less difficulty with later number work. The teacher can provide valuable counting experience at every grade level. Some suggestions for counting in the upper grades are the following:

Grade three 1. Tom and Bill were arguing. Tom said that if you count by 4's starting with 5, one of the numbers that you would count would be 21. Was he right?

2. Can you count backwards by 2's? Let's try. We'll start at 16.

Grade four 1. Tom and Bill were working on the chart of numerals I've started on the board. Can you tell me what numeral will appear above the 15? What numeral will be three rows above the 12?

13	14	15	16	17	18
7	8	9	10	11	12
1	2	3	4	5	6

2. A friend told me that she didn't think it would be possible to count by using fractions. What do you think? Let's try counting by one-thirds. Ready $\frac{1}{3}$, $\frac{2}{3}$, $\frac{3}{3}$, (pause) what's another name for $\frac{3}{3}$?

Grade five 1. Some of you seem to be having trouble with addition. Counting practice will often improve your addition. Start at 23 and count by 8's to the first number you reach that is beyond 60. What is that number? Count from 75 by 9's to the first number you reach beyond 100.

2. How well do you know fractions? How well do you know how to count? Let's see. Start at 8 and count by $\frac{2}{3}$'s to the first number you reach that is beyond 10.

Grade six   1. Counting by using fractions often helps you to improve your ability to add and subtract fractions.

Try these:

a. Start at 8 and count by $\frac{5}{6}$'s until you count a number larger than 12.

b. Start at 15 and count backwards by $\frac{2}{3}$'s until you reach a number smaller than 10.

Reading numerals

When the teacher felt that most of the pupils understood the names of the numbers for sets containing up to ten objects, she began work on the reading of numerals. This work was not designed to have every student "master" the reading of numerals, but was to develop background for further work. There was little pressure placed on the slow students, while the faster students were given an opportunity to work at a high level of proficiency.

The teacher asked, "How many fish do we have in our fishbowl?" The pupils responded that there were four fish in the bowl. The teacher asked one of the pupils to place four felt fish on the flannel board. Then the teacher commented, "Larry has placed a set of four fish on the flannel board. Do any of you know the symbol we use to indicate the number four?"

Because of previous experiences with sets, counting, and the use of the chart shown in the section on "counting experiences for children," many of the pupils knew the symbol for the number four. The teacher gave each pupil a set of plastic numerals (they could be paper ones) and asked if they could hold up the one which indicated four.

Next, the teacher placed three flannel cutouts of children on the flannel board and asked, "Do you know how we could write three?" One of the pupils went to the board and wrote the numeral 3, explaining that his older brother had helped him learn to write. The teacher placed a felt numeral 3 on the flannel board. Then she asked a number of children to show her sets that contained three objects. During the discussion that followed, the teacher's questions brought out the idea that the various sets that contained three objects were not the same set, although they were alike in that they each contained three objects. Discussion also emphasized that the "3" was a way of writing three, just as the teacher often wrote "Bill" on the chalkboard but did not actually put the boy Bill on the chalkboard.

The following day all of the children received a chart like the one below. They also received magazines that contained colored pictures. The teacher explained that she had filled in a set of three objects which was represented by the "3." She said, "Now let's talk about some other number ideas and see if you can fill in your chart. How many of you ride the bus?" (Two hands were raised.) "How many is that?" (Several children gave the answer 2.) "When you work on the chart you are to cut any two objects you wish and paste them next to the "2." The teacher wrote a "2" on the board.

Before the chart work began, the teacher asked, "How many members in the set of pupils who rode their bicycles to school today?" The pupils explained that this would be the empty set because they were not allowed to ride bicycles to school. The teacher asked, "How many objects should be put in to represent the empty set?" The pupils agreed that there would be no object for the empty set. The number associated with the empty set was discussed and the pupils noted that "zero" (0) was used to name the empty set.

0	
1	
2	
3	
4	
5	
6	
7	
8	
9	
10	

While the pupils worked on their charts, the teacher moved about the room asking questions and giving aid to the pupils. At no time during the kindergarten program was stress placed on writing the numerals. However, when a pupil wished to write a numeral, the teacher helped him to write it in the correct manner.

Writing numerals

While numeral writing often appears to be a very mundane part of the curriculum, there are several reasons why correct numeral writing should be stressed. They are the following:

1. In the majority of schools, the first handwriting a child is taught involves numeral writing.[8]

2. Current use of numerals in addresses (ZIP codes), telephone exchanges (237-2090 rather than AD 7-2090), credit cards, bank accounts, and social security numbers on income tax returns requires a high level of legibility. In-

[8] Gwen F. Arnold, and others, *Handwriting in Wisconsin* (Madison, Wisconsin: School of Education, University of Wisconsin, 1951).

correct formation of numerals can cause costly delays in delivering mail and in processing data.

3. Illegible numeral writing causes errors which nationally cost victims well over a million dollars. Many persons have had experience with the difficulties that arise when one of the persons using a joint checking account writes a numeral illegibly.

The need to write numerals arises early in the elementary school program. The first need to write numerals usually occurs when the student needs (1) to indicate a page number, (2) to record the date or the temperature, or (3) to keep score for a game.

The pupils have had experience in reading the number names and thus refer to sample numerals posted on the bulletin board. Several use situations should precede a systematic numeral writing program.

Traditionally the handwriting period has focused upon "what's wrong" with "your" numeral writing. Comments on "what's right" usually produce better results. The teacher may begin a numeral writing period in the following manner: "Yesterday I asked each of you to write on your papers the numeral which would tell me how many pictures you had collected of objects which begin with the same sound as 'dog.' I was very pleased with the way that many of you wrote the numerals. I've copied some of the numerals you wrote on these large pieces of oak tag and I've dittoed a sheet containing the correct forms of the numerals for you to refer to. Compare the way in which you wrote the numerals with the board and with the sheet I've given you. (pause) Now let's see if we can write the numerals even better. I'm going to count and then stop. You write the numeral that would represent the number which occurs next. If you aren't sure which number would be next, raise your hand and I'll be happy to give you some help. All right, is everyone clear on the instruction? Let's begin—1, 2, 3, 4, 5, 6 (pause) 8, 9, etc.

"Now that we've finished, take a look at the numerals you've written and compare them with your chart or the chart on the board. I'd like to know how you began to write each numeral. Would you please draw an arrow like this (→) to indicate where you started each numeral." When the class members had indicated the direction in which they had begun each numeral, the teacher set up a chart such as the one below, and the pupils compared their writing with the chart.

Detailed accounts of the research done on numeral writing and of the many ideas that classroom teachers have found helpful in teaching numeral writing are beyond the scope of this book. However, the following comments are offered as an aid to teachers:

1. The strongest factor in good numeral writing is the student's motivation. Most children can write numerals legibly (if not beautifully) if they have a real desire to do so. Thus the teacher should be constantly on the lookout for situations that will positively motivate the student to increased effort in numeral writing.

2. Most handwriting programs begin with the student writing very large numerals. In such cases, the student usually draws rather than writes the numerals. While such drawing practice is helpful, the student should also have an opportunity right from the beginning of instruction to write numerals of standard size.

3. While different pupils experience difficulty with various numerals, research reveals that the three numerals which cause the greatest difficulty are 5, 0, and 2. The numerals 3, 6, 7, 8, and 9 also cause some difficulties.

4. A large pencil is often suggested for primary work in handwriting. Research does not support the contention that it is important for primary school children to use large pencils.[9]

5. There should be a reintroduction of numeral writing at each grade level. This reintroduction should present a challenge. The teacher might use such approaches as comparing the numerals of today with those used in the past.

A Comparison of Numerals[10]

	1	2	3	4	5	6	7	8	9	10
Sanskrit										
Arabic										
Later Arabic										

6. Normally, short intensive periods of instruction are preferable to longer periods. If a teacher plans to spend 60 minutes on numeral writing, four 15-minute periods would produce better results than two 30-minute periods.

7. Normally, instruction begins in grade one with manuscript numerals. Cursive numerals usually are introduced in grades two or three. There is little evidence for or against this procedure.

[9] Virgil E. Herrick, "Handwriting and Children's Writing," *Elementary English*, Vol. XXXVII, No. 4 (April 1960).
[10] *From History of Mathematics* by D. E. Smith, Vol. II, pp. 70–71. Copyright 1953 by Eva May Luce Smith. Published by Dover Publications, Inc., New York 14, N.Y. at $5.00, and reprinted through permission of the publisher.

1234567890

Manuscript Numerals

1234567890

Cursive Numerals

8. Paper placement for manuscript writing is at right angles to the desk. When cursive writing begins, the paper should be placed as illustrated below. Note: When the paper is placed in the same manner for both left-handed and right-handed pupils, the left-handed pupil will usually develop a hook. The teacher should carefully check to see that the left-handed pupil has placed his paper correctly.

Manuscript   Cursive

right-handed   left-handed

VERBAL PROBLEM SOLVING AT THE PREREADING LEVEL

Many teachers feel that the solution of the verbal problem is one of the most difficult portions of the elementary school mathematics curriculum. They often find that in many cases pupils have difficulty with problems and do not enjoy working them. This difficulty may well be caused by the delay in starting the problem-solving program. The majority of commercial mathematics programs of both traditional and modern content have very little verbal problem solving until late in the second grade. This lack of problem-solving material usually stems from the assumptions that (1) problem solving cannot or should not begin until the pupil can read the problems; and/or (2) problem solving as such is unimportant to the mathematics program.

A careful study of the two assumptions listed will reveal little sound evidence to support these positions. First, it is not necessary for the pupil to have reading facility to work with verbal problems. These problems can be presented orally by the teacher and solved by the use of concrete sets of objects. Oral presentation is in keeping with the typical problem situations that children and adults encounter, for most physical world problem situations are in an orally presented context rather than in a written context. Second, work in verbal problem solving at the early primary level is consistent with the modern emphasis upon sets and concrete materials. A problem situation concerning things (sets) provides the pupil with an opportunity to work with sets in a situation where he sees a need for their use. Also, continued use of problems helps the pupil to abstract the number idea from sets.

At the beginning of the year, the kindergarten or first-grade teacher can make use of situations such as the following:

1. Mike wants to start a collection of model boats. To start his collection his brother gave him 3 boats, and his father gave him 2 boats. How many boats does he have in all?

2. Nancy brought in 3 records for us to use, and Carol brought us 4 records. How many records did the girls bring to us?

3. I bought 7 clay pots for us to plant flowers. On the way to school I dropped 2. How many pots do I have left?

4. Billy has 8¢ in his pocket, and Ken has 5¢. How much more does Billy have than Ken?

The above problems are only representative. The kindergarten and first-grade teacher can isolate many simple problem situations from occurrences in the room and contrived situations which she has developed.

How would the problem situations be used? The following classroom description is typical where orally presented problems form a major portion of early mathematics instruction.

The following problem was read to the children: "Mark has been telling me about his fishing trip. His father caught 4 fish and Mark caught 3 fish. How many did they catch in all?" Each pupil was directed to try to find the answer and then be able to show that his answer was correct. Each pupil had a set of plastic counters and paper and pencil at his desk. Some pupils began to use the counters to find an answer, while others thought for a moment and raised their hands. The following explanations are typical of the different levels of thinking that occurred:

Jim: I drew 4 fish on my paper because Mark's father caught 4 fish. Then I drew 3 fish on my paper because Mark caught 3 fish. Then I counted all of the fish. They caught 7 fish.

Nancy: I laid down 4 counters to show the fish that Mark's father caught and then I laid down 3 counters to show the fish that Mark caught. I counted all of the fish and got an answer of 7 fish caught.

Tim: I know that Mark's father caught 4 fish and that Mark caught 3 fish. I said to myself four—five, six, seven. I knew I could start with four and then count three more.

Jill: I just know that 4 and 3 combine to equal 7.

More difficult problems may be worked by total class consideration. Such total class experiences should involve problems that are significant to the members of the class.

The problems involve the union or separation of sets and are excellent background for the later study of addition and subtraction.

Place value

Knowledge of place value is important to an understanding of the algorithms of addition, subtraction, multiplication, and division and to the later development of decimals and percent. The lack of understanding concerning such procedures as regrouping in addition and subtraction originates from a lack of understanding of place value.

It is the responsibility of the children's first teacher to develop an understanding of place value and that of succeeding teachers to deepen this understanding. The descriptions that follow suggest ways to teach place value. The procedures assume an ability to do rote and rational counting beyond ten.

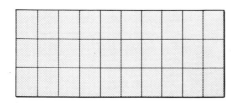

"Ken is anxious to fill in his savings stamp book." (The teacher pointed to the drawing on the board.) "How many stamps will he need to fill the first row?" (The pupils counted and answered, "ten.") "How many tens will he need to cover the page?" (Pupils responded, "Three tens.")

"How many groups of ten stamps has he pasted in the book." (Pupils responded, "2 tens.") "How many stamps in all?" (Pupils responded, "2 tens and 4 ones" or "24 stamps.")

"How many markers are there on the hundred board?" Several children immediately raised their hands and answered, "Thirty-four." The teacher asked, "How did you know so fast? You didn't have time to count them." The pupils responded that they knew that there were ten markers in each row on the hundred board. This meant that there were 3 tens and 4 ones or 34 markers.

"I've given each of you a number of popsicle sticks and some rubberbands. Group the popsicle sticks so that one of your friends or I can easily tell how many sticks there are." There was no attempt to give the same number of sticks to every child. The majority of the class grouped the sticks into bundles of ten each. Some of the pupils used bundles of other sizes. The pupils then discussed the grouping of the sticks. They found that if the sticks were in groups such as 8, 11, or 12, it was still necessary to count the entire number of sticks. After discussion it was agreed that any size group could be used, but that grouping by tens and ones helped the pupils tell how many sticks were on another desk.

Then the teacher gave each pupil a ditted sheet containing several place-value frames. She referred to a frame drawn on the board and asked, "How could I represent this number of sticks on the place-value frame? Show this on your place-value frame."

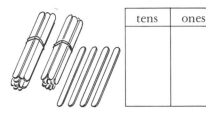

tens	ones

After the pupils filled in the frames, discussion revealed that the two methods shown at the right were considered to be good representations.

tens	ones
ll	llll

tens	ones
2	4

The class agreed that it would not be good form to use the method at the right because a person looking at the frame could not tell if it meant 2 tens or 2 groups of 10 tens.

tens	ones
~~HHH HHH~~ ~~HHH HHH~~	IIII

Devices such as Cuisenaire rods, tens and ones blocks, Stern materials (strips of ten and single squares), counting disks in plastic bags, and a simple abacus may be used.

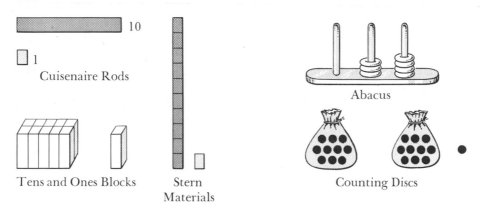

Cuisenaire Rods

Tens and Ones Blocks

Stern Materials

Abacus

Counting Discs

As children in succeeding grades mature in their understanding of the number system, first expanded notation and then exponents are used to continue work on place value. (See chapter 9.)

STUDY SUGGESTIONS

1. Obtain a manual from a handwriting series and trace the development of steps in learning to write numerals.
2. Compare the kindergarten program presented by the School Mathematics Study Group with the program advocated in a current book on instruction in the kindergarten. How do these programs differ? How are they alike?
3. Plan a lesson at the primary-grade level which makes use of a children's book that has reference to numbers.
4. It has been stated that the majority of the kindergarten and first-grade mathematics programs could be based upon orally presented verbal problems. State some of the advantages and disadvantages of such a program.
5. Prepared materials for kindergarten and first-grade instruction are often criticized because they present little challenge. Explain how a teacher can provide challenging material without teaching second- and third-grade material?

SUGGESTED REFERENCES

Beard, Virginia, "Mathematics in Kindergarten," *The Arithmetic Teacher,* Vol. 9, No. 1 (January 1962), pp. 22–25.

Dwight, Leslie A., *Modern Mathematics for the Elementary Teacher* (New York: Holt, Rinehart and Winston, 1966), Chap. 4.

Holmes, Emma E., "First Graders' Number Concepts," *The Arithmetic Teacher,* Vol. 10, No. 4 (April 1963), pp. 195–196.

Hollister, G. E., and Gunderson, A. G., *Teaching Arithmetic in the Primary Grades* (Boston: Heath, 1964), Chap. 2.

Howard, Charles F., and Dumas, Enoch, *Basic Procedures in Teaching Arithmetic* (Boston: Heath, 1963), Chaps. 1 and 3.

Spencer, P. L., and Brydegaard, M., *Building Mathematical Competence in the Elementary School* (New York: Holt, Rinehart and Winston, 1966), Chaps. 3, 6, and 7.

Spitzer, Herbert F., "Arithmetic in Kindergarten and Grades 1 and 2," *Instruction in Arithmetic*, Twenty-fifth Yearbook (Washington, D. C.: The Council, 1960), Chap. 5.

Stern, Catherine, *Children Discover Arithmetic* (New York: Harper & Row, 1949), Chaps. 4, 5, and 6.

Swenson, Esther J. *Teaching Arithmetic to Children* (New York: Macmillan, 1964), Chap. 4.

USE OF SUGGESTED REFERENCES

1. Analyze the objectives of the kindergarten mathematics curriculum which are suggested by Beard.
2. Use suggestions by Dwight to develop a lesson that moves from sets to the idea that there are many names for numbers.
3. What implications for the development of kindergarten and first-grade programs can be drawn from the findings of Holmes?
4. Would the report of Hollister and Gunderson on the number concepts possessed by preschool children lend support to a structured kindergarten mathematics program?
5. What do Howard and Dumas mean by "organizing content around 'threads' of activity"?
6. Use Spencer and Brydegaard as a source to develop a sequence for teaching sets, language, and counting.
7. Compare the kindergarten program suggested by Spitzer in *Instruction in Arithmetic* with the suggestions made in a book on kindergarten education. Which suggestions are most specific?
8. What suggestions does Stern make for the use of blocks and rods in developing the number concepts of very young children?
9. When does Swenson believe that a child should be taught to write numerals? What in your opinion is the proper grade level for introducing work concerned with writing numerals? Why?

3

Meeting individual differences

One of the questions uppermost in the minds of future teachers, in-service teachers, and elementary school administrators is, "What can be done to help those children who are far above or far below the average level of arithmetic achievement for their class?" When these persons are questioned further a number of more specific questions arise. For example,

1. Shall I group the arithmetic class in the same manner as I do in reading?

2. Should all of the pupils study the same topic (for example, multiplication) at the same time?

3. What arithmetical content is most worthwhile for the better pupils? For the poorer students?

4. Should I use materials designed for the grade that follows with the better students and materials designed for the previous grade with the poorer students?

5. What should be the basis for assigning different levels of instructional materials?

6. How can I recognize varying abilities?

7. What are some things that I can do to interest the slow learners?

8. Should superior students be used to help the slower pupils? If so, how?

9. What materials are available for the better students? For the poorer students?

Before considering possible solutions to the above questions, certain propositions concerning individual differences should be considered. Jones and Pingry[1] summarize research findings as follows:

1. Children in any classroom, even in those where ability grouping is used, will differ widely in both general and special abilities and aptitudes.

2. Differences in both ability and achievement increase with age, the span or range of general ability increasing almost two-fold from the first to the eighth grade.

3. The various special abilities (for example, numerical fluency) correlate

[1] R. Stewart Jones and Robert E. Pingry, "Individual Differences," *Instruction in Arithmetic*, The Twenty-fifth Yearbook of the National Council of Teachers of Mathematics (Washington, D. C.: The Council, 1960), p. 123.

differentially with each other and with any measure of general ability that is presently in use.

4. Any school subject requires a variety of abilities. Competency in arithmetic, for example, calls for numerical fluency, numerical comprehension, conceptual ability, visual and auditory memory, etc.

5. Differences between the sexes in abilities and skills are slight, with some apparent advantage for the earlier maturing girl, especially in language skills, and some slight advantage for boys in mathematics.

6. Differences within an individual, that is, the variability of traits within a single child, are more than half as great as differences among children.

7. Although various abilities overlap, that is, intercorrelate, they are sufficiently independent to merit separate measurement.

8. Differences not accounted for by mental-age measures are as important in determining school success as intellectual ones. One-fourth of retarded readers, for example, are above average in measured intelligence.

9. The effects of schooling that fails to consider differences among children seem to be cumulative. Children fall further and further away from the attainments of which they are capable at all levels of ability, but particularly at the higher ability levels.

10. Differences are not static. Children vary when they enter school and they develop at different rates. Consequently, diagnosis must be a continuous process.

When the above findings are studied carefully, it is not difficult to understand why elementary school personnel are often in a quandary as to the best means for handling the problem of individual differences.

There are basically two ways of providing a setting in which each member of an arithmetic class has an opportunity to use materials of appropriate difficulty. The first is through special organization of the arithmetic classroom by the administration. The second requires special provisions made by the teacher. In some school systems both means are used, while in others only one of the two is found.

ADMINISTRATIVE PROCEDURES

Homogeneous grouping

In some schools the pupil is assigned to a section of a grade by an estimate of his ability. Normally the criteria used include the results of tests of mental ability, achievement tests, and the judgment of the professional staff. Because major weight is given to the pupils' reading abilities when determining the sections of a grade, it is not uncommon to have wide differences in arithmetic achievement within a so-called "homogeneous" classroom. Studies do not reveal any clear-cut advantages for the homogeneously grouped classroom.[2]

[2] See O. L. Davis, Jr., "Grouping for Instruction: Some Perspectives," *Educational Forum,* XXV (January 1960); O. L. Davis, Jr., "Arithmetic Achievement and Instructional Grouping," *The Arithmetic Teacher,* Vol. 10, No. 1 (January 1963); A. Harry Passow, "The Maze of the Research on Ability Grouping," *Educational Forum,* XXVI (March 1962); Paul V. Rogler, "Some Observations on the Value of Homogeneous Grouping to Achievement in Seventh Grade Mathematics" (Unpublished Ed.D. dissertation, Teachers College, Columbia University, 1957).

Departmentalization

Departmentalization in which a teacher works only in the area of arithmetic may be found in a number of school systems. Administrators have felt that making a teacher responsible for teaching only arithmetic should allow the teacher to study the field carefully and to develop materials appropriate to children of varying abilities. Each generation has attempted this approach to improving elementary school mathematics. The results of such programs have been varied. Recent evidence to support departmentalization is lacking.[3]

Since the teacher may at some time teach departmentalized mathematics, the following suggestions are offered:

1. There is a tendency in departmentalized classes to spend the entire period in class discussion and teacher explanation. This should be avoided. The teacher needs an opportunity to observe individuals at work and to give individual aid. As a rule of thumb, not more than half of the total class time should be spent in discussion and total class involvement.

2. Teachers often forget that the pupils are also studying other subjects. Therefore, the amount of work expected outside class time should be realistic.

3. Enrichment and remedial materials should be available to the students.

4. Other instructors should be consulted.

   a. An interchange on individual pupil performance and traits is usually helpful.

   b. Joint planning of projects and assignments is of value. For example, the social studies teacher may plan with you so that your teaching of longitude and latitude may correspond with the need for its use in social studies. Pupils may develop graphs and charts that use mathematical principles but are of use in the science or social studies class. The teacher of language arts may work with you on "the mathematics theme."

   c. There should be some sort of joint agreement on evaluation and promotion policies.

5. It should be remembered that every teacher is a teacher of language arts and that pupils will be learning some science and social studies in the mathematics classroom. They will also be learning some mathematics in the other classes they take.

6. Since the departmentalized teacher spends less time with her students, she should pay particular attention to pupil cumulative records and make a concerted effort to "get to know" each student.

Team-teaching

Team-teaching allows for the use of very large and very small groups and enables teachers working cooperatively to give particular help to

---

[3] E. Glenadine Gibb and Dorothy C. Matala, "Study on the Use of Special Teachers of Science and Mathematics in Grades 5 and 6: Final Report," *School Science and Mathematics,* Vol. LXII, No. 8 (November 1962), pp. 565–85.

those below average and those above average in mathematics achievement. For example, individual classroom teachers might introduce a unit on the study of multi-digit division at the fourth-grade level. Near the middle of the unit, as the children in each room were moving further and further apart in the understanding and skill of division, one teacher might prepare special enrichment materials and work with those with superior achievement, while another teacher might work with special materials teaching those with below average achievement. On other occasions the entire group of fourth-grade children might be brought together to view a mathematics enrichment film of historical interest. The cooperative planning developed in a team-teaching plan also provides an opportunity for a group of teachers to prepare special materials that all may use with the below average or above average student.

There are many forms of team-teaching ranging from the simple cooperative planning of teachers to a modified departmentalized system. For a more complete look at team-teaching the reader is directed to the sources listed below.[4]

The Dual-Progress program[5]

The Dual-Progress program normally begins with a nongraded primary and moves to a modified departmental plan in grades four through six. In these higher grades students are grouped in grade level classes in language arts. The classes for mathematics, science, art, and music are nongraded. Thus, the best students from grades four through six meet in one group for forty minutes a day to receive mathematics instruction from teachers who teach only mathematics. This is also true for the average and below average student.

In order to teach mathematics in this nongraded plan, a sequence of levels of achievement is developed. As the student finishes one level he advances to the next level. All students are not expected to complete the entire sequence in the elementary school. A brief outline of one such nongraded mathematics sequence is reproduced below.[6]

Levels:

1. Meaning and use of numbers from one to ten
2. Meaning and use of numbers from eleven to one hundred
3. Addition with carrying and subtraction with exchanging

[4] See Judson T. Shaplin and Henry F. Olds, eds., *Team Teaching* (New York: Harper & Row, 1964); Robert H. Anderson, "Team Teaching," *NEA Journal*, Vol. L (March 1961), pp. 52–54; Harold D. Drummond, "Team Teaching: An Assessment," *Educational Leadership*, Vol. XIX (December 1961), pp. 160–165; Philip Lambert, "Team Teaching for the Elementary School," *Educational Leadership*, Vol. XVIII (November 1960), pp. 394–396.
[5] See George D. Stoddard, *The Dual Progress Plan* (New York: Harper & Row, 1961).
[6] Glen Heathers and Morris Pincus, "The Dual Progress Plan in the Elementary School," *The Arithmetic Teacher*, Vol. 6 (December 1959), pp. 302–305. See also Samuel Steinbert, "A Non-Grade Sequence in Elementary Mathematics" (New York: The New York University School of Education, Experimental Teaching Center, July 15, 1960).

4. Multiplication and division by one-place multipliers and divisors
5. Meaning and use of common fractions
6. Geometry, graphs, and maps
7. Meaning and use of large numbers
8. Multiplication by two-place multipliers; division by two-place divisors
9. Comparing fractions
10. Operations with unlike fractions
11. Meaning and use of decimal fractions
12. Graphs, maps, and Cartesian coordinates
13. Multiplication and division of fractions
14. Ratios and percentages
15. Squares and square roots
16. Variables and number sentences
17. Probability and statistics

The Dual-Progress plan has been attempted in a number of schools with varying success. Only further experience with the plan will determine the effectiveness of this innovation.

Enrichment and remedial classes

Some schools provide special instruction once or twice a week for pupils above or below average in mathematics achievement. These special sessions are usually thirty to fifty minutes long. Although the pattern or organization varies, usually some form of team-teaching is used. For example, in a school containing four fifth grades with a total of 120 fifth graders, one teacher may work on enrichment materials with the top students, another teacher on remedial work with students in need of a particular kind of remedial aid, and the other two teachers with the average achievers on an appropriate topic. In other schools, a special mathematics consultant may work with enrichment materials with all classes. Still another pattern is for a teacher with a special interest in mathematics to work with gifted children from several rooms during the period in which music or art is taught in her homeroom. The success of such programs has varied with the enthusiasm and capabilities of the teachers involved.

Evaluation

A careful study of the research done on administrative organizational programs to meet individual differences is inconclusive. A proponent of one plan can find studies that verify his stand. Conversely, an opponent of the same program can find studies that show that this plan works no better than the typical administrative single-teacher, graded pattern. Perhaps the most important implication of the various studies is that good teachers are effective regardless of the nature of classroom organization.[7]

[7] J. Fred Weaver and E. Glenadine Gibb, "Mathematics in the Elementary School," *Review of Educational Research*, Vol. XXXIV, No. 3 (June 1964), p. 278.

WITHIN-A-CLASS GROUPING

The three-group pattern

There are a number of patterns of within-a-class grouping. The most typical type resembles the three-group pattern normally found in reading instruction. In such a pattern the time devoted to arithmetic is divided into three equal portions, and the teacher devotes an equal amount of time to each group. (See table.)

DISTRIBUTION OF TIME DURING A 45-MINUTE ARITHMETIC PERIOD

Time	Group I	Group II	Group III
9:00–9:15	Pupil Work	Pupil Work	Discussion of Previous Work and Introductory Material
9:15–9:30	Pupil Work	Discussion of Previous Work and Introductory Material	Pupil Work
9:30–9:45	Discussion of Previous Work and Introductory Material	Pupil Work	Pupil Work

During the course of the school year two patterns can be followed. The normal pattern is for the advanced group to cover the material for the year and part of the material for the next school year. The average group finishes the year's work, and the slower group does not complete the year's work. Another pattern calls for all three groups to cover the year's program, with the upper group spending time on supplementary materials and the slower group working on shortened assignments.

There are inherent weaknesses in either of the patterns described. In the first case, it is essential that all of the teachers in an elementary school work together closely. If they do not, the upper group often covers the same material the following year, and the lower group misses important content. As can be readily noted, if there is not meticulous coordination, a program such as this can lead to lack of interest and dislike of arithmetic. In the second case, the three-group pattern offers no more advantages than a pattern of introducing new topics to the entire class and then using supplementary materials for the above average and below average students.

Another weakness of the three-group pattern is the limited amount of teacher time available for the teacher to spend aiding individuals. In the superior classroom one of the major roles of the teacher is to ask questions, offer suggestions, and observe individual pupil work. This is difficult in the traditional three-group situation.

A weakness of any form of grouping is the negative attitude that may be developed by students who are not in the top group. While most pupils realize that they are not of equal ability with the top students, they often feel that the better students are given more than their fair share of opportunities to work on interesting assignments. Also, while it is always recommended that groups within a classroom be kept flexible with changes often occurring, observation of grouping in action reveals that once a child is placed within a group the chances are great that he will remain in that group for the entire year, even though his achievement has greatly improved or he has made very slow progress. In fact, he may continue in the same level group for several years, since the teacher who next teaches him will tend to use the records of his past group placement as the major criterion for his group placement in her class.

In addition, a number of research studies have indicated that programs of ability grouping do not produce results superior to regular classroom procedures.[8]

A suggested pattern for providing for individual differences

If the "reading-type" grouping pattern is rejected, what can be done? The instructional procedures that are described below attempt to provide answers to the questions raised earlier in the chapter. Those that are not answered by the narrative are then considered.

A sixth-grade teacher noted that many of the word problems presented in the textbook were not challenging the better students, while the poorer students were experiencing extreme difficulty with them. She devised a period-length problem-solving test made up of typical sixth-grade problems. The test was tape-recorded to give pupils with reading difficulty a chance to hear the problems. Each pupil also received a duplicated copy of the problems. The test was administered and corrected by the teacher.

The next class period she began by saying, "Yesterday we took a test in problem solving designed to help you gauge your present problem-solving ability and to serve as a basis on which to check the improvement you make. I've developed two sets of problem exercises. The problems on the yellow sheet of paper are the more difficult ones. Those on the white sheet are not so difficult. I am giving you either a yellow or a white sheet on the basis of the score you made on the tests. Those who made below the median (half-way score) will get the white sheets. The others will get the yellow ones. After you've worked a while with the problems, we can more easily decide which sheet is best for you. Some of you may want to work with both sheets."

[8] O. L. Davis, Jr., and Neal H. Tracy, "Arithmetic Achievement and Instructional Grouping," *The Arithmetic Teacher*, Vol. 10, No. 1 (January 1963), pp. 12–17.

The first two problems occurred on both the yellow sheet and the white sheet. These were used as a basis for discussion and to acquaint the pupils with the materials. Pupils then began to work, with the teacher going about the room offering encouragement and help to those in need. After the pupils had been at work for a little while, the teacher called their attention to the fact that the last exercise, headed "How's Your P.Q.?" (How's Your Problem Quotient), was the most difficult on the page and was to be worked only if the pupil wished to do so. The teacher also suggested that when the students had finished all the exercises, they might compare their answers first with a companion and then with a check sheet on the teacher's desk.

A sample of the problem and answer sheets is reproduced below.

PROBLEM-SOLVING LESSON—USING DRAWINGS AND DIAGRAMS (BELOW AVERAGE)

Read the problem carefully, and then make a drawing or diagram to use in solving the problem. Try to check your work by using another method of solution.

1. Alice wants to divide 3 candy bars equally among 4 people. What fraction of a candy bar will each person's share be?

2. Clyde and his father set out for the mountains. In 3 hours they had gone 140 miles. They still had 28 miles to go. How far was it to the mountains?

3. One Friday George rode his bicycle $\frac{3}{10}$ mile to the store, $\frac{7}{10}$ mile to the Y.M.C.A., and $\frac{9}{10}$ mile to school. How far did he ride that day?

4. In the morning the snow behind Rachel's house was $6\frac{1}{2}$ inches deep. It snowed during the day so that in the evening the snow was 12 inches deep. How much had it snowed during the day?

HOW'S YOUR P.Q.?

5. Jack said to his friend Bill, "I met a group of boys practicing marching. There were 2 boys in front of a boy and 2 boys behind a boy and there was a boy in the middle. How many boys did I see?" Try using a drawing to help you answer Jack's question.

CORRECTION SHEET FOR PROBLEM-SOLVING LESSON—USING DRAWINGS AND DIAGRAMS

1. Each person will receive $\frac{3}{4}$ of a candy bar.

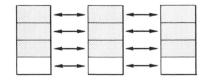

2. The total distance is 168 miles. The 3 hours is unnecessary information.

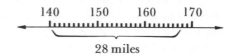

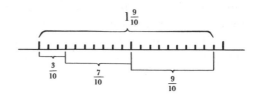

3. He rode $1\frac{9}{10}$ miles in all.

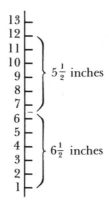

4. It snowed $5\frac{1}{2}$ inches during the day.

5. How's Your P.Q.?
Answer: Three boys in all.

2 boys in the front

1 boy in the middle

2 boys in the back

PROBLEM-SOLVING LESSON—USING DRAWINGS AND DIAGRAMS (ABOVE AVERAGE)

Read the problem carefully and then make a drawing or diagram to use in solving the problem. Try to check your answer by using another method of solution.

1. Two men depart both from one place and both go the same road; the one travels 12 miles every day; the other 17 miles every day; how far are they distant after the 5th day of departure? (Taken from *The Scholar's Arithmetic* by Adams, 1812).

2. Mr. Kramer and Mr. Black are going to put new fence around their farms. Mr. Kramer's farm is in the shape of a square that is 1 mile long and 1 mile wide, and Mr. Black's farm is a rectangle 1 mile long and $\frac{1}{2}$ mile wide. How many times as much fence will be needed by Mr. Kramer as by Mr. Black?

3. Mary is cutting 3-inch-by-5-inch cards to use as tickets for the school play. How many cards can she cut from a sheet of cardboard that is 12 inches by 20 inches?

4. A circular fish pond has a border of red and white bricks. If it has 20 red bricks spaced evenly around the edge and follows a pattern of two red bricks, one white brick, two red bricks, etc., how many white bricks are there?

HOW'S YOUR P.Q.?

5. If a brick balances evenly with a $\frac{3}{4}$ lb. weight and $\frac{3}{4}$ of a brick, what is the weight of a whole brick?

CORRECTION SHEET FOR PROBLEM-SOLVING LESSON USING DRAWINGS AND DIAGRAMS

1. Use a number line

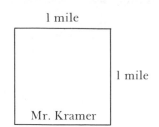

2. Make a drawing of the two
farms. Compare the distances

$\dfrac{4}{3}$ Kramer
    Black

$= 1\frac{1}{3}$ times as much

Total = 4 miles of fence.

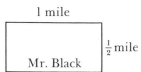

Total = 3 miles of fence.

3. Twelve tickets can
be cut from the 12-inch
by 20-inch piece of
cardboard.

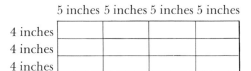

4. Ten white bricks.

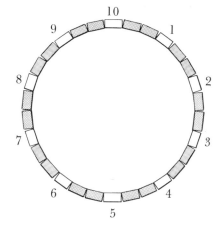

5. How's Your P.Q.?
Answer: Thus $\frac{1}{4}$ of a brick must weigh $\frac{3}{4}$ lb. A whole brick = 3 lbs.

$\frac{3}{4}$ of a brick, $\frac{3}{4}$-lb. weight   1 brick

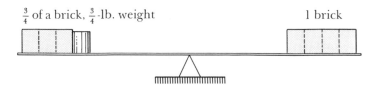

During the weeks that followed the teacher made use of the supple-mentary worksheet plan when working on problem solving. At times all of the students were assigned a few problems from the text and their choice of problem-solving sheets.

Several features of the approach suggested can be noted:

1. Materials on the same topic but with varying levels of difficulty were provided. Note that the "How's Your P.Q.?" problem provided an opportunity for both the fast student and the slow student to work with challenging supplemental problems.

2. The introductory test demonstrated to the pupils who were having difficulty a need for the study of problem solving. One of the most important aspects in improving a pupil's achievement is to have the pupil see a need for an intensive study.

3. The pupils were allowed leeway in choosing material of varying levels of difficulty. Teachers using such materials have found that pupils who are experiencing some difficulty with problem solving will often ask to work both sets of materials. They are encouraged to get the majority of the exercises on the easier sheets right and feel a sense of achievement if they are able to get any of the exercises on the more difficult sheets correct.

4. The opportunity to check answers upon completion of the work pro-vided for a correction of errors while the material was still fresh in the pupil's mind.

5. Class unity was still maintained since class discussion occurred on some problems worked in common. Class discussion also gave the pupils a chance to hear the explanations from their classmates. Often another pupil is able to explain an idea in a manner that is understandable to the slow learner. These explanations also allow the able pupil to clarify in his own mind his method of solution.

6. The procedure provided the teacher with an opportunity to work with individual pupils. If the "reading-type" grouping is used, the teacher has no time during the mathematics period to work with individual children. The time spent with individual pupils also provides an opportunity for the teacher to suggest specific materials for individual class members. In such cases, one or two pages from a supplementary book or worksheet may help to correct difficulty experienced by only one pupil.

7. A program such as the one described allows for a study in "depth" by the above average pupil. This procedure has applications in all areas of the mathematics curriculum. The recognition of the fact that pupils with vary-ing degrees of mathematical ability can work on materials at several levels of abstractness allows the class to move from topic to topic together. Some pupils will use concrete materials, some drawings, some the standard algorithms, and some will work beyond the level of the standard form. Examples of pupils working at these levels will occur in the chapters that follow.

Source: United Feature Syndicate

Nothing succeeds like success!

In addition to the suggested grouping procedure, the teacher may provide many opportunities for "enriching" the program for all students. Several suggestions for "enrichment" and "depth" learning follow.

1. Emphasize the multiple solution to number operations and verbal problems. The inventive pupil may develop several alternate situations to an exercise while the slower student is developing one. Such a procedure not only adds to the learning situations but is also a valuable means of balancing the length of time required for the class to finish an exercise.

2. Make use of historical materials. Such materials help to reveal the number system as a "man-made" invention and to develop cultural appreciation of the number system.[9]

3. Make use of a mathematics bulletin board. Such a bulletin board should act as a motivation for a unit. In addition, the bulletin board should always include several challenging problems, puzzles, or exercises. These should be developed at several different levels of difficulty so that all of the pupils have a possibility of working at least one.

4. Provide supplemental worksheets containing challenging material. It should be noted that for many years supplemental puzzle-type exercises have been used by the better teachers. It is suggested that a somewhat different stress be placed on these exercises. That is, not only should "figuring out an answer" be stressed, but the pupil should be directed to "figure out what mathematical principle is involved in the solution."

5. Provide books and booklets which emphasize the use of mathematics in various careers [for example, National Council of Teachers of Mathematics, *Careers in Mathematics* (New York: The Council, 1961)]. Pupils are often amazed at the need for mathematics in apparently nonmathematical occupations.

6. At the end of units make use of "review study questions."[10] In addition to providing a general review of understanding, some of these questions

---

[9] Frances Flournoy and Helen Marie Kreitz, "A Bibliography of Historical Materials for Use in Arithmetic in the Intermediate Grades," *The Arithmetic Teacher,* Vol. 7, No. 6 (October 1960), pp. 287–292.
[10] Paul C. Burns, "Study Questions for Reviewing Arithmetic," *The Arithmetic Teacher,* Vol. 7, No. 8 (December 1960), pp. 414–417.

should encourage investigation and exploration. Examples of such questions follow.

Grade three (addition). How could you rename one of the 8's in $8 + 8$ so that a friend who knew only addition combinations with sums of ten or less could probably understand? (Answer: $8 + (2 + 6) = (8 + 2) + 6 = 10 + 6 = 16$.) Use of the associative principle.

Grade five (multiplication of fractions). What is the smallest number and the largest number that could be the product of a little less than 3 times a little more than 4? Note: A little less than 3 would be $> 2\frac{1}{2}$, but < 3; a little more than 4 would be > 4, but $< 4\frac{1}{2}$. (Answer: 10 plus to $13\frac{1}{2}$ minus.) Smallest: $2\frac{1}{2} \times 4 = 10$. Largest: $3 \times 4\frac{1}{2} = 13\frac{1}{2}$.

Team-learning

On occasion the idea of "team-learning" may be employed. In the team-learning situation, two pupils of about the same ability level work on materials as partners. On occasion three pupils may work as a team. The pupils study the materials together or work with the teacher.

Some programs have been developed in which the "learning teams" work through a series of assignment or "job" sheets.[11] When they have successfully completed one topic, they go on to the next. Such a procedure probably does not give the individual pupil a chance to "discover" ideas for himself. Because of this feature, the author feels that the team-learning aspect is best used after a new topic has been introduced to the entire class.

Programmed materials

Recent developments in self-instructional materials reveal that well-constructed materials based upon the ideas of "programmed instruction" can be a valuable adjunct to the regular classroom program. In order to provide materials for the extremes in achievement levels two approaches to programmed instruction are needed. The below average students need very small-step programs with a minimum of possibility of pupil errors. The above average student requires rather large-step programs which challenge his thinking.

Programs for the below average. There are several basic features of programmed instruction which should be helpful to the slow learner: (1) the learning is active; (2) the student receives immediate knowledge of his results and thus can correct quickly his errors in thinking; (3) spaced review is pro-

[11] Walter J. McHugh, "Team Learning in Skills Subjects in Intermediate Grades," *Journal of Education*, Vol. 142 (December 1959), pp. 22–51.

vided; and (4) anxiety is often reduced since the pupil is not threatened by the task.[12]

Since the slow learner very seldom achieves success in his endeavors, programs developed for these pupils should move along very slowly, giving the pupil a chance to experience success. Success with such small-step programs may improve not only the mathematics achievement of the pupil but also his attitude toward learning. The old adage, "Nothing succeeds like success" is particularly true for the slow learner.

The following illustrative situation depicts one way that programmed materials may be effectively used with the mathematics class: During the first half of the arithmetic period the fifth grade discussed a number of multiplication problems and exercises. Then the teacher said, "I've noticed that some of you are having trouble with the work we have been doing on multiplication, while others of you seem to know the majority of the answers. Those who are interested in improving their multiplication skill may wish to work on the booklets that I have placed on the arithmetic table. There are two booklets, 'Be a Speed Demon,' and 'Improve Your Skill.' Try the speed demon one if you think you know multiplication quite well. If you're having some trouble, try the 'Improve Your Skill.' When you finish the skill booklet, you may want to try the speed demon booklet. There are instructions inside each booklet." (The teacher holds one up.) "They say, 'Make use of the cardboard slider to cover the answers until you have attempted to answer the question.' Use the blank sheets provided for writing your answers."

Portions of an enrichment program and of a remedial program are illustrated below.[13]

ENRICHMENT PROGRAM

(1) When asked to work the multiplication example

$$38$$
$$\times 42$$

Bob went to the board and wrote 1596 almost immediately. His teacher and classmates were surprised at his speed. Do you think that you could work the example without paper and pencil?

(1) If you answered yes, try to work another example by your method and then see if your procedure is the same as the one shown on the next few pages.

[12] Ernest R. Hilgard, "What Support from the Psychology of Learning?" *NEA Journal*, Vol. L, No. 8 (November 1961), p. 20.
[13] C. Alan Riedesel, "Arithmetic Enrichment Through the Use of the Modified Program," *The Arithmetic Teacher*, Vol. 10, No. 8 (December 1963), pp. 501–503.

(2) Bob said that his method was called the "lightning" method of multiplying. How would working by the lightning method compare in speed with the regular procedure?

(2) It should be faster.

Now you will try the lightning method. You'll need paper and pencil. Perhaps you'll need an eraser too. Copy this example on your paper:

$$\begin{array}{r} 36 \\ \times 24 \\ \hline \end{array}$$

(3) Now multiply the digits in the ones' place. What is the answer?

(3) 24
$4 \times 6 = 24$

(4) How many tens and ones are there in 24? _____ tens _____ ones

(4) 2 tens   4 ones

(5) Write the 4 on your paper as shown.

$$\begin{array}{r} 36 \\ \times 24 \\ \hline 4 \end{array}$$

You should remember the tens numeral. What is it?

(5) 2 tens
Remember 4×6 $= 2$ tens and 4 ones.

(6) How many ones will there be in your final answer?

(6) 4 ones

(7) Next it is necessary to multiply the 4 ones in the multiplier by _____ tens in the multiplicand.

$$\begin{array}{r} 36 \\ \times 24 \\ \hline 4 \end{array}$$

(7) 3 tens

(8) Then multiply the 2 tens in the multiplier times the _____ ones in the multiplicand.

$$\begin{array}{r} 36 \\ \times 24 \\ \hline 4 \end{array}$$

(8) 6 ones

(9) This is a total of _____ tens + _____ tens.
Or a total of _____ tens.

(9) 12 tens + 12 tens
24 tens

(10) How many tens were you to remember from the 4 × 6?

(10) 2 tens
Remember 4 × 6
= 24, 2 tens 4 ones.

(11) How many tens are there in all?

(11) 26 tens.
24 + 2 = 26

(12) Write the 6 in the tens place of your answer. How many hundreds do you need to remember?

$$\begin{array}{r} 36 \\ \times 24 \\ \hline 64 \end{array}$$

(12) 2 hundreds

(13) You still need to multiply 2 tens × 3 tens. How many hundreds is this?

(13) 6 hundreds

(14) Add the 6 hundreds to the 2 hundreds you were to remember. How many hundreds in all?

Write down the 8 hundreds.

$$\begin{array}{r} 36 \\ \times 24 \\ \hline 864 \end{array}$$

(14) 8 hundreds

That took a long time to do, but it should be a help in learning the lightning method of multiplication. Study this diagram carefully. It shows the steps you took in working the lightning method.

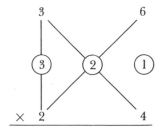

(15) Try to write a rule for working the lightning method. Compare it with the one on the right.

(15) Multiply ones times ones. Multiply the ones times tens and the tens times ones and add them. Multiply the tens. Carry when you need to.

As a final aid in learning the lightning method, it may help you to study this example:

$$\begin{array}{r} 23 \\ \times 46 \\ \hline \end{array}$$

Multiply $6 \times 3 = 18$. Write the 8, remember the 1. "Cross-multiply" $6 \times 2 = 12$ and $4 \times 3 = 12$; add 12 and 12 and the 1 you remembered to carry $= 25$. Write 5, remember the 2. Multiply $4 \times 2 = 8$ plus the 2 you remembered $= 10$. Write 10. Answer: 1058.

The lightning method takes a lot of thought and practice. If you aren't sure of it go back through the previous pages. When you think you have the idea, work the examples that follow. Remember you will need a lot of practice with the lightning method, but once you are skillful in its use, you can multiply two-digit examples quickly. Try these examples:

(16) $\begin{array}{r} 56 \\ \times 43 \\ \hline \end{array}$ (16) 2408

(17) $\begin{array}{r} 74 \\ \times 63 \\ \hline \end{array}$ (17) 4662

(18) $\begin{array}{r} 83 \\ \times 27 \\ \hline \end{array}$ (18) 2241

(19) $\begin{array}{r} 25 \\ \times 32 \\ \hline \end{array}$ (19) 800

(20) $\begin{array}{r} 32 \\ \times 23 \\ \hline \end{array}$ (20) 736

After you have become skillful in multiplying two-digit numerals using the lightning method, try to figure out a way to multiply three-digit numerals.

Jane plans to have a tulip bed like the one shown in the drawing.

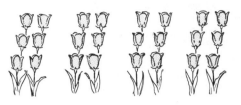

(1) How many flowers are in the flower garden diagrammed above? _____

    (1) 24

(2) Can the answer be found by counting? _____

    (2) Yes

(3) Can the answer be found by addition? _____

    (3) Yes

(4) Can the answer be found by multiplication? _____

    (4) Yes

(5) Can the answer by found by subtraction? _____

    (5) No

(6) Can the answer be found by division? _____

    (6) No

(7) Which way is the fastest way to find the number of flowers in the garden? _____

    (7) Multiplying

(8) What is the multiplication question used to find the answer to the question, "How many flowers in the garden?" _____ × _____ =_____

    (8) How many are four 6's or how many are three 8's?
$4 \times 6 = 24$
$3 \times 8 = 24$

(9) Jim and his younger brother Joe were arguing over the cost of the stamps in their collections. Jim said that the cost of six 4¢ stamps was 24¢. Joe was in second grade and could only write addition and subtraction number questions. How could Jim show Joe that six 4's equal 24 if he used addition? _____

    (9) $4 + 4 + 4 + 4 + 4 + 4 = 24$

$$\begin{array}{r} 4 \\ 4 \\ 4 \\ 4 \\ 4 \\ +4 \\ \hline 24 \end{array}$$

Think the answers to the following multiplication questions and show that your answers are correct by adding. Write your answers on your answer pad.

(10) 4×5 The answer is _____

(11) 6×7 The answer is _____

(12) 8×6 The answer is _____

(13) 7×5 The answer is _____

(14) 4×8 The answer is _____

(15) 6×9 The answer is _____

(16) 9×5 The answer is _____

(10) 20
$5 + 5 + 5 + 5 = 20$

(11) 42
$7 + 7 + 7 + 7 + 7 + 7 = 42$

(12) 48
$6 + 6 + 6 + 6 + 6 + 6 + 6 + 6 = 48$

(13) 35
$5 + 5 + 5 + 5 + 5 + 5 + 5 = 35$

(14) 32
$8 + 8 + 8 + 8 = 32$

(15) 54
$9 + 9 + 9 + 9 + 9 + 9 = 54$

(16) 45
$5 + 5 + 5 + 5 + 5 + 5 + 5 + 5 + 5 = 45$

A good, quick way to check your knowledge of basic multiplication facts is to take a set of numbers and multiply each number by another number. What are the products when each number written below is multiplied by 4? Write the answer in your answer pad for the exercise below, and then compare your answers with those given at the right.

Multiply each of these numbers by 4.

(17) 5 _____   (20) 7 _____   (17) 20   (20) 28

(18) 6 _____   (21) 9 _____   (18) 24   (21) 36

(19) 8 _____   (22) 4 _____   (19) 32   (22) 16

If it was hard for you to think the answers to the multiplication questions that you just worked, you need to study the multiplication facts. Turn to the back of the book for some practice exercises. You will want to use these exercises often if you have any trouble thinking the answers to multiplication questions. Cover the answers to the exercises in the back of the book in the same manner that you have in your work in this book.

(23) Jack and Tom lived on a farm and raised sweet corn to earn spending money. One day Tom, who was seven, was alone at the vegetable stand. A customer stopped and asked for 3 dozen ears of corn. Tom knew there were 12 ears in a dozen, but because he didn't know how many three 12's are, he counted to 12 three times. Would that be a good way to get 3 dozen ears? _____

(23) Yes

(24) How far would Tom have had to count if he had just continued to count 13, 14, and so on? _____

(24) 36

(25) Would counting from 1 to 36 have been easier than counting to 12 three times? _____

(25) Yes, but not much.

(26) Jack, who is Tom's older brother, said counting through to 36 was really easier and besides it was a good check. "But," he said, "you might have known that three 12's = 36." If you didn't know

(26) Counting
Adding
Multiplying

that, what are three good ways of finding out how many three 12's are?

_____

_____

_____

(27) To find how many three 12's are, is it better to add or multiply? _____

(27) Multiply, it is normally faster.

Jack explained to Tom a method of finding how many are three 12's. He asked these questions. Answer them.

$$\begin{array}{r} 12 \\ \times\ 3 \\ \hline \end{array}$$

(28) How many are three 2's? _____

(28) 6

(29) How many are 3×1 ten? _____

(29) 30

(30) How many are three 12's? _____

(30) 36

(31) In multiplying 3×12, why did Jack say 3×1 ten? _____

(31) The 1 is in the tens place.

The following exercises should improve your skill in multiplying. Find the answers by multiplying:

$$\begin{array}{r} 21 \\ \times\ 3 \\ \hline \end{array}$$

(32) $3 \times 1 =$ _____ ones or just _____

(32) 3 ones or 3

(33) 3×2 tens $=$ _____ tens or _____

(33) 6 tens or 60

(34) The answer is _____

(34) 63

(35) $\begin{array}{r} 22 \\ \times\ 4 \\ \hline \end{array}$ The answer is _____

(35) 88

(36) $\begin{array}{r} 23 \\ \times\ 5 \\ \hline \end{array}$ The answer is _____

(36) 115

(37) $\begin{array}{r} 12 \\ \times\ 4 \\ \hline \end{array}$ The answer is _____

(37) 48

$$\begin{array}{r} 42 \\ \times\ 5 \\ \hline \end{array}$$

(38)   The answer is _____   (38) 210

Chapter 16 provides suggestions for developing programmed materials.

The previous situations and suggestions have dealt with the first five questions developed on page 46. Questions six through nine are discussed below.

How can I recognize varying abilities? There are several common means of identifying pupils with above or below average ability in mathematics. They include: (1) analysis of tests of ability, commonly called I.Q. tests; (2) analysis of results on standardized tests of mathematics achievement; (3) analysis of tests of creativity;[14] (4) comments from a previous teacher; and (5) observation of pupils and analysis of their work.

The teacher will also want to be on the lookout for traits that are usually present in pupils of atypical ability levels. Two lists follow: (1) a composite of traits frequently possessed by gifted students; and (2) a composite of traits usually present in slow learners.

Gifted pupils in mathematics often[15]
1.   Are more persistent in pursuing a task than others.
2.   Are able to perceive mathematical patterns, structures, and relationships.
3.   Possess a greater amount of intellectual curiosity and imagination.
4.   Are physically stronger, socially more secure, and emotionally more stable than average.
5.   Possess a superior vocabulary.
6.   Are able to transfer mathematical learning to new or novel situations that have not previously been taught.
7.   Are able to remember longer what they have learned.
8.   Are flexible in their thinking.
9.   Are able to discover new principles from the principles which they already know.
10.   Are able to think and work abstractly and enjoy working with abstractions.
11.   Have a high verbal comprehension and are able to communicate mathematical ideas to others.
12.   Are able to objectively self-analyze strengths and weaknesses in their mathematical thinking.
13.   Often are bored with "drill-type" work.

Slow learners in mathematics often[16]
1.   Possess little motivation or drive. They are willing to just sit.
2.   Enjoy "drill-type" work.

[14] E. Paul Torrance, *Guiding Creative Talent* (Englewood Cliffs, N.J.: Prentice-Hall, 1962).
[15] Adapted from Charlotte Junge, "The Gifted Ones—How Shall We Know them?" *The Arithmetic Teacher*, Vol. 4, No. 4 (October 1957), pp. 141–146 and J. Fred Weaver and Cleo Fisher Brawley, "Enriching The Elementary School Mathematics Program for More Capable Children," *Journal of Education*, Vol. 142, No. 1 (October 1959), pp. 6–7.
[16] Adapted from Mary Potter and Virgil Mallory, *Education in Mathematics for the Slow Learner* (Washington, D. C.: National Council of Teachers of Mathematics, 1958), pp. 11–14.

3. Possess short attention spans. They are easily distracted.

4. Possess a less than average memory. They may forget material from day to day.

5. Are low in verbal comprehension. Have difficulty in interpreting written material.

6. Are unable to be original in their thinking.

7. Are physically weaker, socially less secure, and emotionally less stable than average.

The above traits will vary from pupil to pupil, but they should serve the teacher as a guideline in observation. Also, the power of motivation should not be overlooked. It is possible for one of the slower pupils to do very fine work on a topic in which he is greatly interested or that he believes that he has a chance of mastering.

What are some things that I can do to interest the slow learners? The suggestions that follow are designed to improve the interest of the slow learner. The reader should realize that many of the suggestions apply equally well to the average student and the above average student.

1. Show interest yourself. Interest inventories reveal that arithmetic rates at or near the top as a favorite subject of children.[17] Teachers do not rate arithmetic as high.[18] Often below average pupils will reflect the enthusiasm or lack of enthusiasm of the teacher.

2. Often the bright pupils are provided with attractive supplemental materials. Provide appropriate supplemental materials of equal attractiveness for the below average.

3. During a class discussion use the "levels of depth" approach to discussion. In this approach the teacher allows the pupils who have used a very simple means of arriving at an answer to express their views first. Then she builds on their explanations by getting next suggestions from the average pupils and last the suggestions of the bright. By such an approach all ability levels are able to make a contribution to the class consideration of a topic in mathematics.

4. Slow learners have few opportunities to present unique contributions to the class. During the course of the year, work out a "special" presentation with one of the slower pupils. "Knowing something first" is often a good incentive to continued work.

5. Provide situations which "make sense" to the slow learner. Bright pupils in mathematics are often interested in the abstract puzzle aspects of mathematics. While some slow learners are also interested in these aspects, in general it is important for them to see a use for the mathematics they study.

6. Know the interests of the pupils. Capitalize on these interests in the mathematics class. Many boys who are below average in arithmetic understand "baseball percentage very well."

[17] Clare E. Faust, "A Study of the Relationship Between Attitude and Achievement in Selected Elementary School Subjects" (Unpublished Ph.D. dissertation, State University of Iowa, February 1962).
[18] C. Alan Riedesel, "Teachers and Elementary School Mathematics" (Unpublished study, Kansas State University).

7. Be impartial. Let each pupil know that you like HIM. He should know that you are interested in his work, even if he will never be a good mathematician. Be positive rather than negative. Almost all slow learners react much better to—"You're coming along better, Bill. Let's see if we can do well on the next lesson"—than to—"Bill, if you don't improve you're going to fail mathematics."

8. Point out the value of praise to the parents. Encourage the parents to take pride in some of the good work a slow learner accomplishes.

9. Be patient. It is very discouraging to a pupil to hear, "Hurry-up, quit loafing!" when he is trying very hard and working at his fastest pace.

Should superior students be used to help the slower pupils? If so, how? Probably the best answer to this question is—sometimes. On occasion both the bright pupils and the slow pupils can gain from working together. The bright pupil has to understand the mathematical content well enough to explain it clearly to the slower pupil, and often the thought processes the bright pupil goes through in verbalizing an explanation are helpful to him as well as to the slower pupil. If the "team-learning" approach is sometimes used in a classroom, there will be occasions on which the teacher can profitably team a slow student with a fast student.

This approach can be, and often is, overdone. The better student should not have the responsibility of being a tutor to a slower student. A rule of thumb might be this: Use this technique in situations in which you believe both parties will derive benefit from the exchange.

What materials are available for the better students? For the poorer students?

The hardcover books, paperbacks, and pamphlets listed below are representative of the types of materials available to the teacher for use in developing materials for pupils.

ENRICHMENT AND REMEDIAL MATERIALS

The materials listed below are examples of arithmetic aids for the teacher's use in providing vertical enrichment or remedial activities. Those marked with an asterisk (*) can be used for enrichment or remedial purposes.

ADDISON-WESLEY PUBLISHING CO., INC., READING, MASSACHUSETTS.

Davis, Robert, *Discovery in Math.* Madison project; supplementary math enrichment.

ENCYCLOPEDIA BRITANNICA FILMS, INC., WILMETTE, ILLINOIS.

*Rasmussen, L., *Mathematics Laboratory Materials.* Gr. 1, 2, 3. Individualized materials to provide primary school pupils with a wide variety of opportunities to develop insight, sequence, and independent work.

*Wirtz, R., Botel, M., and Sawyer, W. W., *Math Workshop for Children.* Complete supplementary program K-6.

FEARON PUBLISHERS, INC., SAN FRANCISCO, CALIFORNIA.

Dumas, E., *Arithmetic Games.*

GINN & COMPANY, BOSTON, MASSACHUSETTS.

Marks, J. L., Smart, J. R., and Sauble, I., *Ginn Arithmetic Enrichment Program.*
    *Exploring Mathematical Ideas. Gr. 4.
    *Enlarging Mathematical Ideas. Gr. 5.
    Extending Mathematical Ideas. Gr. 6.
    Principles and Patterns of Numeration Systems.

Marks, J. L., Smart, J. R., and Purdy, C. R., *Ginn Enrichment Program.* For advanced sixth graders.
    Sentences—Properties—Probability. Gr. 7–8.
    Sets, Geometry, Other Systems. Gr. 7–9.
    Understanding and Using Sets. Gr. 7–9.
    Sets in Geometry. Gr. 7–9.
    Other Bases in Arithmetic. Gr. 7–8.
    Introduction to Mathematical Sentences. Gr. 7–9.
    Graphing Mathematical Sentences. Gr. 7–9.
    Properties of Our Number System. Gr. 7–9.
    Thinking About Probability. Gr. 7–9.
    Introduction to Sets and Numbers. Elementary.
    Operations on Sets and Numbers. Elementary.

HARPER & ROW, NEW YORK, NEW YORK.

*Peterman, W. J., editor, *Enrichment Program for Arithmetic, Grades 3 through 8.* A series of booklets containing interesting and challenging problems for children, historical material, and puzzles.

HOLT, RINEHART AND WINSTON, INC., NEW YORK, NEW YORK.

Ready for Numbers. Gr. 1.

Using Numbers. Gr. 2.

LAIDLAW BROTHERS, RIVER FOREST, ILLINOIS.

Gundlach, B., *Student's Glossary of Arithmetical—Mathematical Terms.*

*Lennes, N. J., and Traver, L. R., *Essential Drill and Practice in Arithmetic.* Gr. 3–6.

*——, *Arithmetic Readiness Parts I and II.* Gr. 1–2.

MACMILLAN COMPANY, NEW YORK, NEW YORK.

Page, D. A., *Number Lines, Functions, and Fundamental Topics.*

NATIONAL COUNCIL OF TEACHERS OF MATHEMATICS, WASHINGTON, D. C.

Johnson, D. A., *Paper Folding for the Mathematics Class.* For advanced students.

NEW AMERICAN LIBRARY OF WORLD LITERATURE, NEW YORK, NEW YORK.

*Adler, Irving, *Golden Key to Math.* Three workbooks for gr. 1–3.

SCIENCE RESEARCH ASSOCIATES, INC., CHICAGO, ILLINOIS.

Computational Skills Development Kit. Gr. 2–7.

Advancing In Mathematics. Gr. 7–8.

SCOTT, FORESMAN AND COMPANY, CHICAGO, ILLINOIS.

Seeing Through Arithmetic: Special Book A. Gr. 5–6.

Seeing Through Arithmetic: Special Book B. Gr. 5–6.

L. W. SINGER COMPANY, INC., SYRACUSE, NEW YORK.

Suppes, P., *Sets and Numbers.* Complete program K-6.

HARR WAGNER PUBLISHING CO., SAN FRANCISCO, CALIFORNIA.

Irving, H. F., and Eastman, G., *Highway to Math Fun.*

Arithmetic Foundation Series Levels I, II, II. Gr. 1–20.

WEBSTER DIVISION, McGRAW-HILL BOOK COMPANY, ST. LOUIS, MISSOURI.

Johnson, D. A., and Glenn, W. H., *Exploring Mathematics on Your Own.* Set of eighteen booklets mainly for junior and senior high school. Four booklets—Sets, Sentences, and Operation; Number Patterns; Fun with Mathematics; and Understanding Numeration Systems—are better for elementary children.

PROGRAMMED INSTRUCTION—REMEDIAL AND ENRICHMENT

ADDISON-WESLEY PUBLISHING CO., INC., READING, MASSACHUSETTS.

O'Malley, R. H., *Basic Math: A Problem Solving Approach.*

———, *Enrichment Topics in Basic Math.*

ALLYN AND BACON, INC., BOSTON, MASSACHUSETTS.

Smith, M. D., *Decimals and Per cents.* Upper elementary grades.

DOUBLEDAY & COMPANY, GARDEN CITY, NEW YORK.

Friel, B. K., *Decimals and Percentages.* Gr. 4–8.

———, *Fractions.* Gr. 5–9.

ENCYCLOPEDIA BRITANNICA INC., CHICAGO, ILLINOIS.

TEMAC materials.

Gentry, F. C., Devine, J. V., Doran, L. L., and Hunt, A. D., *Fractions I and II.* Gr. 4–5.

Pearsall, L. J., and Hunt, A. D., *Problems in Percentage.* Advanced sixth graders.

Smith, J. A., *Arithmetic of the Whole Numbers.* Advanced sixth graders.

———, *Whole Numbers and Numerals.* Advanced sixth graders.

Basic Mathematics and Basic Mathematics—Measurement. Advanced sixth graders.

Modern Mathematics for the Junior High School. Advanced sixth graders with mod/math book.

Ratios and Proportions. Advanced sixth graders.

Seventh Grade Mathematics. Advanced sixth graders.

GINN & COMPANY, BOSTON, MASSACHUSETTS.

Programed Problem Solving. Adding and subtracting whole numbers.

GRAFLEX, INC., ROCHESTER, NEW YORK.

Dippold, J., *Addition of Fractions.* Gr. 4–5.

Faegre, *Arithmetic Facts Practice Program.* Gr. 1–6.

Kuehne, E., *Time Telling.* Gr. 2.

Syage, K. J., *Perimeters.* Gr. 4–6.

HARCOURT, BRACE & WORLD, INC., NEW YORK, NEW YORK.

Spooner, G., Mueller, F. J., and Hach, A., *Mathematics Enrichment.* Five books, A, B, C, D, E, for Gr. 4–8. Books A, B, and C are programmed; D, E are self-help. Can be utilized in a variety of patterns for Gr. 3–6 as enrichment and remedial work.

D. C. HEATH & COMPANY, BOSTON, MASSACHUSETTS.

Fitzgerald, J. F., and Blyth, J. W., *Logic.* Gr. 4–6.

Fitzgerald, and Raytheon Co., *Introduction to Sets.*

———, *Set Operations.* S-2.

———, *Set Operations.* S-3.

HOLT, RINEHART AND WINSTON, INC., NEW YORK, NEW YORK.

Nichols, E. D., Kalin, R., and Garland, H., *Arithmetic of Directed Numbers.*

———, *Equations and Inequalities.* Advanced sixth graders.

Odom, M. and Nichols, E. D., *Introduction to Exponents.* Gr. 5–8.

LEARNING, INC., CORONET FILMS, CHICAGO, ILLINOIS.

Number Bases and Binary Arithmetic, 8–10. Advanced sixth graders.

Understanding Problems in Arithmetic, 4–6.

McGRAW-HILL BOOK COMPANY, NEW YORK, NEW YORK.

Hauck, W., Moore, J. W., and Smith, W., *Decimals and Percent.* Advanced fifth and most sixth graders.

Hauck, W., Moore, J. W., and Smith, W., *Fractions.* Gr. 6.

MACMILLAN COMPANY, NEW YORK, NEW YORK.

Series can be judiciously used with sixth graders.
    Number Sentences, An Introduction to Equation Solving.
    Points, Lines and Planes: An Introduction to Geometry in Two Dimensions.
    What Are the Chances? An Introduction to Probability.
    Factors and Primes: An Introduction to Number Theory.
    Bases and Numerals: An Introduction to Numeration.

Reigh, M., Moore, J. W., and Smith, W., *Finite Arithmetic.* Advanced sixth graders.

NOBLE AND NOBLE PUBLISHERS, INC., NEW YORK, NEW YORK.

Progressive Elementary Mathematics Series
    Arithmetic With Sets. Gr. 4.
    Arithmetic In Use. Gr. 5.

TEACHING MATERIALS CORPORATION, DIVISION OF GROLIER, INC., NEW YORK, NEW YORK.

De Baca, P. C., and Tosti, D. T., *Decimal Numbers.* Advanced fifth and most sixth graders.

———, *Time Telling.* Gr. 2–3.

Evans, J. L., and Tosti, D. T., *Multiplication and Division Facts.* Gr. 2–3.

Glascock, G., and Evans, J. L., *Fractions: Basic Concepts.* Advanced third and most fourth graders.

Homme, L. E., *Introduction to Numbers.* Gr. 1.

1. Use the *Education Index, Reader's Guide,* and *Books in Print* to update the materials listed in this chapter for below average and above average students.
2. Review several textbooks designed for the same grade level. How does the level of difficulty of the texts compare? What suggestions and provisions are made to provide for individual differences?
3. Work out a lesson plan that provides for learning at several ability levels. Provide further help for slow students and opportunities for "depth" learning for the better students.
4. Prepare a list of arguments for and against "horizontal" and "vertical" enrichment. (Horizontal enrichment involves broadening or depth learning of topics. Vertical enrichment involves studying some topics normally taught at higher grade levels.)
5. Prepare a mathematics bulletin board designed to motivate the slow learner in mathematics.
6. Prepare an "enrichment" bulletin board.
7. Examine a puzzle-type mathematics exercise to determine the basic principles used for a solution.
8. Develop a short remedial program in division for a fourth-grade student.
9. Prepare a letter to parents explaining the manner in which you handle individual differences in the elementary school mathematics classroom.

SUGGESTED REFERENCES

Brewer, Emery, "A Survey of Arithmetic Intraclass Grouping Practices," *The Arithmetic Teacher,* Vol. 13, No. 4 (April 1966), pp. 310–314.
Brown, Gerald, "Magic Squares—More Than Recreations," *School Science and Mathematics,* Vol. LXVI, No. 1 (January 1966), pp. 23–28.
Brueckner, Leo J., and Bond, Guy L., *The Diagnosis and Treatment of Learning Difficulties* (New York: Appleton-Century-Crofts, 1955), Chaps. 3, 8, and 9.

Junge, Charlotte, "The Gifted Ones—How Shall We Know Them?" *The Arithmetic Teacher*, Vol. 4, No. 1 (October 1957), pp. 144–146.

Marks, John L., Purdy, C. Richard, and Kinney, Lucien B., *Teaching Arithmetic for Understanding* (New York: McGraw-Hill, 1958).

National Council of Teachers of Mathematics, *Enrichment Mathematics for the Grades,* Twenty-seventh Yearbook (Washington, D. C.: The Council, 1963).

———, *Instruction in Arithmetic,* Twenty-fifth Yearbook (Washington, D. C.: The Council, 1960), Chaps. 6, 7, 8, and 9.

National Society for the Study of Education, *Individualizing Instruction,* Sixty-first Yearbook, Part I (Chicago: Distributed by the University of Chicago Press, 1962).

Paschal, Billy L., "Teaching the Culturally Disadvantaged Child," *The Arithmetic Teacher*, Vol. 13, No. 5 (May 1966), pp. 369–374.

Read, Cecil B., "The History of Mathematics—A Bibliography of Articles in English Appearing in Seven Periodicals, *School Science and Mathematics,* Vol. LXVI, No. 2 (February 1966), pp. 147–179.

Spencer, P. L., and Brydegaard, M., *Building Mathematical Competence In the Elementary School* (New York: Holt, Rinehart and Winston, 1966), Chap. 14.

Spitzer, Herbert F., *Enrichment of Arithmetic* (St. Louis: Webster Division, McGraw-Hill Book Company, 1964).

Stevenson, Gordon K., "Attitudes Toward Reading and Arithmetic Instruction: Why the Contrast?" *The Arithmetic Teacher*, Vol. 5, No. 3 (April 1958), pp. 161–162.

Weaver, J. Fred, and Brawley, Cleo Fisher, "Enriching the Elementary School Mathematics Program for More Capable Children," *Journal of Education*, Vol. 142, No. 1 (October 1959), pp. 1–40.

USE OF SUGGESTED REFERENCES

1. What did Brewer find to be the current grouping practices? What suggestions does he make?

2. How could you use the magic square development presented by Brown to develop worksheets for above 'average and below average pupils?

3. Are the step-by-step remedial procedures suggested by Brueckner and Bond in keeping with the current emphasis on mathematical structure? Give reasons.

4. Develop a lesson around one of the suggested enrichment topics contained

in the Twenty-seventh Yearbook. Develop a list of procedures suggested in the Twenty-fifth Yearbook.

5. What are the feelings of Marks, Prudy, and Kinney concerning homogeneous grouping?

6. Study the characteristics of students described in *Individualizing Instruction.*

7. What suggestion does Paschal make for teaching culturally disadvantaged children mathematics?

8. Read's bibliography of historical articles should be helpful in developing teacher materials and pupil reports. How could it be condensed for strictly elementary school use?

9. Spencer and Brydegaard devote a chapter to "Errors with Numerical Computation." How could their suggestions be used in developing a program that considers individual differences?

10. Select materials from *Enrichment of Arithmetic* which would be helpful in giving students challenging material for further development of counting.

11. Contrast the opinions on grouping of Stevenson with those advocated in this chapter.

12. Read Weaver's analysis of acceleration versus enrichment.

4

Addition of whole numbers

WHAT IS ADDITION?

If you were to stop almost any person on the street and ask him, "Do you know what addition is?" he would say without hesitation, "Certainly I know what addition is." If you were then to ask for a precise definition, some difficulty might result. Often we are able to make use of mathematical ideas without being able to explain them concisely.

Before addition can be defined, certain terms must be defined. *Addition* is a *binary* operation. That is, the operation is always performed on *two numbers*. Note that to add $5 + 7 + 3$ it is necessary to first perform addition on two numbers and then another addition on two numbers. Thus, $5 + 7 + 3$ becomes $(5 + 7) + 3 = 15$. To be an operation, a process must be *performable* and the *result must be unique*. The numbers to be added $(5 + 7)$ are called *addends*. The result of the operation is called the *sum* $(5 + 7 = 12)$.

In modern terminology, addition is defined from the set operation of union performed on disjoint sets (sets which have no members in common). Recall that the union of two sets is the set composed of all the elements that belong to either of the sets. An element that belongs to either set also belongs to their union. Example: Suppose the Smith children, Mary, Bob, and Ken go over to play with the Jones children, Harry and Nancy. This can be thought of as forming the union of two sets.

{Mary, Bob, Ken} $\cup$ {Harry, Nancy} = {Mary, Bob, Ken, Harry, Nancy}

The sum of two cardinal numbers[1] can be defined to be the cardinal number of the union of the sets.

N {Mary, Bob, Ken} + N {Harry, Nancy} =
     3   +   2   =

                           N {Mary, Bob, Ken, Harry, Nancy}
                                      5

---

[1] When natural numbers are used to indicate "how many?" they are said to be used in the *cardinal* sense.

If the two sets are not disjoint (if they have members in common), a difficulty arises.

$$\{\text{Tom, Fred}\} \quad \cup \quad \{\text{Mary, Fred, Alice}\} \quad = \quad \{\text{Tom, Fred, Mary, Alice}\}$$

$$\text{N } \{\text{Tom, Fred}\} \; + \; \text{N } \{\text{Mary, Fred, Alice}\} \; \neq \; \{\text{Tom, Fred, Mary, Alice}\}$$
$$2 \quad\quad + \quad\quad 3 \quad\quad \neq \quad\quad 4$$

The sets must be disjoint if addition is to be defined in terms of their union.

In order to avoid a common difficulty, the operation "union of sets" should not be considered the same as "addition of numbers." Children have often been told, "You cannot add unlike things." One does not add things, but numbers.

It is possible to form a union of a set containing three pears and a set containing six apples. The set formed is a set of fruit containing three pears and six apples. We may also think of the union of three pears and six apples as a set containing nine pieces of fruit.

Use of union of sets and addition of numbers also clears up another common stumbling block to teachers and pupils. Often a problem arises such as, "If I have 2 dimes and 1 nickel and add these amounts, this 'equals' a quarter." But 2 dimes and 1 nickel are equal in *value* to a quarter, not the same thing physically.

Using the distinction between union of sets and addition of numbers, it can be noted that the union of the set of 2 dimes and 1 nickel is *equivalent in value,* but not equal or equivalent, to a set composed of a quarter. The addition of $(10 + 10) + 5$ is equal to 25.

Also, three sticks 1 foot long are not the same thing as one stick 3 feet long, although $1 + 1 + 1 = 3$. They are equivalent in length, however.

FOUNDATION EXPERIENCES

Counting and addition

While the addition of numbers is "finding the sum without counting," the basis of addition of whole numbers is founded upon counting. The beginning of the addition idea starts in the earliest days of school life when pupils combine groups of objects and count to find "how many?" Soon many children recognize without counting that the result of combining a set of 3 objects with a set of 2 objects is a set of 5 objects. At this time, they are adding.

Verbal problems

Orally presented verbal problems form the framework for this early addition readiness. They provide a purpose for finding "how many?" and also provide the physical world setting from which the child can begin to abstract number ideas by physically combining sets.

The following materials are helpful in the solution of pre-addition problems.

1. The actual object described in the problem: "Ken brought us 3 pictures and Mary brought us 4 pictures. How many pictures is this? How can we find out? Lloyd, do you want to count the pictures to see? Don't count aloud; we'll count along with you silently." "Yesterday I gave each of you 4 crayons. I have 4 more for each of you." (She passes out the crayons.) "How many do you now have?"

2. The number line:
"John said he has 3 new books. Jill said she has 5 new books. Use the number line to find out how many new books the two children have. Would it make any difference whether we started with 5 books or started with 3 books?"

3. Use of representative objects to be counted in place of the actual objects: "Nancy has 4 dolls and Jill has 5 dolls. How many dolls do they have in all? If you need help, use popsicle sticks to represent the dolls."

Other representative objects that may be used include: beads, buttons, pictures, bottle caps, beans, paper strips, washers, grains of corn, building blocks, and play money.

It is often suggested that pupils should follow a three-step program in developing mathematical abstractions: first, a *concrete stage* in which pupils work only with the actual objects; second, a *semiconcrete* stage in which counters and pictures are used to replace the actual objects; third, the *abstract stage* in which numerals are used to represent numbers. In actual practice, children often do not need all three stages. If orally presented verbal problems are used, some pupils can think from the concrete problem to semiconcrete material or to the actual number idea. Because children vary greatly in their maturity in abstract thinking, opportunities should be provided for the pupil to choose appropriate methods of attacking early addition situations.

Use of set ideas

The previous foundation work in addition made use of counting as a basis for solving a verbal problem. Joining (forming the union of sets) is also a valuable pre-addition experience. The teacher may use a flannel board containing several objects.

"I've placed a set of apples on the flannel board. How many apples in the set?" (The children either recognize that there are three apples or count the three apples.) "Now I'm placing a set of oranges in the other corner of the flannel board. How many oranges? How many members in the set of fruit if I combine (form a union) the apples and the oranges?" Pupils match in one-to-one correspondence the members with a set of a known size.

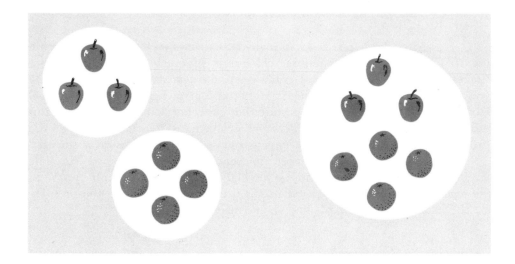

"I've drawn a set of fish to represent those that Bill caught. Also, the set of fish that Nancy caught. How many fish are in Bill's set? In Nancy's? If the two sets are joined, how many fish in all?" In this case the pupils counted to find the total as a check. The number of the set formed by the union of the two sets was matched with the counting numbers on the number line.

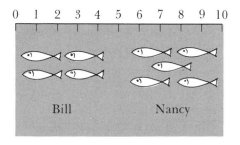 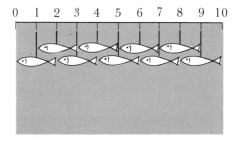

THE BASIC ADDITION FACTS

The basic addition facts are formed by the combination of all one-digit addends. When the zero facts are included, there are 100 basic addition facts. The addition facts are often grouped into combinations having sums of 10 or less, and facts having sums of more than 10. The first are often called the "easy" addition facts, and the latter, the "hard addition facts." The terms "easy" and "hard" actually have little meaning in terms of actual difficulty. For example, many pupils find 9 + 2 is easier than 5 + 4.

Discovering the addition facts

After the pupils had had many experiences with joining sets, counting to find "how many," and matching sets in one-to-one correspondence (sometime about the middle of grade one), the teacher asked, "How could you find an answer to this problem? Mary has 5 arrowheads in her collection. How many will she have if her grandfather gives her 3 more? See if you can think of the exact question which the problem asks, and then solve the problem. Try to show in as many ways as you can that your answer is correct."

The children made use of paper and pencil in working the problem. The teacher moved about the class noting methods of attacking the problem. When the majority were finished, several pupils drew their solution to the problem on the chalkboard and explained their reasoning.

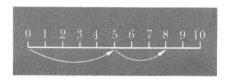

Gene: I used the number line. I moved to 5 to represent Mary's arrowheads. Then I counted 3 more to represent the arrowheads her grandfather will give to her.

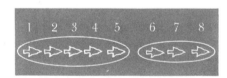

Sally: I drew a picture of the 5 arrowheads Mary has. Then I drew a picture of the 3 arrowheads her grandfather will give her. Then I counted the total number of arrowheads.

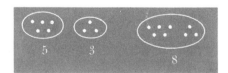

Mike: I drew a set of 5 dots to represent the arrowheads. Then I drew a set of 3 dots to represent the arrowheads that Mary's grandfather will give to her. Then I drew a picture of the union of these two sets. I counted the number of dots in the union of the sets.

Claudia: I know that Mary has 5 arrowheads. Then I thought, "How many arrowheads would 3 more be?" The answer 8 popped into my head.

After some discussion the teacher asked the pupils if they had been able to identify the exact question which the problem asked. After some argument the pupils agreed that the question was "What is 5 and 3 more?" The teacher restated the question, "Five with three equals what number?"

Several other addition problems were worked and then the teacher said, "When we combine two numbers such as 6 and 3, we usually say, 'Six *plus* three equals what number?' " (The teacher writes on the board.) "In mathematics we have a shorter way of writing a sentence which uses numbers. Do any of you know how to write a number sentence in a short way?"

Several of the pupils raised their hands and said, "We could replace the six and the three with numerals." "I think that my older brother uses '+' to mean plus. He also uses '=' to mean equals." "We could use a question mark to stand for the 'what number?' "

Following the suggestions of the pupils, the teacher wrote "6 + 3 = ?" on the board. Then she said, "You may also want to use a box □ to indicate the number you are seeking. Then, when you have an answer you may fill in the box." (She wrote 6 + 3 = □.) "We call what I have written on the board a 'number sentence' or a 'mathematical sentence.' Which name would you like to use for the sentence?"

Second day. The teacher began the lesson with several verbal problems. The pupils were asked to write the number or mathematical sentence which described the problem and then to solve the mathematical sentence. The pupils were also directed to show in as many ways as they could that their answer was correct. Pupils who were experiencing difficulty writing the mathematical sentence that described the problem were asked to solve the problem in another manner and then to raise their hands. The teacher gave individual help to those experiencing trouble.

Later in the period the pupils were given a worksheet containing several mathematical sentences, were asked to write the numeral in the box which made the sentence correct, and were told to show that their answer was correct.

$$2 + 3 = \square \qquad 6 + 3 = \square$$
$$5 + 1 = \square \qquad 2 + 2 = \square$$
$$4 + 2 = \square \qquad 4 + 4 = \square$$

Pupils counted to themselves and made use of the number line, rods, sticks, etc. to arrive at the correct answer to the addition combination.

Third through fifth days. Several days were spent in solving problems involving addition and developing further the use of the mathematical sentence.

Sixth day. On the previous days the pupils had had many opportunities to develop by inductive discovery the answer to addition questions. For the sixth day's work the teacher felt that it would be worthwhile to make use of some deductive methods of discovery. This took the form of "If—then" statements. She began by developing with the class the pattern for addition involving six. She said, "What is $6 + 1$? If $6 + 1 = 7$, then what will $6 + 2$ equal? What will $6 + 3$ equal?" Pupils were then given a dittoed sheet.

If	If
$6 + 1 = 7$	$5 + 1 = 6$
and	and
$6 + 2 = 8$	$5 + 2 = 7$
then	then
$6 + 3 = \Box$	$5 + 3 = \Box$
$6 + 4 = \Box$	$5 + 4 = \Box$
$6 + 5 = \Box$	$5 + 5 = \Box$
$6 + 6 = \Box$	$5 + 6 = \Box$
$6 + 7 = \Box$	$5 + 7 = \Box$
$6 + 8 = \Box$	$5 + 8 = \Box$
$6 + 9 = \Box$	$5 + 9 = \Box$

It should be noted that at no time during the addition work did the teacher suggest that the pupils memorize the combinations. Rather, each was to make use of the method he felt most appropriate for arriving at an answer.

During the remainder of the addition work in grade one, the teacher continued to make use of verbal problems and mathematical sentences with no stress on memorization of addition facts. The teacher did not limit herself to the addition combinations involving smaller numbers but made use of situations using all of the addition facts.

Using the basic properties of addition

The commutative property. Recognition of the fact that the order of the addends does not affect the sum $(4 + 5 = 5 + 4)$ is a valuable aid to work with the addition combinations. This property of addition continues to be of great value throughout the study of mathematics.

The commutative property can be developed by pupil analysis of addition situations. At the beginning of a mathematics period the teacher commented, "At the end of class yesterday one of you told me, 'I think I can save a lot of time in addition because if I know what $4 + 5$ is, I know that $5 + 4$ will give me the same amount'. Do you think that he was right? If so, will this be true of all of the addition combinations? Try this on several addition combinations, and then if it works, try to develop a means of showing that it is true."

Pupils tried several combinations and then developed their method of "proof." It should be noted that while the proofs developed by the pupils were not "mathematical proofs," they served a very useful purpose in stressing the need to carefully check number properties.

Several of the "proofs" given by the pupils follow.

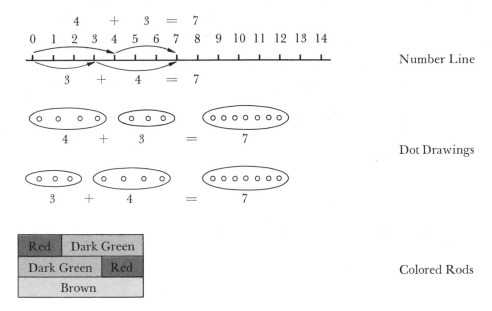

Number Line

Dot Drawings

Colored Rods

First-grade pupils can generalize the commutative property by making statements such as, "It doesn't matter whether you say 3 + 4 or 4 + 3; the answer is the same," or "the numbers

$$\begin{array}{r} 3 \\ + 4 \\ \hline \end{array}$$

can be added up or down." After the students thoroughly understand this number property (usually not until a later grade), the teacher may ask the children to state the number property in their own words, have pupils check their definition with a standard definition, and then say, "The number property we have been discussing is called the *commutative property* for addition." From this time on the property may be referred to by its name. The teacher should be sure that the stress is placed upon the understanding of the commutative property, not upon the learning of the words "commutative property." It is better to wait too long to introduce the term than to introduce the term before meaning has been developed.

The associative property. Rather early in problem-solving work the need to add more than two numbers develops. Since it is not possible to add three or more numbers at the same time, it is often valuable to regroup numbers for addition. Children should discover that the numbers can be regrouped in computation. For example, in adding $7 + 8 + 2$, most pupils will find that adding $7 + (8 + 2) = 7 + 10 = 17$ is easier than adding $(7 + 8) + 2 = 15 + 2 = 17$.

Another valuable use of the associative property of addition is the idea "a number has many names." Since $(3 + 2)$, $(4 + 1)$, $(2 + 3)$, and $(1 + 4)$ all represent the number "five," they may be considered to be other names for five. This understanding, coupled with the associative property, allows a primary-level pupil to solve many addition situations that would otherwise be beyond his grasp. To illustrate: early in the year one second-grade pupil was asked to find the sum of $97 + 8$. He thought of $3 + 5$ as another name for 8. Then he added $97 + 3 = 100$, and he knew that $100 + 5 = 105$. In written form this thinking could be represented as follows:

$$97 + 8 =$$
$$97 + (3 + 5) =$$
$$(97 + 3) + 5 =$$
$$100 + 5 = 105$$

The use of another name for a number and the associative property may be introduced in a situation such as the following:

The teacher said, "A boy I had last year had trouble with addition combinations such as $8 + 7 = \square$. He changed the name of one of the numbers and added twice. Can you figure out what he did? Look at the way he handled the addition."

$$8 + 7 = \square$$
$$8 + (2 + 5) = \square$$
$$(8 + 2) + 5 = \square$$
$$10 + 5 = 15$$

After studying the procedure the pupils explained that the boy had renamed 7 as $2 + 5$ and had made use of the enclosures (parentheses) to show that he had added $8 + 2$ first. He knew that $10 + 5 = 15$.

Since the majority of mathematical work is based on the system of place value, the teacher should emphasize often the regrouping of two numbers into tens and ones.

Zero, the identity element for addition. Zero is the *additive identity* and thus $5 + 0 = 5$. Some authorities in the field of elementary school mathematics have advocated that addition combinations such as $5 + 0 = \square$ should not be taught, since normally such situations do not arise in physical world settings.

Pupils should have experience with zero combinations since many pupils have a tendency to arrive at the answer 6 when they add $5 + 0$. Also, they may believe that when zero is added to a number, no addition occurs. This is not true. There are a number of physical world situations in which it is necessary to know whether addition of zero has occurred or whether no addition has occurred. The situations that follow are illustrative of those in which it is necessary to be sure that addition has occurred.

1. Each player gets two turns in a game. We need to know if a player has a score of $2 + 0$ or hasn't had a second turn.

2. Tom and Alan go fishing. They have a contest with Nancy and Elaine to see whether the girls or the boys have caught the most fish. Tom catches 3 fish; Alan catches 0 fish. Nancy catches 2 fish; Elaine catches 2 fish. It is necessary to know that the boys have caught $3 + 0$ fish and the girls have caught $2 + 2$ fish.

3. It is the ninth inning. The Cardinals and the Braves tied 3-3 at the end of the eighth inning. The Cardinal third baseman hits a home run. Do the Cardinals win? Yes, if the Braves' runs are $3 + 0$. That is, if the Braves have batted in the ninth. We're not sure if the Braves' score is 3 and they haven't as yet batted in the ninth.

Other generalizations concerning basic addition facts. The following generalizations can be developed through exploratory exercises. They are helpful in developing patterns in mathematics and are useful for many phases of mathematics.

1. Adding ones is equivalent to counting by ones.

2. The sum of a number and the next number larger is one more than the first number doubled. $8 + 9 =$ one more than $8 + 8$.

3. The sum of a number and the next number smaller is one less than the first number doubled. $8 + 7 =$ one less than $8 + 8$.

4. The double of any number is two more than the double of the number that is the next smaller number or two less than the next number larger.

$$8 + 8 = 16 \quad \text{thus} \quad 7 + 7 = 14$$
$$8 + 8 = 16 \quad \text{thus} \quad 9 + 9 = 18$$

"If—then" exercises can be used to develop this idea.

5. The addition of 9 to any number can be found by adding ten and subtracting 1.

$$8 + 9 = (8 + 10) - 1$$

Analysis of the procedures for developing the basic addition facts

1. The suggested program differs from the many traditional and experimental programs in that pupils have an opportunity to explore all of the addition combinations in grade one. In most programs first-grade pupils are

limited to the addition facts with sums of ten or less, with a study for mastery of these facts.

There are several reasons for this departure from standard procedure. These include:

a. First-grade pupils often encounter situations requiring the use of addition facts with sums greater than ten.

b. Limiting the study of addition in grade one to sums of ten and less is not in keeping with the emphasis placed upon place value in current programs. The importance of place value becomes more evident when pupils make use of renaming in dealing with large sums such as $8 + 7 = (8 + 2) + 5$.

c. By avoiding any study for mastery in grade one pupils have a greater opportunity to become completely familiar with the operation of addition. Early study for mastery of a number operation often leads to rote learning with little understanding.

d. If the teacher emphasizes the uses of addition in problem situations and solving number sentences, many pupils can learn a rather large number of addition facts without drill work.

2. The use of multiple solutions (solving an addition problem or addition combination in several ways) provides for individual differences and also develops student confidence. When a student realizes that often there are several ways of finding an answer, he is not as hesitant to attempt new or difficult material.

3. The introductory addition situations make use of verbal problems. A number of new programs in elementary school mathematics develop the addition facts without verbal problems and then use problems after addition has been developed. The use of verbal problems to introduce addition has two advantages.

a. It provides a setting in which the pupil can abstract the mathematical idea from the physical world.

b. It shows a reason for the study of addition.

4. The program stresses the relatedness of addition combinations, thus encouraging pupils to form generalizations rather than memorize each combination as a separate entity.

5. Formal addition is first introduced with a situation requiring the addition of larger numbers, such as $5 + 3$. This is at variance with many programs which use combinations such as $1 + 1$ or $2 + 1$ for the first work in addition. Since foundation work has given pupils an opportunity to solve many addition situations by counting, the first situation used in the study of addition should make use of a combination in which addition has a definite advantage over counting. Also, $1 + 1$ or $2 + 1$ is not a very challenging combination, even for the slower than average pupil.

6. The approach makes use of two early ideas of addition: the combining of two sets and counting to find a total.

7. Developing the mathematical ideas of commutativity, associativity, and the identity element for addition lays a strong foundation for a structural

approach to the study of mathematics. Pupils develop understanding of essential number properties. These basic properties are important to all phases of mathematics.

8. Stress is placed upon writing the mathematical sentence that could represent the problem situation. The use of the mathematical sentence is one of the most important tools in problem solving at all mathematical levels.

Techniques for studying the basic addition facts

It was previously suggested that while all single-digit addition combinations be studied at grade one, the practice for mastery be delayed until grade two. Teachers have often asked questions such as "Harry understands addition very well but just doesn't seem to learn the addition combinations. He always counts. What kind of material can I give him to help him to learn the addition facts?" "Nancy gets bored with the addition practice I give to the class. However, she still doesn't know the combinations as well as she should. What kind of practice that will maintain her interest can I give her?" "When I begin practice on the addition combinations, my third graders say, 'We had all of that in second grade.' How can I vary the treatment?" One of the best procedures for developing mastery of basic number combinations is to present to children a situation in which they must quickly give the sums of a number of addition combinations. A game or a timed exercise can be used. This presentation helps pupils to see that they need further practice in basic number combinations.

The practice material suggested below is designed with two purposes in mind. One is to develop facility in working with basic addition facts. The other is to further the understanding of addition. Some of the suggestions do both; others develop only facility with addition.

Semi-programmed study sheets. Teachers have found that a sheet of scrambled addition combinations with a slider serves as a valuable study aid. Children are interested in the self-correction feature and in the similarity of the study aid to programmed or teaching machine materials.

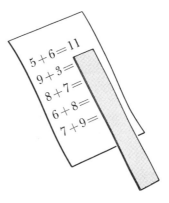

Use of the addition table. The addition table is useful in studying the structural properties of addition. The teacher may give each pupil a partially completed addition table and make a statement such as, "I found this table in an old arithmetic textbook. See if you can fill in the remainder of the table."

	0	1	2	3	4	5	6	7	8	9
0			2							
1				5						
2										
3									11	
4						9				
5										
6										
7										
8										17
9										

When the pupils have finished the table, the teacher may ask questions such as, "What do you notice about the zeros? Try folding the table in various ways. What patterns can you notice? Why do they work? How many rows with values two larger than the preceding number can you find?"

Frame arithmetic. The use of many names for the same number and the use of frames provide many worthwhile addition exercises. Questions such as those that follow can be effectively used.

1. What are all the replacements we could use for the box and the triangle?

$$\square + \triangle = 9$$

2. What replacements can we use in each of the following? How many addition facts fit each model? ($\triangle = \triangle$; $\square = \square$; $\bigcirc = \bigcirc$)

$\bigcirc + \bigcirc = \square$ 　　　　 $\square + \_\_ = \square$
Example: $2 + 2 = 4$ 　　 Example: $5 + 0 = 5$

$\square + \triangle = \bigcirc$ 　　　　 $\square + \square = \square$
Example: $5 + 6 = 11$ 　　 Example: $0 + 0 = 0$

Note: The examples are for teacher use. In working with children, the examples should be developed by discussion.

3. What are the pairs of one-digit addends which will fit each of these models?

$\square + 5 = \triangle$ 　　　 Example: $3 + 5 = 8$
$6 + \triangle = \square$ 　　　 Example: $6 + 3 = 9$

4. Review of the commutative and associative principles may be accomplished with frames.

$$5 + \square = \square + \triangle$$ What is the value of $\triangle$, if $\square = \square$? (Answer 5)

$$(\square + 6) + \triangle = \square + (\bigcirc + \triangle)$$ What is the value of $\bigcirc$, if $\square = \square$ and $\triangle = \triangle$? (Answer 6)

What principles are involved in the above frames?

Use of fact finders.   A simple addition fact finder can be made from a piece of coat hanger and 18 beads. (See illustration.) The beads may be all of one color, or the first ten may be of one color and the remaining eight of another color.

Source: Still Photo Services U. D. I. S., Pennsylvania State University.

Devises such as the addition wheel to reinforce basic addition knowledge.

The fact finder allows the pupils to count the answer to a forgotten addition combination or to discover the answer to a new combination by counting.

Other materials. Various commercially prepared colored rods, the number line, popsicle sticks, electric addition games, and dice provide materials that lend themselves to practice with addition.

Study exercises. Materials such as those illustrated below can be used to give variety in addition practice materials.

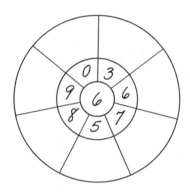

Find the sum of the number named in the center ring added to a number named in the second ring.

Fill in each box with the appropriate numeral.

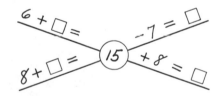

Fill in the boxes on the right with the numeral that represents the number that can be added to the number on the left to equal the top number.

MULTI-DIGIT ADDITION

Adding multiples of ten

Rather early in the addition experiences of children, situations that require the addition of numbers such as $40 + 30 = \square$ can be introduced.

The teacher may begin with a verbal problem such as, "Ken's mother has 30 trading stamps on one page and 50 trading stamps on another page. How many stamps does she have in all? Is this enough to get a serving spoon which requires 90 stamps?"

When given an opportunity to explore various means of answering the question, pupils can find a solution in several ways. They may find 30 + 50 by (1) counting by tens—30, 40, 50, 60, 70, 80; (2) using tens and ones blocks and counting them; (3) counting the tens rod of colored rods; (4) adding 3 tens + 5 tens = 8 tens; (5) using an abacus (see below); (6) using a place-value chart (see below).

Abacus

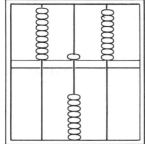

Place-Value Chart

tens	ones
3	0
5	0

8 ten 0 ones = 80

tens	ones
III	
IIIII	

 IIIII / III tens = 80

Pupils quickly move to combinations such as 53 + 30 = □ and 23 + 34 = □ by using the same procedures. While many programs do not introduce this type of addition until third grade, if verbal problems and concrete materials are used, second-grade pupils can benefit from such instruction. Also, multi-digit addition provides a good reason for extensive study of place value, further insight into the addition process, and new settings for basic addition facts.

Renaming in addition

Renaming or "carrying" in addition is the most difficult form of the addition algorithms. It is based on two mathematical properties of addition, the commutative property and the associative property. Consider the following:

$$57 + 35 = N$$

We may expand our notation to $(50 + 7) + (30 + 5) = N$. Using the commutative and associative properties of addition, we arrive at $(50 + 30) + (7 + 5) = N$.

Next, 5 tens + 3 tens = 8 tens or 80. Seven ones + 5 ones = 12 ones. We then expand 12 ones to 1 ten + 2 ones. Thus we have: $80 + (10 + 2) = N$. Using the associative property $(80 + 10) + 2 = N$, $90 + 2 = 92$. By using two basic properties, a rather complex process may be developed.

Introductory work in renaming can be begun by the teacner saying, "I've given you a set of four problems. Write the mathematical sentence you would use to find the answer to the problems and then solve them in as many ways as you can."

The first problem with the solution suggested by several class members is reproduced below:

1. Mary sold 37 tickets for the school play. Jill sold 25 tickets. How many tickets did the two girls sell?

Jim: I used the number line. I marked off 30, 20, 7, and 5. I don't believe that this is the best way to solve the problem because it takes quite a while.

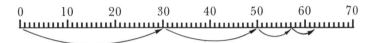

Jane: I used expanded form. I then renamed 12 as 10 + 2 and added again.

$$37 = 30 + 7$$
$$+ 25 = 20 + 5$$
$$\overline{ 50 + 12} = (50 + 10) + 2 = 62$$

John: I used rods. I combined the 5 tens rods and changed the 7 and 5 to 10 and 2. This gave me 62.

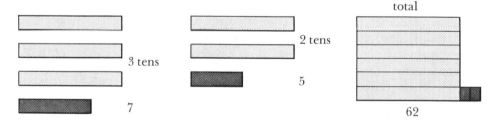

Chris: I used the abacus. I added the 20 + 30. Then I added 5 + 7. I changed the 12 to 10 and 2. I recorded the 10 in the tens place.

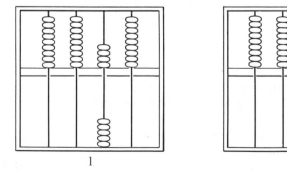

Kevin: I added in the regular way. I first added 7 + 5. I recorded the 12. Then I added 30 + 20. I recorded the 50. Then I added the 50 + 12.

Paula: I used tens and ones blocks. I laid out 3 tens and 7 ones, and 2 tens and 5 ones. Then I grouped them together. This gave me 5 tens and 12 ones.

I traded 10 ones for another tens block. This gave me 6 tens and 2 ones, or a total of 62.

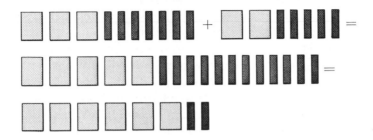

George: I added twice or used the associative property.

$$37 + 25 = 37 + (20 + 5) = (37 + 20) + 5 = 57 + 5 = 62$$

Jean: I used the place-value frame.

tens	ones
3	7
2	5

5 + 12 = 6 tens + 2 ones = 62

tens	ones
I I I	I I I I I I I
I I	I I I I I
I I I I I	I I I I I I I I I I
	I I
I I I I I I	I I = 62

After the completion of several problems, the class members were given a set of addition exercises, a number of which involved renaming. They were instructed to find answers to the exercises in a manner which made sense to them and then to show that their answers were correct by working the exercises in another manner.

During discussions on the following days other methods of solution were discussed. Several of the students had found a more efficient method of solving addition exercises involving renaming. One pupil explained, "Add

$$\begin{array}{r} 57 \\ + 36 \\ \hline 93 \end{array}$$

7 ones and 6 ones; this is 13 or 1 ten and 3 ones. Write down the 3 ones and place the 1 ten in the tens place. Then add the tens."

Another pupil suggested, "To add

$$
\begin{array}{r}
57 \\
+\ 36 \\
\hline
93
\end{array}
$$

I add $7 + 6$, which is 13. I write the 3 and remember the 1 ten. Then I add the 5 tens and the 3 tens. This gives me 8 tens plus the 1 ten I remember equals 9 tens. I write 9 in the tens place. My answer is 93."

As the study of multi-digit addition progressed, the teacher stressed understanding of the basic idea of renaming and the continued development of mature forms of the algorithm. Those who were not ready for the standard algorithm were not forced to use this form. Periodically, review study questions similar to the following were used. (1) What does the 2 that is circled mean? (2) Why do some parents make statements such as "remember to carry the one?" What do they mean by "carrying the one?" (3) What basic properties of addition allow us to compute situations such as $345 + 468$?

Late in the study the pupils were asked to write a mathematics theme as an assignment for both mathematics and language arts. In this theme they were to present in as interesting a manner as possible the ideas behind renaming in addition and to suggest methods of solving renaming situations. Pupil research for the themes brought out historical notes such as, "Probably the reason for 'carrying the one' came from the early sand board abacus in which the person computing picked up ten pebbles in the ones place, dropped nine of them and carried one pebble to the tens place."

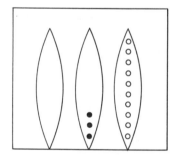 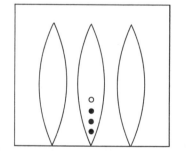

Higher decade addition

Addition situations in which a one digit addend is combined with a two-digit addend are often called higher decade addition. Combinations such as $35 + 3 = 38$ offer little difficulty to most pupils. Situations such as $35 + 8 = 43$ can on occasion cause difficulty. Such situations are often found in column addition and in adding the partial products in multiplication.

Two approaches can be taken to adding $35 + 8$. One method is "adding by endings," that is, add $5 + 8$ and "bridge" to the next decade. The thinking is, "What is the sum of $35 + 8$? $5 + 8 = 13$; this is greater than ten. My answer will be in the next decade, the 40's. The answer is 43." This method is most commonly taught. The other method is often called "adding to make tens." The thinking of this method is, "What is the sum of $35 + 8$? Rename 8 so that I can make an even ten; $35 + 5 + 3 = (35 + 5) + 3 = 43$." This method makes use of renaming and the associative property of addition and thus is in keeping with an emphasis upon structure in the teaching of elementary school mathematics. Also, most adults and children often use this method quite naturally. For example, in adding a column such as $8 + 9 + 7 + 6$, the thinking might be 8, 17, 20, 24, 30. In this case the 7 was thought of as $3 + 4$ to form even tens.

Since both methods are used in column addition, there is reason to make use of both approaches in the elementary school. Pupil explanations and guided discussion should be used to develop both. Also, since most addition situations occurring in life situations involve column addition, the teacher should take care to emphasize these two procedures.

CHECKING ADDITION

Teachers often say, "My pupils hate to check their work in arithmetic." This statement is probably true. It is often difficult for children to realize that in most instances when an adult does a computation, he checks the work. This reluctance to check addition (or any other) computation can be partially reduced by making use of the suggestions that follow. (1) Pupils often feel that "checking their work" means that they will have twice as much work to perform. This is usually true. The teacher can reduce this feeling by giving fewer exercises when checking is expected. It is usually of greater value to work fewer exercises with a check than a greater number without checking. (2) In some cases pupils see little reason to check. It is suggested that pupils may compare the accuracy of papers which they have checked with those that are not checked. If the class members see a real value in terms of increased accuracy, the use of checking will be better accepted. (3) Often the use of varied and imaginative checks increases pupil interest. Several such checks are illustrated below.

Checking basic facts

The idea of solving an exercise in several different ways provides a check. In addition exercises pupils can use counting, the number line, adding twice $[9 + 5 = 9 + (1 + 4) = (9 + 1) + 4 = 10 + 4 = 14]$, the abacus, and the commutative property to reverse the addends. All are acceptable checks.

Checking multi-digit addition

Casting out nines.   While casting out nines is not a particularly efficient check, it is usually of interest to intermediate grade pupils and is useful in developing further insight into the number system. The teacher may illustrate the check on the chalkboard (see below) and ask questions such as "This check is often called casting out nines. Is that what we're doing? Try dividing each addend by nine. What is the remainder? Why does this check work?"

$$
\begin{array}{rl}
562 & 5 + 6 + 2 = 13 \longleftrightarrow 1 + 3 = 4 \\
291 & 2 + 9 + 1 = 12 \longleftrightarrow 1 + 2 = 3 \\
243 & 2 + 4 + 3 = \ \ 9 \longleftrightarrow 0 \\
+122 & 1 + 2 + 2 = \ \ 5 \\
\hline
1218 & \qquad\quad\ \ \overline{12} \longleftrightarrow 1 + 2 = 3 \\
& 1 + 2 + 1 + 8 = 12 \longleftrightarrow 1 + 2 = 3
\end{array}
$$

Study of the nines multiplication table reveals that in every multiple of nine the sum of the digits is equal to nine. A dot drawing such as the one below is also helpful in understanding the procedure.[2]

Associative Checks.   Changing the order of the addends by use of the associative property provides a number of ways of checking.

		(a)	(b)		(c)
3,821		4,653	3,821	7,982	3,821
4,653		7,982	4,653	6,051	4,653
7,982		6,051	8,474	14,033	6,051
6,051		18,686	14,033		14,525
22,507		3,821	22,507		7,982
		22,507			22,507

Casting out elevens.   For an explanation of the procedure see page 131 on which the check is developed in a subtraction situation.

---

[2] For a further explanation of the check of nines see J. Houston Banks, *Learning and Teaching Arithmetic,* 2nd ed. (Boston: Allyn and Bacon, 1964), pp. 60–62, 200.

USE OF THE ABACUS FOR ADDITION

The abacus is an excellent physical model of a base ten numeration system and thus a valuable aid to the teacher of elementary school mathematics. A simple version of the abacus, along with the record for several numbers, is shown below.

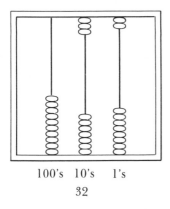

100's   10's   1's
32

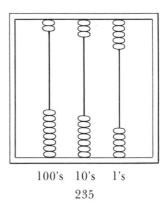

100's   10's   1's
235

Addition using an abacus may be accomplished in the following manner: Add 223 + 145 + 16

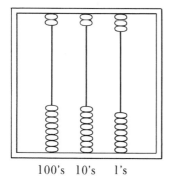

100's   10's   1's

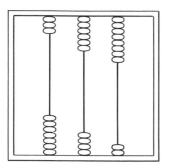

Record 223.

Add the second addend by moving up 5 beads in the ones column 4 beads in the tens column and 1 bead in the hundreds column.

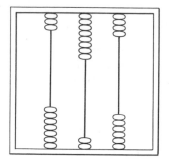

Add the third addend, 16. Only two beads remain in the ones column. Therefore, count 1, 2. This uses all of the beads in the ones column. Exchange 10 ones for 1 ten by moving the beads on the ones rod down and moving one bead in the tens column up. Now continue counting 3, 4, 5, 6. Next add the 1 ten by moving up a bead in the tens column. Sum = 384.

ADDITION OF INTEGERS

A teacher began the development by stating, "The temperature outdoors was −5 degrees when I got up this morning. The weatherman said that it should get 20 degrees warmer during the day. If he is right, what will be the high temperature? Try to visualize the situation. You may want to use the demonstration thermometer or a number line."

Pupils made use of the two devices to answer the question.

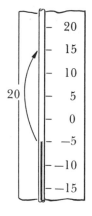

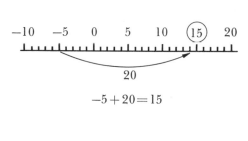

$$-5+20=15$$

Then the teacher attached a negative portion to the large number line displayed above the chalkboards. Several other verbal problems were presented on a dittoed sheet.

1. Two teams, the Cardinals and the Yankees, are playing a quiz game. For each right answer they get 5 points. For each wrong answer they go 5 points in the hole. One round the Cardinals score −5, 5, 5, and −5. What is their total score? ($-5 + 5 = 0$, $5 + -5 = 0$, Total = 0) The Yankees

score −5, −5, 5, −5. What is their total score? (−5 + −5 = −10, 5 + −5 = 0, −10 + 0 = −10, Total = −10) Which team is the winner? (the Cardinals)

2. In an afternoon in the winter the temperature was 15 degrees above zero. During the night the temperature fell 25 degrees. What was the temperature then? (+15 + −25 = −10: 10 degrees below zero)

3. After the first round of a game Floyd was 3 "in the hole." The next round he went 8 more "in the hole." What was his total at the end of the two rounds? (−3 + −8 = −11)

After pupils develop intuitive ideas of negative integers from problem situations, a mathematical approach can be effectively used. Mathematical sentences can be written to show the addition diagrammed on the number line.[3]

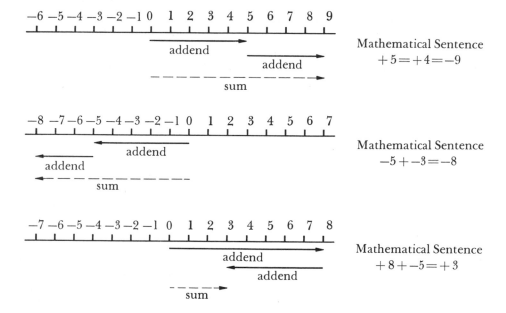

Development of the idea of the additive inverse of a whole number can begin with discussion of situations such as −5 + 5 = ☐ and −8 + 8 = ☐. Problems such as, "Ken owes his father 25¢ and his mother 15¢. How much money will he need to get out 'of the hole?'" can be used to help in the development of the inverse relationship.

[3] School Mathematics Study Group, *Mathematics for the Elementary School, Grade Six, Teacher Commentary*, Part I (New Haven: Yale University Press, 1963), pp. 349–376.

REINTRODUCTION OF ADDITION

There are many situations in elementary school mathematics which call for a review or further practice on a topic. At times there has not been enough review on basically mathematical understandings. Often a high school mathematics teacher states, "The pupils do not understand the basic principle of renaming in addition. They use 'carry the one.' I wish that the elementary teachers would teach them the basic ideas of mathematics." Such indictments probably arise not so much from a lack of teaching basic principles at an early grade as from a lack of reviewing basic principles at an upper grade level. Too often the computational procedure is reviewed, but the mathematical meaning is not reviewed.

The writer suggests that to make reintroduction or review an active learning experience for the pupils, the material should be introduced in a new or novel setting. Pupils who need further study on addition often attack reintroduction work with a lack of fervor. They feel, and justly so, "We had that in the same way last year; we're doing the same old thing." The situations that follow are illustrative of the type of reintroduction materials designed to vary the setting so that pupils may get further insights into addition and also be able to study "something new."

Basic addition facts

The teacher said, "I noticed a boy doodling with addition combinations. Can you tell what he did?

1	2	3	4
$1 + 1$	$1 + 2$	$1 + 3$	$1 + 4$
2	3	4	5
$1 + 2$	$2 + 3$	$3 + 4$	$4 + 5$
3	5	7	9
?	?	?	?
?	?	?	?
?	?	?	?

"See if you can complete his chart." The teacher then moved about the class and helped those pupils who hadn't discovered the pattern of computation.

Follow-up exercises

Basic Facts (grade four).   The teacher began the year by saying, "Classes I've had usually enjoy 'follow me' exercises in mathematics. See how good you are at 'following me.' Without using pencil and paper, work the addition and subtraction which I give you orally. Keep up. See if you have the correct answer at the end. Let's begin—7 plus 2 plus 5 minus 4 plus 50; the answer is

——right——60. Try again, 3 plus 5 plus 8 plus 4 minus 10; the answer is
——10." The teacher gave several other "follow-me" situations and suggested
that class members having trouble keeping up might benefit from the use of
the flash cards, rods, or semi-programmed sheets on the arithmetic table. Pupils
using the material at the arithmetic table often worked in pairs, with one
child presenting flash cards for the other. In the days that followed the
teacher often used "follow-me" exercises while waiting for the music teacher
or for the lunch bell, directly after recess, or at other times in which there
were a few moments of uncommitted time available.

Continuous addition

Column addition (grade five).   The teacher reintroduced column addition by
asking, "Have any of you ever heard of persons who could add the numbers
named on the side of box cars as a train moved by at a railroad crossing?"
The majority of pupils had heard of such persons or had actually witnessed a
performance of rapid addition. The teacher continued, "I was talking to a
person who can do this rapid type of addition and asked him to explain it to
me so that I could show it to you. He said that he would give you an idea
of his method on a sheet of paper and see if you could figure out how he does
the addition. This is what he wrote. Can you find out what he did?"

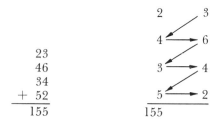

After a little thought the pupils found the idea was to total as they went
along. Think 23, add 40, add 6, add 30, add 4, add 50, add 2, total 155. Many
of the pupils did not feel that this method was faster than their normal method
and a short argument followed. The teacher suggested that it would be necessary to practice using the new method in order to compare. The class was
broken into two teams. One team was to study the new method by working
a set of addition exercises using this method. They checked their exercises using
the conventional algorithm. The other team worked the exercises in the conventional way and checked using the new form. Several days later a contest
was held.

The above reintroduction accomplished at least two things. First, the
pupils had a reason for working on column addition—to find out which procedure was most effective. Second, the computational procedure introduced
is often handy and is the basis of some forms of rapid addition.

Front-end addition

Column addition (grade five).   Adding the most important digits first is a method often used by businessmen and can be a means of estimation or checking. It is also a good review of place-value concepts.

An introductory statement that may be used is, "When I bought some clothing the other day, the clerk added my purchases on a sales slip. I've drawn the sales slip on the board. At first I wasn't sure how he added the amounts. Can you find out what procedure he used?" [4]

Sport Coat	$45.75
Tie	2.25
Top	58.50
Shirt	5.95

Step 1	9	Step 4	11
Step 2	20		2.45
Step 3	2.3		112.45
	.15		

After a discussion, the teacher asked, "Would this method always work? What do you like about the method? What don't you like about the method? Try using this 'front-end' arithmetic to solve the addition exercise in your text. Check using the regular method."

Sand board addition

Column addition (grade five or six).   The teacher introduced sand board addition by saying, "Before the development of pencil and paper, the Hindus in India often performed their calculations in the sand or dirt. Often they had a board covered with sand on which they did their work. When they had finished a portion of an addition, they smoothed out the sand. I'll show you the way the sand board looked at various stages. How did they add 589 ?"
$$+876$$

589 876	89 76 13	9 6 1 135	9 6 145
1 1455	1465		

Hindu method

Column addition (grade six).   The pupils were asked to see if they could find
the reason for a method of addition used by the Hindus in the twelfth
century. The following problem and computational algorithm was given to
the pupils.[5]

. . . if thou be skilled in addition . . . , tell me the sum of two, five, thirty-two, a
hundred and ninety-three, eighteen, ten, and a hundred added together.

Sum of the units	2,	5,	2,	3,	8,	0,	0	20
Sum of the tens			3,	9,	1,	1,	0	14
Sum of the hundreds				1,	0,	0,	1	2
Sum of the sums								360

Pupils were asked the following questions concerning the procedure (1)
Why does it work? (2) Is it really very different from the form we use? (3) Why
can the addition exercise be solved without regrouping? Or, is there regrouping? (4) Solve 234 + 12 + 92 + 7 using the Hindu method.

[5] From *History of Mathematics* by D. E. Smith, Vol. II, p. 91. Copyright 1953 by Eva May
Luce Smith. Published by Dover Publications, Inc., New York 14, N.Y. at $5.00, and reprinted
through permission of the publisher.

1. Choose a grade level and then develop a set of "follow-me" exercises to present to a class of elementary school pupils.
2. Develop a lesson plan for reintroducing a topic in addition.
3. It has been suggested by some writers in the field of elementary school mathematics that technical vocabulary such as commutative property and associative property be developed at the time the topic is first studied. Others believe that introduction should be delayed until the concept is understood. Defend one of these positions.
4. Develop a set of remedial materials for pupils experiencing difficulty with column addition such as: 3 + 306 + 23 + 457.
5. Explain why it is important for a pupil to know several methods of solving an addition exercise.
6. Work the following addition exercises using an abacus.

347	23	4562
+259	86	+8988
	+59	

7. Develop a set of test questions which check the basic mathematical properties of addition.

SUGGESTED REFERENCES

Banks, Houston J., *Learning and Teaching Arithmetic,* 2nd ed. (Boston: Allyn and Bacon, 1964), pp. 133–179.
Buckingham, B. R., *Elementary Arithmetic: Its Meaning and Practice* (Boston: Ginn, 1953), Chap. 5.
Cutler, Ann, and McShane, Rudolph (trans.), *The Trachtenberg Speed System of Basic Mathematics* (Garden City, New York: Doubleday, 1960), Chap. 4.
Flournoy, Frances, "A Consideration of the Ways Children Think When Performing Higher-Decade Addition," *Elementary School Journal,* Vol. 57 (January 1957), pp. 204–208.

Grossnickle, Foster, and Brueckner, Leo J., *Discovering Meanings in Arithmetic* (Philadelphia: Holt, Rinehart and Winston, 1959), Chap. 10.

Overman, James R., *The Teaching of Arithmetic* (Chicago: Lyons and Carnahan, 1961), pp. 101–117.

Swenson, Esther J., *Teaching Arithmetic to Children* (New York: Macmillan, 1964), pp. 81–143.

USE OF SUGGESTED REFERENCES

1. What suggestions for column addition are given by Banks?
2. Study the various checks for addition presented by Buckingham.
3. Review Flournoy's findings concerning children's solutions to higher decade addition.
4. Develop an introduction to the use of manipulative materials suggested by Grossnickle and Brueckner.
5. How does Overman suggest that deductive reasoning be used in learning addition combinations?
6. How does Swenson suggest that money be used to help develop understanding of addition?
7. Study the Trachtenberg method of non-pencil and paper addition. How could this system be used in the classroom?

5

Subtraction
of whole numbers

WHAT IS SUBTRACTION?

Basically, subtraction can be thought of as the inverse or "undoing" of addition. It is standard for a mathematician to consider that there are two basic operations on whole numbers. These are addition and multiplication. Thus, $8 - 5 = 3$ if and only if $5 + 3 = 8$. In the general case, $a - b = c$ if and only if $b + c = a$.

When we dealt with addition, the two numbers to be combined were called *addends* and the result the *sum*. In subtraction, we start with the *sum* and take away one of the *addends* to find the other *addend*. Using the terminology of subtraction, the original sum is called the *minuend,* the addend which is being subtracted, the *subtrahend,* and the remaining addend, the *remainder* or the *difference*. For example,

$$
\begin{array}{ccccc}
3 & + & \square & = & 7 \\
\text{addend} & & \text{addend} & & \text{sum}
\end{array}
$$

$$
\begin{array}{ccccc}
7 & - & 3 & = & \square \\
\text{sum} & & \text{addend} & & \text{addend} \\
\text{minuend} & & \text{subtrahend} & & \text{difference}
\end{array}
$$

The joining of two sets offers an approach to addition. In the same manner, removing a subset from a set offers an approach to subtraction. We may start with a set of 8 objects, remove a subset of 5 objects, and then note that there remains a subset of 3 objects.

Another interpretation of subtraction occurs when two sets are compared by means of one-to-one correspondence. A set of 8 may be compared with a set of 5 by matching set numbers. This matching leaves a remainder set of 3 which indicates the difference in size of the two sets.

A third interpretation involves the question of how many set members must be joined to a given set to obtain another set. For example, how many elements must be joined to a set containing 5 objects to form a set of 8 objects. In terms of number, this leads to the mathematical sentence $5 + \square = 8$. This interpretation closely ties subtraction to addition.

FOUNDATIONS EXPERIENCES

As in the foundation work with addition, the orally presented verbal problem lends itself to the use of sets, concrete objects, and the number line in arriving at a solution. Pupils should experience problems involving all three types of subtraction situations during the foundation work. The discussion that follows includes an illustrative problem for each type of subtraction along with procedures pupils can use to "figure out" the problem.

A take-away situation (removing a subset from a set)

"I just received a package of playground balls (6). The principal asked me to take these (3) to another kindergarten. How many will we have for our use?" The class opened the package and removed 3 from the set of 6 playground balls. They counted to find that the remainder set contained 3. Other solutions to orally presented subtraction problems used at the foundation level may include:

The flannel board.

We have a set of 7.

We remove a subset of 4.

Three are left in the remainder set.

The number line. We have 7; we remove 4 (count back 4). We have 3 left.

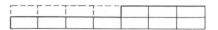

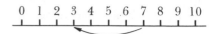

Rods. We have a rod 7 units in length. We remove a rod 4 units in length. We have a rod left that is 3 units in length.

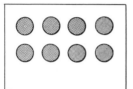

Counters. Tom has 8¢. He spends 5¢. How much money does he have left? Play money or counters can represent the pennies.

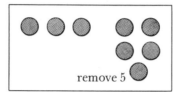

remove 5

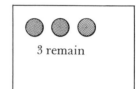

3 remain

Drawings. Notice the picture of Mary's play cups. Her younger brother breaks 2 of them. How many does she then have?

3 remain

How many more are needed situations (looking for the missing addend)

"George wants to buy a candy bar which costs 5¢. He has 3¢. How many more pennies will he need to buy the candy bar?" Early primary pupils may solve problems of this type using the following procedures.

Actual pennies, play pennies, or counters. Begin with a set of 3 pennies and count forward to 5.

1¢   1¢   1¢   1¢   1¢

The number line.

The flannel board.

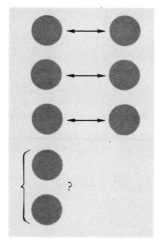

The "how many more" type of problem is often omitted from foundation work in subtraction. However, careful study of situations in which kindergarten and early first-grade pupils actually use subtraction ideas reveals that many of the most common problem situations involve the idea "I have a certain amount. I need a certain amount. How much more do I need?"

Comparison (find the difference between two numbers)

"John and Jill were playing checkers one day. John won 8 games and Jill won 5 games. How many more games did John win than Jill?" Children can develop solutions at the foundation level using these procedures:

Sets of objects and matching in one-to-one correspondence.

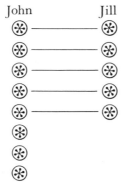

The number line.

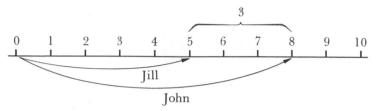

Drawings.

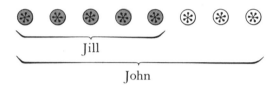

Most pupils find the comparison type of subtraction problem to be the most difficult of the three types. Also, many current textbooks give little attention to the comparison situation.[1] With the small amount of emphasis given comparison situations in current materials, the teacher must constantly supplement instruction with problems of this type.

Discovering subtraction combinations

The teacher of elementary school mathematics is faced with several decisions concerning the introduction of the subtraction algorithm. First, she must decide whether subtraction and addition should be introduced simultaneously. Some writers in the field of elementary school mathematics suggest that subtraction be introduced on the same day as addition in order to highlight the inverse relationship between addition and subtraction. Others suggest that the subtraction algorithm be introduced several days after addition. The author holds the latter viewpoint. While there is little research evidence for either procedure, it is the belief of the author that the inverse operation can be developed more effectively if the pupils possess a good understanding of addition.

Second, the teacher must decide which of the three types of subtraction situations should be used for introductory work. Few authorities suggest the use of the "comparison" type of problem for introductory work. There are, however, proponents of both the "take-away" and the "additive" situations.

---

[1] Leo M. Schell and Paul C. Burns, "Pupils Performance with Three Types of Subtraction Situations," School Science and Mathematics, *Vol. LXII* (March 1962), pp. 208–214.

Additive situations in which pupils search for the missing addend lend themselves to a good development of the inverse relationship of subtraction to addition. Also, some writers believe that if a pupil knows $3 + 4 = \square$, he will know $3 + \square = 7$ and $7 - 3 = \square$. There is little evidence either to justify or repudiate this belief.

Take-away situations are usually easier for pupils to understand [2] and can be developed as the removal of members from a given set. For these reasons it is suggested that the first formal subtraction situations involve the take-away idea.

Introducing subtraction

Following foundation work, initial subtraction was begun with this orally presented problem: "Marcia baked 8 cupcakes. She gave 3 of the cupcakes to friends. How many cupcakes did she have remaining?" The pupils gave answers to the problem. Then the teacher suggested that they discuss the methods they had used in solving the problem. Pupils suggested counting backward from 8, taking 8 objects and removing 3, and using a number line to help count to find the answer.

The class members were directed to solve several other problems printed on a duplicated sheet and to show their answers to be correct by using a different method. All of the problems involved take-away situations. During the work time, the teacher noted the methods used by pupils and gave assistance and encouragement to those who were experiencing difficulty.

When the majority of the pupils had worked several problems, the teacher suggested, "Let's stop for a minute and discuss the process that we are using. When we have worked addition problems, we have written the mathematical sentence which can be used to solve the problem. Can you state in words the mathematical question asked in this problem? Grandmother gave Ken 9 pencils. Ken's mother said, 'You'll have to share these with your brothers and sisters. I'll take 4 to give to them.' How many of the pencils will Ken have?"

Pupils suggested, "Nine take away 4 leaves what number?" "Four from 9 equals what number?" and "Nine remove 4 equals what number?" The teacher then wrote on the board, "Nine take away 4 equals what number?" and asked, "How could we shorten this mathematical question?" Pupils suggested that the equals sign ($=$) replace the word "equals" and that a box ($\square$) replace "what number." The teacher replaced the words with the symbols and then replaced the words "take away" with the minus sign ($-$). She said, "We can read (points to chalkboard: $9 - 4 = \square$) as 'nine minus 4 equals what number?' We call this sign ($-$) the minus sign. Do you know what type of mathematical sentence this is? Remember we've had addition sentences. Is this addition?" The class agreed that the mathematical sentence was not

[2] Glenadine E. Gibb, "Childrens' Thinking in the Process of Subtraction," *Journal of Experimental Education*, Vol. 25 (September 1956), pp. 71-78.

an addition sentence. Several who had older brothers or sisters suggested that it was a subtraction sentence. The teacher verified that the mathematical sentence $9 - 4 = \square$ was indeed a subtraction sentence.

During the next few days the pupils worked problems and found solutions to mathematical sentences which involved both addition and subtraction. Dot drawings, the number line, and objects continued to play a vital role in finding answers to the exercises.

After the pupils had a good understanding of "take-away" subtraction, situations involving "additive subtraction" or "how many more are needed" situations were introduced. These problems were used: (1) Mary wants to give every person attending her birthday party a paper hat. Mary now has 6 paper hats. How many more will she need if 8 persons attend her party? (2) Claudia's mother told her that she would sew a dress for each of her 7 dolls. If her mother has finished 3 dresses, how many does she have left to make? (3) Jim has 3¢. How many more cents does he need to buy a pencil which costs 7¢? The pupils were asked to write the mathematical sentence which could be used to solve the problem, to work the problem, and to prove their answer to be correct by solving the problem in a different manner. Several solutions are illustrated below:

Tim: This is the mathematical sentence which represents the problem. I thought 6 plus what number equals 8. The answer is 2.

$$6 + \square = 8$$

Marcia: I knew that I could find the answer by subtracting 6 from 8. It isn't the same type question as some of the other subtraction questions, but I can get the correct answer in this manner.

$$8 - 6 = \square$$

Phil: The number line can be used to count the answer.

Kim: I used this dot diagram to help me. I need 8. I have 6, so I circle 6 dots. This leaves 2 dots which represent the 2 I need.

The difference between Tim's addition sentence and Marcia's subtraction sentence caused a great deal of class discussion. After a rather heated discussion the class decided that either sentence could be used to solve the problem, that the sentence $6 + \Box = 8$ represented the actions on the sets of paper hats, and that the sentence $8 - 6 = \Box$ represented an effective method of quickly arriving at the answer.

During the remainder of the period the pupils solved a number of addition and subtraction exercises of the type shown below.

$$8 - 5 = \Box \qquad 9 - 5 = \Box \qquad 5 + \Box = 8$$
$$5 + 3 = \Box \qquad 7 + \Box = 9 \qquad 7 - 3 = \Box$$

Discussion on the following day was used to begin the development of the inverse relationship between addition and subtraction. The number line played a key role in this development.

"Comparison" type of subtraction situations were introduced through the following problems: (1) Larry has 6 coins in his collection. Bob has 4 coins in his collection. How many more coins does Larry have than Bob? (2) Gret is 7 years old. Her younger sister Sue is 4 years old. What is the difference in their ages? Again pupils identified the mathematical sentence and showed their answers to be correct by drawings. The majority of the class identified the mathematical sentence as a subtraction sentence. However, they noted that the drawings they needed to show their answer to be correct were different from the type used in their earlier work with subtraction. Examples of the drawings used to solve problem (1) appear below.

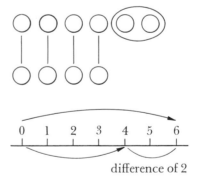

Will: I compared 4 to 6 and found a difference of 2.

Fay: I marked off 6 on the number line and then marked off 4. The difference between them is 2.

difference of 2

When most pupils appeared to be progressing well in subtraction, the class studied the addition table to note similarities between addition and subtraction. Several pupils quickly noted that it was possible to use the addition table to solve any subtraction situation. One pupil said, "To find the combination $16 - 9 = \Box$ I look for a 16 in a sum box that is directly across or directly down from a 9; then I follow the column up (or over) to find the answer."

addend

+	0	1	2	3	4	5	6	7	8	9
0	0	1	2	3	4	5	6	7	8	9
1	1	2	3	4	5	6	7	8	9	10
2	2	3	4	5	6	7	8	9	10	11
3	3	4	5	6	7	8	9	10	11	12
4	4	5	6	7	8	9	10	11	12	13
5	5	6	7	8	9	10	11	12	13	14
6	6	7	8	9	10	11	12	13	14	15
7	7	8	9	10	11	12	13	14	15	16
8	8	9	10	11	12	13	14	15	16	17
9	9	10	11	12	13	14	15	16	17	18

addend (left of table)   sums (right of table)

Subtraction generalization

Once the basic subtraction facts have been discovered, much attention should be given to developing the generalizations or principles which apply to subtraction. In addition to the mathematical understanding involved, such study is helpful to learning the basic subtraction facts. Basically the most important generalization to remember is that subtraction is the *inverse of addition*.

Other related generalizations are the following:

1. When zero is subtracted from a number, the number is unchanged. This holds true since zero is the identity element for addition. Then $7 + 0 = 7$ and $7 - 0 = 7$.

2. Subtracting a number from itself leaves zero. Again, this follows from zero acting as the identity element for addition.

3. Subtracting ones from a number is equivalent to counting backwards by ones.

4. In situations such as $(16 - 5) - 3 = \square$ the subtrahends may be added and the sum subtracted from the minuend, $16 - 5 - 3 = 16 - 8$.

5. The subtrahend may be renamed (broken into parts) and each part subtracted. For example, $18 - 9 = (18 - 8) - 1 = 9$. This is particularly helpful for reviewing subtraction facts in which a number is subtracted from a multi-digit number.

Renaming in subtraction

Subtraction situations such as $34 - 16 = \square$ involve a need to rename one set of tens into ones. ($34 = 30 + 4 = 20 + 10 + 4 = 20 + 14$) The familiar adult term for this process is "borrowing" which is not actually correct. Instead of "borrowing" we rename 34 or $30 + 4$ to $20 + 14$.

Several days before the introduction of renaming, the teacher may use some exercises in which pupils discuss different ways of naming a number such as 34. This discussion should lead pupils to naming 34 as 30 + 4 and 20 + 14. Naming 34 as 3 tens and 4 ones and 2 tens and 14 ones may also be developed.

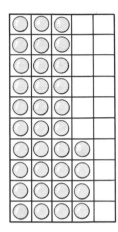

The teacher introduced renaming by stating, "Look at problem one on the duplicated sheet; it says, 'Betty has a box containing 34 Christmas tree ornaments. (See illustration.) If her mother uses 16 of the ornaments, how many will Betty have for use on her own tree?' Write the mathematical sentence which can be used to solve the problem, solve the problem, and then show that your answer is correct in as many ways as you can."

While the pupils worked on the problem, the teacher observed individual class members at work. She suggested to those pupils who were experiencing difficulty that they make use of bundles of sticks or the diagram. Several pupils were asked to show their method of attack at the chalkboard. These procedures and pupil statements are shown below.

The pupils first stated the mathematical sentence as 34 − 16 = ☐ or   34
   −16
   ─────
     ☐

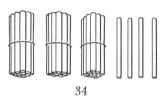

34

Jeff: I used bundles of tens. I had to remove 16. First I removed 10. I couldn't remove 6 more without unbundling one of the tens. I unbundled the ten and removed 6. I had 18 remaining.

Kim: I used place-value frames. I marked 3 tens and 4 ones. I removed 1 ten. I couldn't remove 6 ones so I changed one of the tens to ones. Then I removed 6 ones. My answer was 18.

tens	ones
✳I I	IIII

tens	ones
I	IIII 〥〥〥 IIII

George: I used the place-value frame using numerals. I couldn't subtract 6 from 4 so I changed the 3 tens to 2 tens and 10 ones. Then I subtracted 6 from 14 and 1 ten from 2 tens. My answer was 18.

tens	ones
2	14
−1	−6

1	8

Paul: I wrote the computation in expanded form. Then I remembered that there are many names for the same number. I renamed 30 + 4 into 20 + 14. Then I subtracted. The answer was 18.

$$30 + 4 = 20 + 14$$
$$-10 + 6 \quad 10 + 6$$
$$\overline{\qquad\qquad} \quad \overline{10 + 8} = 18$$

Ray: I used the diagram. I marked out 10 and then marked out 6 more. My answer was 18.

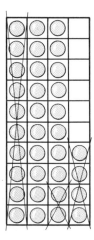

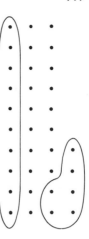

Ned: I made a dot array pattern and circled the 16 I needed to subtract.

Phyllis: I used the abacus. I indicated 34. Then I removed one ten. I needed to remove 6 ones. I removed 4 ones. I still needed to remove 2 ones. I exchanged 1 ten for 10 ones and then removed 2 ones.

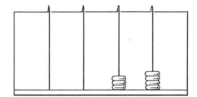

Nan: I had a hard time figuring out what to do, so I counted backwards from 34. I got the right answer, but it took a long time.

The pupils discussed the various solutions. They felt that the solution using renaming suggested by Paul and the tens and ones frame solution suggested by George were probably the best. During this discussion the teacher emphasized the importance of renaming.

If pupils are not able to "discover" the renaming procedure, it is suggested that the teacher use leading questions such as "What does 74 mean?" "How could we rename 74?" "How could we rename 74 in a way to help us subtract 38?"

$$74 = 70 + 4 = 60 + 14$$
$$-38 \quad\ 30 + 8 \quad\ 30 + 8$$

During the next few days pupils were given their choice of method in solving subtraction exercises involving renaming. The slower pupils often used popsicle sticks bundled into tens. As they gained understanding of the process, the teacher helped them to develop the expanded form. The more rapid pupils were directed to try to devise means of shortening the writing process.

When the class members had developed a good understanding of the process, the teacher conducted a discussion of shortening the process. The group moved from illustration (a) to illustration (b) and several of the pupils found that they could think through the renaming without rewriting the algorithm (illustration (c)).

$$
\begin{array}{cc}
\text{tens} & \text{ones} \\
5\!\!\!/ & \not{2}12 \\
-\quad 4 & 8 \\
\hline
1 & 4
\end{array}
\qquad
\begin{array}{cc}
5 & 12 \\
\not{6} & \not{2} \\
-4 & 8 \\
\hline
1 & 4
\end{array}
\qquad
\begin{array}{cc}
6 & 2 \\
-4 & 8 \\
\hline
1 & 4
\end{array}
$$

$$
\text{(a)} \qquad\qquad\qquad \text{(b)} \qquad\qquad \text{(c)}
$$

Subtraction with 3 or more digits can be developed in the same manner. However, some pupils experience difficulty with situations such as $503 - 346 = \square$. The following suggestion is usually helpful.

This can be renamed in several ways.

$$
\begin{array}{cll}
503 & 500 + 3 = 490 + 13 & \text{or} \\
-346 & 340 + 6 = 340 +\ \ 6
\end{array}
\qquad
\begin{array}{l}
400 + 100 + 3 = 400 + 90 + 13 \\
300 +\ \ \ 40 + 6 = 300 + 40 +\ \ 6
\end{array}
$$

In the present program, renaming in subtraction is usually introduced late in second grade or in third grade. Since pupils will be using this process over a period of time, it is suggested that the teacher take care to develop understanding before developing the short-cut algorithm.

The renaming form as presented above is not the only possible means of developing compound subtraction. Four different (or partially) different methods can be used. They are (1) take away-renaming, (2) take away-equal additions, (3) additive-renaming, and (4) additive-equal additions. Type (1), take away-renaming, is the method used for presentation in the teaching situation above. The other methods are explained below.

Take away-equal additions.

$$
\begin{array}{cl}
84 & 80 +\ \ 4 \\
-56 & 50 +\ \ 6 \\
\hline
\end{array}
\qquad \text{Six cannot be subtracted from 4.}
$$

$$
\begin{array}{l}
80 + 14 \\
60 +\ \ 6 \\
\hline
20 +\ \ 8 = 28
\end{array}
\qquad
\begin{array}{l}
\text{Add 10 ones to 4.} \\
\text{Add 1 ten to 50.} \\
\text{Subtract.}
\end{array}
$$

This procedure is based on the principle that if both terms are increased by the same amount, the difference (remainder) is unchanged. This property is referred to as compensation.

$$
\begin{array}{ccc}
6 & 6 + 2 & 8 \\
-3 & 3 + 2 & -5 \\
\hline
3 & & 3
\end{array}
$$

Additive-renaming.

$$\begin{array}{rr} 84 & 80 + 4 \\ -56 & 50 + 6 \end{array}$$

$$\begin{array}{ll} 70 + 14 & \text{Rename.} \\ 50 + 6 & \text{Think 6 plus what number} = 14? \\ & \text{Think 50 plus what number} = 70? \end{array}$$

Note that renaming is done in the same manner as in the classroom situation described above. The difference is in using "additive thinking" rather than "take-away" thinking.

Additive-equal additions.

$$\begin{array}{rr} 84 & 80 + 4 \\ -56 & 50 + 6 \end{array} \quad \text{Six cannot be subtracted from 4.}$$

$$\begin{array}{ll} 80 + 14 & \text{Add 10 ones to 4.} \\ 60 + 6 & \text{Add 1 ten to 50.} \\ & \text{Think 6 plus what number} = 14? \\ & \text{Think 60 plus what number} = 80? \end{array}$$

Students of the teaching of elementary school mathematics have often debated as to which approach (renaming or equal additions) should be used. One of the most thorough studies on the relative merits of the two approaches was conducted by Brownell and Moser.[3] In this study four groups were used. Two groups learned the decomposition (renaming) method, one with understanding and the other mechanically. Two groups learned the equal additions approach, one group with understanding and the other mechanically.

In comparing the four groups they found equal additions to be superior to decomposition when taught by rote and decomposition to be superior to equal additions when taught with understanding. Since a basic tenet of modern programs of mathematics is understanding of the number system, the decomposition method (renaming) is used for initial instruction. A means of making use of the equal additions procedure will be discussed in the section on reintroducing subtraction.

Uses of compensation with multi-digit subtraction

It was noted in the brief discussion on the equal additions approach that *compensation* accounted for the algorithm. This property can be generalized: If $a - b = c$, then $(a + k) - (b + k) = c$. (k is considered to be any integer—whole number.) This principle can be often used in non-pencil

[3] William A. Brownell and Harold E. Moser, *Meaningful vs. Mechanical Learning; Study in Grade III Subtraction* (Durham, North Carolina: Duke University Press, 1949).

and paper solution to subtraction exercises. For example, if a pupil is asked to solve $96 - 38 = N$ without using pencil and paper, he can think $(96 + 2) - (38 + 2) = N$ or $98 - 40 = 58$. This procedure is easier to handle without pencil and paper than the conventional thinking: $96 - 38 = N$; change 96 to $80 + 16$; subtract 8 from 16; subtract 30 from 80; answer $= 58$.

The compensation principle can also be used in this form: If $a - b = c$, then $(a - k) - (b - k) = c$. Thus, a pupil may solve $70 - 32$ by thinking subtract 2 from each term: $68 - 30 = 38$.

The compensation method may be introduced by presenting a number of non-pencil and paper subtraction exercises to pupils and asking them to find the answer as quickly as possible. A discussion of the methods used by pupils will often reveal that one or more pupils have discovered the idea of compensation. If this is the case, the teacher should develop a mathematical understanding of the procedure. The teacher may say, "I worked the exercise in this manner." (She illustrates on the board.) "Why does this work? What mathematical principle allows us to perform subtraction in this manner?"

$$
\begin{array}{ll}
96 & 96 + 2 = 98 \\
-38 & 38 + 2 = 40 \\
\hline
58 & 58
\end{array}
$$

Other techniques for studying subtraction

The suggestions that follow can be used in practice situations, to further the understanding of subtraction, and in developing an understanding of the relationship between addition and subtraction.

Mathematical sentences (primary level).   Work with various types of mathematical sentences involving addition and subtraction, distinguishing between mathematical sentences that are true or false, and making use of greater than, less than, and not equal to in situations using addition and subtraction.

1. Make a true mathematical sentence of the following:

$$5 + \square = 9 \qquad \square + 8 = 15 \qquad 9 - 3 = \square$$
$$18 - 7 = \square \qquad \square + \square = 18$$

2. Insert the correct symbol: $=, <, >$

$$5 - 3 \bigcirc 2 \qquad 17 - 9 \bigcirc 7$$
$$6 - 4 \bigcirc 3 \qquad 9 - 5 \bigcirc 4$$

3. Decide whether each of the following mathematical sentences are true, false, or could be either true or false.

$$16 - 7 = 8 \qquad \text{True, False, Either}$$
$$\square + \square = 17 \qquad \text{True, False, Either}$$
$$\triangle - \triangle = 9 \qquad \text{True, False, Either}$$

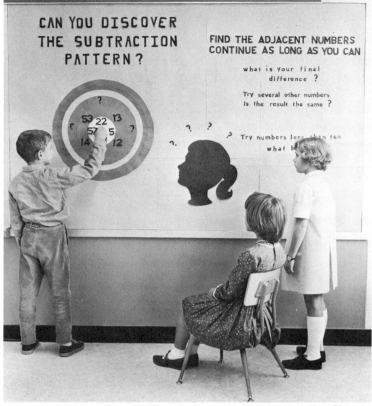

CAN YOU DISCOVER
THE SUBTRACTION
PATTERN?

FIND THE ADJACENT NUMBERS
CONTINUE AS LONG AS YOU CAN

what is your final
difference ?

Try several other numbers
Is the result the same ?

? Try numbers less than ten
what H

Source: Still Photo Services U. D. I. S., Pennsylvania State University

Jim has made some errors in the placement of numerals on the bulletin board. Can you find them?

4. List the possible replacements for the frames: Use only $\{0, 1, 2, 3, \ldots, 17, 18\}$.

$$\triangle - \square = 9 \qquad \bigcirc - \triangle = \triangle$$
$$\square + 5 = \triangle \qquad 9 + \triangle < 16$$
$$\bigcirc - \triangle = \bigcirc \qquad 17 - \triangle < 9$$

Making change (late primary—early intermediate level). "When I bought several items at the drugstore yesterday the cost was \$1.57. I gave the clerk a five dollar bill. He didn't subtract to find how much change I had coming but counted it in the following manner: \$1.57, \$1.58, \$1.59, \$1.60, \$1.70, \$1.75, \$2.00, \$3.00, \$4.00, \$5.00. When I asked (for fun), 'How much change have you given me?' he didn't know. Yet he said that he was sure that it was the correct change. What did he do? Why was he sure he was right? Is this counting, addition, or subtraction? Try a few examples with making change in this manner."

The above situation is helpful in additive thinking in subtraction. Also, it is a situation with which most pupils are familiar, although they have not analyzed it.

The abacus (intermediate grades).   "Many Japanese and Chinese small businessmen in the United States make use of the abacus in doing their business mathematics. In fact, some of them can work much faster than an electric adding machine. See if you can use the Japanese or Chinese abacus. It is somewhat different than the abacuses that we have been using. The beads above the line (one on the Japanese and two on the Chinese) are valued at five of the beads below the line." [4]

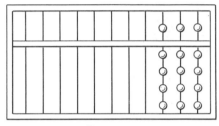
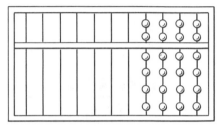

Japanese   Chinese

"Follow-me" oral exercises (all grades).   As in addition, valuable use can be made of oral "follow-me" exercises. They can be used in spare minutes throughout the day. Example: 23 minus 10 plus 7 minus 15 plus 5 plus 8 minus 9 equals what number?

Identification of subtraction types (late primary–early intermediate).   "The problem sheet contains problems of all three subtraction varieties. Identify the type of subtraction situation and illustrate the situation with the number line."

Cross-number puzzles and magic squares (all grades). "I've placed some cross-number puzzles and magic squares on the mathematics table. You may want to spend a portion of the mathematics period working on them. They should be of help to you in subtraction and addition."
    Cross-number puzzle (subtraction). The procedure for use with this type of cross-number puzzle is as follows:
    1. Write the minuend (17) in the upper left-hand box.
    2. Write the subtrahend (8) in the lower left-hand box.
    3. Rename the minuend and write the parts in the spaces to the right of the minuend.

---

[4] For an explanation of the Japanese abacus see Takashi Kojima, *The Japanese Abacus: Its Use and Theory* (Rutland, Vermont: Charles E. Tuttle Company, 1954).

4. Rename the subtrahend and write the part above the subtrahend. (For work with pupils before negative numbers have been introduced: the pupil should always rename the minuend so that each part is larger or equal to the parts of the renamed subtrahend.)

5. Subtract each part of the subtrahend from each part of the minuend $(10 - 6; 7 - 6; 10 - 2; 7 - 2)$. The difference is found by finding the sum of either diagonal $(4 + 5;$ or $8 + 1)$.

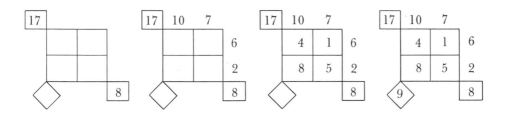

When work with negative numbers has been introduced the pupil no longer needs to rename the parts of the minuend so that each is larger than the parts of the subtrahend. See illustration below.

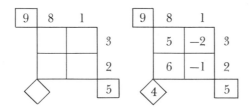

Puzzles of this type are based on the principle that the subtrahend may be renamed and each part subtracted from the minuend. Pupils should be challenged to try to figure out this principle.

Magic squares. A magic square is an array in which the sum of each column across, the sum of each vertical column, and the sum of each diagonal are equal. Study magic square A, and then supply the missing numerals in the other magic squares. When you become proficient, try to develop your own magic squares.

A

10	3	8
5	7	9
6	11	4

B

7	0	
2		6
	8	1

Number families (primary grades).   The relationship between addition and subtraction is often furthered by the study of number families. For example, in the family of 7 how many addition and subtraction facts can you find which have 7 as a sum (addition) or 7 as a minuend (subtraction)?

$$4 + 3 = 7 \qquad 7 - 4 = 3$$
$$3 + 4 = 7 \qquad 7 - 3 = 4$$
$$5 + 2 = 7 \qquad 7 - 5 = 2$$
$$2 + 5 = 7 \qquad 7 - 2 = 5$$
$$6 + 1 = 7 \qquad 7 - 6 = 1$$
$$1 + 6 = 7 \qquad 7 - 1 = 6$$
$$0 + 7 = 7 \qquad 7 - 7 = 0$$
$$7 + 0 = 7 \qquad 7 - 0 = 7$$

CHECKING SUBTRACTION

Checking basic subtraction combinations may be done in several ways. The most common is an application of the inverse relationships with addition and, thus, using addition as the check. Dot drawings, counting backwards, the number line, the abacus, and subtracting twice $[16 - 9 = (16 - 6) - 3]$ are also appropriate checks.

For multi-digit subtraction, addition, subtraction of the remainder from the minuend, casting out nines, and any of the procedures suggested for reintroduction may be effectively used.

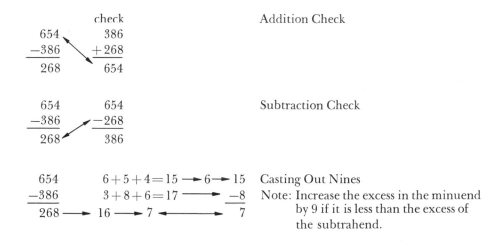

REINTRODUCING SUBTRACTION

As in the case of addition (see chapter 4), the reintroduction of subtraction should involve situations that differ from the original introduction. Suggestions for reteaching follow.

HOW MANY NAMES FOR MR. NUMBER CAN YOU FIND?

Renaming numbers furthers pupils' knowledge of place value, addition, and subtraction.

Associative Property

Basic facts (grade three).   The teacher made use of the principle that the number to be subtracted may be broken up into parts and each of these parts subtracted: $15 - 8 = (15 - 5) - 3 = 10 - 3 = 7$.   She said, "I noticed yesterday that some of you were having difficulty with remembering the answer to a subtraction of one digit from two digits. See if you can think of a means of finding an answer if you have forgotten a subtraction combination." Pupils gave various suggestions such as the number line and counting. Then the teacher said, "Last year I had a boy who found the answer in this manner: To find $17 - 9$ think seventeen, ten, eight. The answer is 8. Can anyone show me what he did?"

Charlie: $17 - 9 = (17 - 7) - 2 = 8$. Subtract the number it takes to reach 10. Then subtract the remaining number. This works in the same manner as adding twice. $8 + 9 = 8 + 2 + 7$. We are renaming and subtracting.

Another class member then suggested that it would also be possible to use additive thinking in solving the exercise. He said, "You could think $9 + \square = 17$; 9 and *one* more equals 10, plus 7 more equals 17. $9 + 8 = 17$. You can think what number do I need to add to reach 10? How much more than 10 is the original number? Then add these."

$$
\begin{array}{r}
16 \\
-\ 7 \\
\hline
9
\end{array}
$$

Think: I need 3 to reach 10.

Sixteen is 6 more than 10.

$6 + 3 = 9.$

Compensation

Basic facts (grade three).   "Last year I had a pupil who was always forgetting basic subtraction facts. Do any of you have this trouble? He often worked an exercise in the manner I've shown on the board. What is his method? Was he right? Will he always be right? Why does this work?"

$$
\begin{array}{r}
17 \\
-\ 9 \\
\hline
\end{array}
\quad \text{change to} \quad
\begin{array}{r}
18 \\
-10 \\
\hline
8
\end{array}
\quad \text{or} \quad 17 - 9 = (17 - 10) + 1
$$

Again the principle of compensation is used. The situation above provides a different look at subtraction facts and can also be used as a check of subtraction exercises.

Review study questions (grade three, four, five or six).   The teacher began, "I know you sometimes get tired of review in mathematics class. Today I'm going to give you a set of questions to check to see if it is necessary to do much review work in subtraction. The questions call for some good thinking. Work on these questions and we'll discuss them later in the period." She then gave each pupil a duplicated set of review study questions.

REVIEW STUDY QUESTIONS (GRADE FOUR)

1. Show $85 - 37 = \square$ using the place-value frame.

tens	ones

2. How many subtraction questions can you write using the numerals 8, 7, 4, and 9? Solve the questions.

3. How could you rename 45 so that you could subtract 29 from it? $(45 = 30 + 15)$

4. Solve the following: $6 + \square = 18$ $8 + \square = 37$
$\square + 24 = 38$ $\square + \ 8 = 20$

Subtraction whizzes

Basic facts in different settings (grade four).   "Yesterday you told me that you were subtraction whizzes. Let's see. Put away your paper and pencils. Now start at 78 and subtract 5's until you reach a number in the 50's. Raise your hand when you know. Yes, the answer is 58. Now start at 156 and subtract 7's until you reach a number in the 130's. What is that number?"

This type of subtraction makes use of a "bridging" situation and a series of subtractions. It also provides a good foundation experience for division.

Additive thinking

Multi-digit (grade five).   "We haven't always renamed in the manner we now use. See if you can figure out the procedure that I've duplicated, the explanation given in *White's Arithmetic,* which was written in 1883. See if you can work the examples using this procedure. Also, see if you can give an explanation for the procedure."

Since 6 units can not be taken from 4 units, add 10 units to the 4 units, making 14 units, and take 6 units from the 14 units, and write 8 units (the difference) below. To balance the 10 units added to the minuend, add 1 ten (equal to 10 units) to the 2 tens, making 3 tens, and take 3 tens from 3 tens, and write 0 (the difference) below.

Process
Minuend	5334
Subtrahend	2726
Difference	2608

Since 7 hundreds can not be taken from 3 hundreds, add 10 hundreds to the 3 hundreds, making 13 hundreds, and take 7 hundreds from 13 hundreds, and write 6 hundreds (the difference) below. To balance 10 hundreds added to the minuend, add 1 thousand (equal to 10 hundreds) to the 2 thousands, making 3 thousands, and take 3 thousands from 5 thousands, and write 2 thousands (the difference) below. The difference is 2608.

Pupils commented on the writing of the explanation. They were surprised at the number of times *and* was used in one sentence. Several subtraction combinations were solved as a total class. Discussion brought out the idea that the procedure made use of the principle of compensation. One gave an explanation as follows:

Mark: Use tens and ones. I added 10 ones to the upper term and 1 ten to the lower term. This makes use of the principle we learned earlier called compensation. If both terms are increased by the same amount, the difference is not changed.

$$\begin{array}{r} 56 \\ -38 \\ \hline \end{array}$$

Tens	Ones
5	6 − 10
3 − 1 ten	8
1	8

Complementary method

Multi-digit (grade five or six).   The question, "Do you know what a complement is?" was asked by the teacher. Pupils suggested that it meant praise or flattery. The teacher wrote "complement" on the board and said, "That would be a homonym which is spelled c-o-m-p-l-i-m-e-n-t. Complement is spelled in the same way as complementary colors." She then said, "Let's see if you can figure out what a mathematical complement is. The complement of 6 is 4; the complement of 3 is 7; what is the complement of 5? ____5____ right. The complement of 25 is 75; what is the complement of 40? ____60____ right. What would be the complement of 350? ____650____right. How can you state a generalization that would cover all complements?

The class decided that the complement of a number was the difference between the number and the next higher power of ten.[5] Then the teacher said, "During the eighteen hundreds the Europeans often used the 'complementary method' of subtraction. Look at the example of the board and see if you can work the other examples."

$$\begin{array}{r} 32 \\ -18 \\ \hline \end{array}$$ The complement of 18 is 82. $$\begin{array}{r} 32 \\ +82 \\ \hline \cancel{1}4 \end{array}$$

Add the complement to the sum (minuend).
Mark the numeral in the hundreds place.
Answer 14.

After working several of the exercises, the class attacked the problem, "Why does the complementary method work?" Herb suggested that they might get an idea of the workings of the complementary method by recording the entire operation as a mathematical sentence. He worked $74 - 36 = \square$ in the manner shown below.

$$(74 - 36) = 74 + (100 - 36) - 100$$

He said, "If we look closely we can see that 100 has been added to the sentence and then subtracted. This makes use of the principle that the value of a number is not changed if we add and take away the same amount from it. It's just like $(5 + 7) - 7 = 5$." After further clarification of the complementary

[5] Note: There are other complements, such as the complement of an angle.

method, the teacher assigned several exercises to be worked by the complementary method and checked by the regular subtraction algorithm.

Casting out elevens

Multi-digit (grade six).   "We've checked addition and subtraction by 'casting
out nines'; could we cast out other numbers?" The class agreed that any
number could be 'cast out' as a check, but that it would be difficult to find
the excess without going through the process of division. Then the teacher
said, "There is one number which we can use that doesn't involve the division
process. That is 11. Look at the illustration. What has been done?"

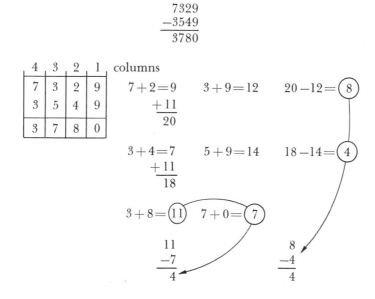

$$7329$$
$$-3549$$
$$\overline{3780}$$

After thoughtful consideration and several questions by the teacher, the
pupils said, "We find the excess of 11's by subtracting the sum of the even-place
digits from the sum of the odd-place digits. We label the digits from left to
right. If the sum of the odd-place digits is less than the sum of the even-place
digits, we add 11 to the odd-place digits."

The efficiency of the check was discussed. Most class members agreed
that while it was not a very efficient method of checking subtraction, it was
rather unusual. The teacher suggested that some of the class members might
be able to figure out why the procedure worked. It was suggested that looking at a multiplication table of 11's might be an aid.

Consider $11 \times 15 = 165$

$$
\begin{array}{r}
51 \\
\times\ 11 \\
\hline
51 \\
51 \\
\hline
561
\end{array}
$$

From the property of multiplication by 11, the sum of the even
digits in the partial products is always equal to the sum of the
odd digits.

Thus, the amount over a multiple of 11 is equal to the difference
between the sum of the even and odd digits.

Austrian method

Multi-digit (grade six).   The teacher began, "The other day we were having a contest to see who could find the newest or the oldest method of subtracting. Paul brought in a method called the Austrian method. It was used in Austria in the early 1800's (at least as early as 1821). See if you can follow the suggestions given for this method. Think of the number which added to 483 will give 826.

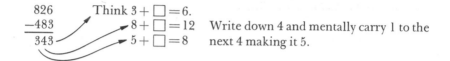

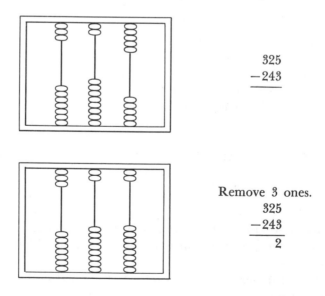

```
826      Think 3 + □ = 6.
−483            8 + □ = 12   Write down 4 and mentally carry 1 to the
 343            5 + □ = 8    next 4 making it 5.
```

"Upon what principle is the method based?—compensation—right. Try several exercises using the Austrian method. See how it works for non-pencil and paper subtraction."

SUBTRACTION USING THE ABACUS

Subtraction may be performed by moving the beads representing the sum (minuend) up and then moving beads down to perform the subtraction. The regrouping is accomplished by exchanging 1 ten for 10 ones or exchanging 100 for 10 tens.

```
325
−243
```

Remove 3 ones.
```
 325
−243
   2
```

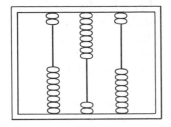

Four beads cannot be moved down.
Move 2 beads down. Exchange 10
tens for one 100. (Move one 100
down.) Move the other 2 beads
down.

$$\begin{array}{r} 2\ 12 \\ \not{3}\ \not{2}\ 5 \\ -2\ 4\ 3 \\ \hline 8\ 2 \end{array}$$

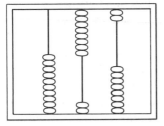

Move 2 beads down in the hundreds place. Answer: 82

$$\begin{array}{r} 2\ 12 \\ \not{3}\ \not{2}\ 5 \\ -2\ 4\ 3 \\ \hline 8\ 2 \end{array}$$

SUBTRACTION OF NEGATIVE INTEGERS

Subtraction involving negative numbers is a more difficult process
for children to rationalize than is addition. Typically pupils were taught
to subtract a number, change its sign, and add. While such a rule holds true
for subtraction of signed numbers, it often has little meaning to elementary
school pupils.

Readiness for subtraction involving negative integers can be developed
by emphasizing the idea of finding the *difference* in many cases with positive
integers. Once the idea of finding the difference is developed, examples involving negative integers should cause little difficulty.

An intuitive understanding of subtraction involving negative integers
can be introduced in the following manner:

Look at the illustration on the chalkboard.
It should help you to solve the problem
I'm going to read to you. Two miners began digging at a location 5 feet above sea
level. They struck uranium at 5 feet below
sea level (-5). What was the difference in
feet between the level at which they began
digging and the level at which they struck
uranium? Draw an illustration of your
own if you need it to help with the question. Solve the problem. Then try to write
the mathematical sentence which illustrates
the situation.

After the pupils had worked a short time, the teacher asked for the answer to the problem and the method of solution that pupils had used. One pupil explained, "I drew a line like the one on the board on my paper. I wanted to find the number of feet between the two points, one at 5 feet above sea level, one at 5 feet below sea level. I counted the distance between the points. My answer came out 10 feet."

Another pupil suggested, "I looked at the illustration. I noticed a distance of 5 feet above sea level and a distance of 5 feet below sea level. I added $5 + 5$ and got an answer of 10 feet."

After the class had reached agreement that the distance between the two points was 10 feet, the teacher asked, "Could you figure out the mathematical sentence that could be used to solve this problem?"

Pupils gave responses similar to the following: "I can't give the mathematical sentence in numbers, but I can give you a 'word sentence.' I think it is, 'What is the difference between 5 feet above sea level and 5 feet below sea level?' " "I think I can make the previous sentence a bit more mathematical. 'We want to find the difference between $+5$, and a -5.' " "Couldn't we write the difference between $+5$ and -5 in this way, $+5 - (-5) = N$? We found the answer to be 10. Therefore, $+5 - (-5) = 10$. But I'm not exactly sure why this is true."

After further discussion the teacher suggested that the class work the several problems contained on a duplicated sheet to see if their concept of subtraction of negative numbers improved and to see if any generalizations could be drawn. The three problems which follow are illustrative of the type used.

1. The high temperature for a winter day was $+12$. The low temperature was -5. What was the difference between these two temperatures?

$+12 - (-5) = 17$

2. What was the difference in temperature on a very cold day when the high was -6 and the low was -16?

$(-6) - (-16) =$

difference $= +12$

3. The highest mountain in the United States is Mt. McKinley, which is about 20,320 feet above sea level. The lowest point in the United States, in Death Valley, California, is about 280 feet below sea level. What is the difference in elevation between these locations?

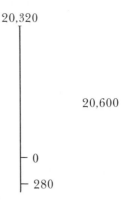

Pupils solved the problems using various forms of the number line. The generalization that subtracting a −5 gave the same result as adding a +5 was noted.

Later in the study the teacher had the pupils develop a small addition-subtraction table to see the relationship between addition and subtraction and between positive and negative integers.

addend

+	−3	−2	−1	0	+1	+2	+3
+3	0	+1	+2	+3	+4	+5	+6
+2	−1	0	+1	+2	+3	+4	+5
+1	−2	−1	0	+1	+2	+3	+4
0	−3	−2	−1	0	+1	+2	+3
−1	−4	−3	−2	−1	0	+1	+2
−2	−5	−4	−3	−2	−1	0	+1
−3	−6	−5	−4	−3	−2	−1	0

addend (left label) ← sum

To perform a subtraction using the table, the following method may be employed:

To subtract:

$$\overset{\text{sum \quad addend \quad addend}}{1 \; - \; (-2) \; = \; \square}$$

Change to the appropriate addition sentence:

$$\overset{\text{sum \quad addend \quad addend}}{1 \; = \; -2 \; + \; \square}$$

Use the addition table. Find the addend -2; move to the $+1$ in the sum portion; move up to the missing addend; answer $+3$.

$$\overset{\text{sum}}{-3} - \overset{\text{addend}}{(-3)} = \overset{\text{addend}}{\square}$$

Change to the appropriate addition sentence:

$$\overset{\text{sum}}{-3} = \overset{\text{addend}}{-3} + \overset{\text{addend}}{\square}$$

Use the addition table. Find the addend $+3$; move to the -3 in the sum portion; move to the missing addend; answer 0.

To subtract:

$$-6 - (-3) = \square$$

Change to the appropriate addition sentence:

$$-6 = -3 + \square$$

Use the addition table.

Instruction in subtraction of negative numbers at the elementary school level should be exploratory. Probably no attempt should be made to master facts. In most cases a form of the number line provides the best means of solving a problem of computational exercise. In other cases the addition table can prove useful in developing concepts.

STUDY SUGGESTIONS

1. Develop a lesson which contrasts the associative property of addition with the idea that $(18 - 6) - 4 = 18 - (6 + 4)$.
2. Outline the advantages and disadvantages of additive versus take-away algorithms for subtraction.
3. Check the terminology of subtraction in three current third-grade mathematics books. How does it differ from books used when you were in third grade?
4. Use the abacus to solve several subtraction computations which involve regrouping.
5. Explain under what conditions the complementary method of subtraction is a labor-saving device.

SUGGESTED REFERENCES

Brownell, William A., and Moser, H. E., *Meaningful vs. Mechanical Learning* (Durham, North Carolina: Duke University Press, 1949).

Hollister, G. E., and Gunderson, A. G., *Teaching Arithmetic in the Primary Grades* (Boston: Heath, 1964), Chap. 6.

Olander, H. T., and Brown, B. I., "Research in Mental Arithmetic Involving Subtraction," *Journal of Educational Research,* Vol. 53 (November 1959), pp. 97–102.

Schell, L. M., and Burns, P. C., "Pupil Performance with Three Types of Subtraction Situations," *School Science and Mathematics,* Vol. 62 (March 1962), pp. 208–214.

Weaver, J. Fred, "Whither Research on Compound Subtraction," *The Arithmetic Teacher,* Vol. 3, No. 2 (February 1956), pp. 17–20.

USE OF SUGGESTED REFERENCES

1. The study by Brownell and Moser is one of the classic studies in meaning-ful subtraction. What would you do to replicate the study today? Keep in mind changes in the content of elementary school mathematics.
2. What implications for grade placement of subtraction topics can you draw from suggestions made by Hollister and Gunderson?
3. How could the suggestion for promoting relation thinking made by Mark, Purdy, and Kinney be used in a second-grade addition-subtraction lesson?
4. How could you incorporate the findings of Olander and Brown into the teaching of subtraction at the intermediate grades?
5. If the suggestions made by Schell and Burns were followed, what would be the order of presentation of the three types of subtraction situations?
6. Using Weaver's article as the basic starting point, trace the research in "compound subtraction" to date.

6

Multiplication of whole numbers

WHAT IS MULTIPLICATION?

An analysis of sources concerned with arithmetic and arithmetic teaching reveals several different means of viewing the operation of multiplication. The three descriptions that follow suggest various means.

1. Multiplication of whole numbers may be viewed as a special case of addition in which all of the addends are of equal size. In set terms, 3×4 can be defined to be the cardinal number associated with a set formed by the union of 3 disjoint sets of 4 elements each.

2. The cross-product or Cartesian product of two sets can be used to interpret multiplication. The cross-product is formed by pairing every member of one set with every member of the other. For example, if we asked 4 boys and 3 girls to form as many mixed dancing couples as possible, we arrive at a product set of 12 elements (couples). Thus, the product of two numbers can be associated with a rectangular pattern or array.

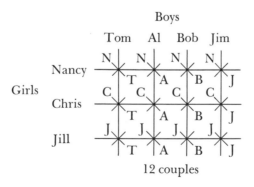

12 couples

3. Multiplication may be viewed in terms of finding a number that has the same ratio to the multiplicand that the multiplier has to 1. Thus, the

product of 3×4 can be found in this manner: 3 is to 1 as N (the product) is to 4. $3:1 = N:4 = 12:4$. In developing this meaning, $4 \times 3 = \square$ may be referred to as finding the number 4 times as large as 3 rather than as finding four 3's. The two problem situations that follow exhibit this meaning.

1. How far will the Johnson family travel in 6 hours at a constant speed of 50 miles per hour?

2. Bill lives 2 blocks from school. How far from school does Mary live if she lives 3 times as far as Bill?

The first time that the ratio definition has major importance to pupils is when the multiplication of rational numbers (fractions) is begun.

There is a great deal of difference in the three approaches described above, and in order for elementary school pupils to develop a mature understanding of the multiplication operation, they should be familiarized with the different multiplication definitions. However, if maximum understanding is to be developed, a logical sequence of these ideas is important. The sequence that follows makes use of the previous mathematical experiences of the pupils to develop a mature viewpoint toward the operation of multiplication.

FOUNDATION EXPERIENCES

As in the case of addition and subtraction, the orally presented problem is well adapted to foundation work in multiplication. The three problems that follow are representative of the type used by successful first- and second-grade teachers to develop background for formal multiplication work.

1. Jill placed 3 cookies on each of 3 plates. How many cookies were on the plates?

2. Ken bought three 4-cent stamps. How much did they cost?

3. How much will 6 pieces of candy cost if each one costs 2 cents?

To make full use of work problems of the type listed above, the following approaches are suggested: (1) provide children with actual objects so that it is possible to use counting to find an answer; (2) use tens and ones blocks and Cuisenaire rods; (3) make use of the number line for solutions; (4) encourage the children to think of as many ways as possible to solve the word problems; and (5) solve the more difficult problems by total class consideration.

When children have had experience with a variety of these problem situations, they usually experience a minimum of difficulty in developing the "equal additions" concept of multiplication. Recently, groups of children with background experiences but no formal multiplication experience scored a median of 18 correct on a 21-item test that consisted of questions such as the following:

1. Alice is serving ice cream at her birthday party. If 1 package of ice cream will serve 4 children, how many children will 3 packages serve?

2. Ann gets 2 cents each day for helping with the dishes. How much will she get for helping with the dishes for 4 days?

3. How many are four 5's?

4. How many are three 7's?

5. How many are five 4's?

Pupils who have had an opportunity to explore number relationships will often demonstrate a grasp of numbers far beyond their level of study. One child in the second month of third grade (multiplication had not been introduced at that time) read in *Little Women* that Amy couldn't think of the answer to 9×12. In about a minute the girl asked the teacher, "Is $9 \times 12 = 108$?" The teacher answered, "Yes, how did you figure out that answer?" "I left out the 2's and added all the 10's. That was 90. Then I added all the 2's. That was 18. I added $90 + 18$ for the answer of 108."

Such reactions are typical in programs in which an emphasis is placed upon a strong foundation of orally presented problems.

TEACHING THE CONCEPT OF MULTIPLICATION

One teacher introduced multiplication in the following manner: "Look at the first problem on the duplicated sheet that I've given you. It says, 'Alice pasted 3 pictures on each of 4 pages of her scrapbook. How many pictures did she paste?' Solve the problem and then show that your answer is correct in as many ways as you can. If you finish early, try to solve the next problem."

As the children worked on the problem, the teacher moved about the room offering encouragement and making suggestions. She often aided the pupil by asking a question which helped him to see the situation involved. As the teacher noted the different means the pupils used to solve the problem, she asked them to record their thinking on the chalkboard. Several pupil responses are recorded below.

Ken: I drew a picture of the situation and then counted the number of pictures. My answer is 12.

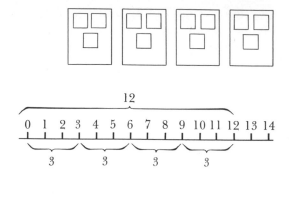

Joe: I marked off four 3's on the number line. This made a total of 12.

$$
\overbrace{}^{12}
$$

0 1 2 3 4 5 6 7 8 9 10 11 12 13 14

$$\underbrace{}_{3}\ \underbrace{}_{3}\ \underbrace{}_{3}\ \underbrace{}_{3}$$

Phil: I made use of rods I took 4 rods that were equal to 3 each and matched them against the 10 rod. I still needed 2 of the 1 rods. My answer is 12.

Mary: There were 3 pictures on each page so I added four 3's. My answer is 12.

$$3 + 3 + 3 + 3 = 12$$

Nancy: I marked 4 groups of 3 marks and counted them. My answer is 12.

/ / /   / / /   / / /   / / /

The children were directed to work the remainder of the problems on the worksheet. The problems involved finding three 3's, three 7's, four 5's, and three 4's. When the work was completed, several pupils who had not participated in the original problem situation were asked to describe the methods they used to solve the problems.

Then the teacher asked, "What number question did you answer in the first problem?" The pupils suggested "How many are four 3's?" or "How much is three plus three plus three plus three?" as possible number questions.

The difference between the two number questions was discussed, and the first question was identified as a multiplication question. The children knew that the second question was an addition question. Multiplication and addition questions were then stated for the problems.

Next the pupils identified $3 + 3 + 3 + 3 = \square$ as the mathematical sentence used to answer the first addition number question. Then they learned the multiplication question, "How many are four 3's?" could be written as $4 \times 3 = \square$.

Then next day a number of multiplication situations were studied. Terminology such as *factors* and *product* was developed during this time. Care was taken to ascertain that the characteristics of factors and of the product were understood before they were given names.

The commutative property and developing the cross-products of the sets idea

In introducing ways to develop cross-products of the sets idea, a teacher presented the following problem: "Jane plans to plant 4 rows of tulips with 6 tulips in each row. How many tulips does she need?"

The children were asked to write a mathematical sentence that could be completed, to answer the question, and then to make a diagram of the situation.

The mathematical sentence was identified as $4 \times 6 = \square$ and a diagram of the type shown at the right drawn by most pupils.

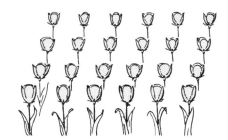

The diagram was drawn on the board and then the teacher said, "How many rows do we have? How many tulips in each row?"

One pupil answered, "Four rows with 6 tulips in each row." Another said, "That's right, but we could say that we have 6 rows of tulips with 4 tulips in each row. Just turn the paper sideways and you can see this."

The teacher made use of this suggestion to question the children concerning the relationship of 6×4 and 4×6. The class tentatively decided that the order of the factors does not change the value of the product (the commutative property of multiplication). The teacher explained, "Patterns such as the one we have made are often called array patterns. Can you think of any other way that we could show that the order of the factors does not affect the product?"

The number line, Cuisenaire rods, and series of additions were used by class members to demonstrate this relationship. The teacher suggested that several other multiplication situations be diagrammed to "check" the "rule" further. When the class had found the property to be true of several situations, the teacher asked the pupils to write a sentence that would describe the "rule." After this, the pupils were told to check their statements against those in their textbooks.

The teacher asked, "How can the property that we have discovered today help us with our work in multiplication?" Class members suggested that it would save them time in learning the multiplication combinations, for if they learned a combination such as 7×9, they would automatically know the combination 9×7. At this time the "rule" was identified as the communative law for multiplication. However, no stress was placed upon the learning of this terminology.

During the early study of multiplication a wide variety of problem situations were used to give the pupils experience with multiplication combinations. No attempt was made to use only simple combinations, and no pressure was exerted to master the combinations. The teacher continued to develop the cross-products of sets idea making use of problems such as those that follow. Periodically, the pupils were asked to diagram the situation.

ARRAY PROBLEMS

1. A man liked 4 makes of cars (Ford, Plymouth, Chevrolet, and Rambler). His wife liked 3 colors (green, white, and yellow). How many combinations did they have to choose from? What were they?

2. An art class was arranged with desks in pairs. There were 3 boys and 3 girls. The teacher told them to arrange themselves with a boy sitting with a girl. How many combinations were there? What were they?

3. A boy had 2 books (a play and a novel) and he had 4 bookcovers (red, green, blue, and white). He wanted to cover each of the books. How many combinations did he have to choose from? What were they?

4. A woman wanted to cover 3 pieces of furniture (a rocker, a sofa, and an arm chair). She had 5 different types of material (striped, print, plaid, solid, and checked). How many different combinations did she have to choose from? What were they?

5. A girl was going on a date and she had a choice of wearing heels, flats, or loafers. She also didn't know whether to wear a pleated or a straight skirt. How many choices did she really have? What were they?

6. Three boys, Tom, George, and Ralph, were working in a shop class. There were 4 woods available (pine, maple, cedar, and oak). Each boy could use only one type of wood. How many different combinations could have been made? What were they?

TYPES OF WOOD				
Boys	Pine	Maple	Cedar	Oak
Tom	T,P	T,M	T,C	T,O
George	G,P	G,M	G,C	G,O
Ralph	R,P	R,M	R,C	R,O

12

Order of presentation of basic multiplication combinations

Early work in multiplication should emphasize understanding, clarify the uses of multiplication, and aid pupils in developing mathematical insight. Before 1960 the majority of elementary school textbooks followed the unchallenging pattern of introducing multiplication with combinations such as the following:

$$2 \times 1 = ?$$
$$2 \times 3 = ?$$
$$2 \times 5 = ?$$

In fact, this pattern is still found in many textbooks. Such an introduction is of questionable value since there is no reason to multiply; the solution can be found just as advantageously by addition. Also, if the teacher is interested in fostering pupil discovery, a more challenging situation will provide greater stimulation for pupils to try to find novel solutions. When well over half of the pupils can answer questions such as "How many are four 5's?" "How many are three 7's?" "How many are four 2's?" without any formal study of multiplication, then the use of more elementary examples, such as "How many are two 4's?" and "How many are two 2's?" to introduce multiplication is certainly to be questioned.

The author suggests that during third grade pupils be provided an opportunity to work with all of the multiplication situations, often making use of materials such as Cuisenaire rods, the number line, arrays, and tongue depressors. Much of multiplication study may well be provided through verbal problem situations and situations in which children are asked to look for number relationships. Counting by 2's, 5's, 10's, and 3's is also helpful in developing multiplication.

Early in fourth grade a systematic study for mastery of all the basic multiplication combinations can be undertaken. While these suggestions differ from typical current usage, they provide the following advantages:

1. Early work with a variety of multiplication combinations challenges students and allows for a better grasp of the basic ideas of multiplication.

2. The use of a variety of combinations allows the teacher to develop good pupil understanding of the commutative and associative properties of multiplication in situations in which pupils can see real value in their application.

3. Such a program helps to prevent the boredom that ensues when pupils think that because they studied the 3's this week and the 2's last week, they will probably study the 4's next week.

4. If practice or drill on the combinations is delayed until after understanding of the majority of multiplication facts is developed, it results in a great savings in time necessary for practice. If pupils understand the following generalizations, the number of basic multiplication combinations to be memorized is reduced from 100 to 32.

a. The order of the factors does not affect the product.

b. Any number multiplied by one remains unchanged, or any number times one equals the original number.

c. Any number multiplied by zero or zero times any number equals zero.

Development of the role of zero and one

Normally the elementary school pupil does not need to know multiplication sentences that involve 0 and 1 until he deals with multi-digit multiplication ($10 \times 23 = \square$). However, teachers may wish to teach the role of 0 and 1 during the time that pupils are developing the multiplication table. Problems such as $5 \times 1 = \square$ and $5 \times 0 = \square$ are easily understood in terms of addition, and the commutative property can be used to develop the answer to $1 \times 5 = \square$ and $0 \times 5 = \square$. Stress should be placed upon the study of *one* as the identity element for multiplication.

It is suggested that these multiplications be learned through generalizations. In some cases, it may still be necessary to provide practice materials on specific 0's and 1's combinations.

Mastering the basic multiplication facts

After the pupils have had a wide variety of experiences in solving problems and exercises dealing with multiplication, the teacher may hand out a dittoed sheet such as the one shown below.

Complete the multiplication sentences.

$7 \times 5 = \square$	$6 \times 4 = \square$
$5 \times 3 = \square$	$7 \times 4 = \square$
$4 \times 4 = \square$	$3 \times 6 = \square$
$2 \times 6 = \square$	$3 \times 7 = \square$
$5 \times 5 = \square$	$2 \times 8 = \square$
$9 \times 2 = \square$	$3 \times 3 = \square$
$7 \times 5 = \square$	$4 \times 8 = \square$

The pupils may then be directed to answer as many questions as they can in ninety seconds. This procedure points out that while all of the pupils can arrive at an answer to a multiplication question if given time to use addition, an array, or counting, they may not be able to quickly answer multiplication questions. Thus, the time test is a means of showing pupils that they need some direct practice on the multiplication combinations.

Multiplication table. One teacher developed the multiplication table in the following manner: "When I told my grandfather that we were studying the basic multiplication facts, he suggested that I use the multiplication table. He started to fill it in, but I thought that you would be able to do it by yourselves." She then handed out a sheet similar to the one below.

+	0	1	2	3	4	5	6	7	8	9
0	0				0					
1										
2				6						
3									24	
4										
5							30			
6										
7			14							
8										
9										81

The multiplication table may be used to study various structural patterns. Questions such as those which follow help students to see relationships, as well as to master the multiplication combinations.

1. Look at the 9's column. What do you notice about the digits?

2. Draw a line from the upper left-hand corner of the table (the corner where the multiplication sign is located) to the corner containing the 81. What do you notice? (This procedure is helpful in emphasizing the commutative principle.)

3. Use the table to complete these multiplications:

3×2 then multiply this by 8
8×2 then multiply this by 3
           What do you notice?
2×4 then multiply this by 7
4×7 then multiply this by 2
7×2 then multiply this by 4
           What do you notice?

This procedure is helpful in emphasizing the associative property of multiplication.

The multiplication table also allows the teacher to introduce the idea of associating two numbers with a third, or mapping. Thus the pair (3,4) can be shown by the table to be associated with 12. This relationship can be written as

$$(3,4) \xrightarrow{\ \times\ } 12.$$

The following exercises help the pupil to think about this relationship and to practice the basic multiplication combinations.

$(5,6) \xrightarrow{\ \times\ } \square$ $(7,9) \xrightarrow{\ \times\ } \square$

$(7,8) \xrightarrow{\ \times\ } \square$ $(9,7) \xrightarrow{\ \times\ } \square$

$(9,8) \xrightarrow{\ \times\ } \square$ $(6,5) \xrightarrow{\ \times\ } \square$

Cross number puzzles.   Cross number puzzles of the variety shown below serve as challenging practice material. Not only do they help to fix multiplication combinations, but they also further the understanding of basic multiplication principles.[1]

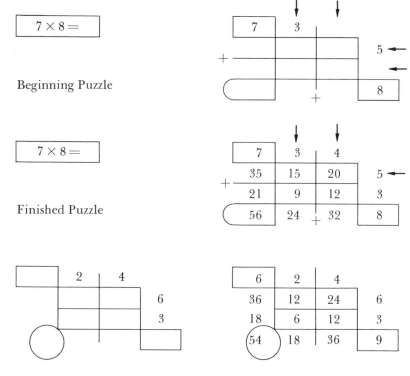

Beginning Puzzle   Finished Puzzle

[1] See Robert W. Wirtz and others, *Math Workshop for Children*, Books A, B, C, D, E, and F (Chicago: Encyclopedia Britannica Films, Inc., 1962), for a set of children's materials that makes wide use of challenging practice materials. Also see Robert W. Wirtz, and others, *Discovery in Elementary School Mathematics* (Chicago: Encyclopaedia Britannica Press, 1963), for material for teachers making use of similar materials.

Additional study procedures. A study procedure such as that used to learn the spelling of words is also helpful. Normally the following steps are taken: (1) look at the multiplication combination; (2) cover the answer; (3) think of the answer; (4) look at the answer; (5) if the answer is correct, write the answer; if not, go through steps 1 to 4 again.

The tapping test can be used to identify combinations on which practice is needed. This procedure consists of giving the pupil a sheet of multiplication combinations and instructing him to look at each combination, to think the answer, and then to tap the paper with his finger. The pupil can note troublesome combinations by the break in the regularity of his tapping.

Semi-programmed sheets may also be used in the same manner as they were for addition.

Source: Still Photo Services U.D.I.S., Pennsylvania State University.

Frame arithmetic provides an opportunity for children to discover multiplication relationships.

Race-type games such as arithmetic baseball can be used periodically to review and fix multiplication combinations. Care must be taken to avoid fierce competition and to not overdo arithmetic games. Children can become bored with a steady diet of arithmetic games, especially those that require only memorized responses.

Developing the distributive property

The need to check or to find an answer to a forgotten multiplication combination provides a good setting for the study of the distributive property. This basic property is also used in multiplying numbers written as multi-digit numerals; for example, $8 \times 23 = 8 \times (20 + 3) = (8 \times 20) + 8 \times 3)$ or, written in the general form, the distributive principle is

$$a \times (b + c) = (a \times b) + (a \times c)$$

or

$$(a \times b) + (a \times c) = a \times (b + c)$$

In developing the distributive principle, a teacher said, "I've written some of the ways that you checked the answer to $4 \times 8 = \square$ on the board. Study them carefully."

(a) $4 \times 8 = \square$

(b)
$$\begin{array}{r} 8 \\ 8 \\ 8 \\ + 8 \\ \hline 32 \end{array}$$

(c) Array

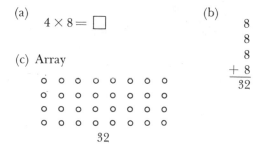

32

(d) Number Line

After handing each pupil a dittoed array pattern, the teacher commented, "Look at the 4 by 8 array that I've dittoed for each of you. How could you find the number of dots on the array without counting?" One of the pupils suggested, "We could multiply 4 times 8."

"What if you weren't sure of the answer to 4 times 8? How could you use the array and still not count? (pause) Tom, I see that you have your hand up. Can you show us?"

Tom suggested, "I could fold the array down the middle. This gives me two 4 by 4 arrays. Four time 4 equals 16. Sixteen plus 16 equals 32."

$$16 + 16 = 32$$

Class members suggested other means of folding the array as shown in the diagrams below.

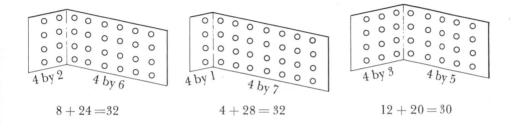

$$8 + 24 = 32 \qquad\qquad 4 + 28 = 32 \qquad\qquad 12 + 20 = 30$$

The teacher suggested that the experiments with the array be recorded with numerals. A class member suggested that parentheses could be used to clarify the record.

$$4 \times 8 = (4 \times 4) + (4 \times 4) = 16 + 16 = 32$$
$$4 \times 8 = (4 \times 2) + (4 \times 6) = 8 + 24 = 32$$
$$4 \times 8 = (4 \times 3) + (4 \times 5) = 12 + 20 = 32$$
$$4 \times 8 = (4 \times 1) + (4 \times 7) = 4 + 28 = 32$$

Various other combinations could also be used.

The teacher directed the students to try Tom's check with the examples on page 56 in their book. She pointed out that it should be helpful not only as a check but also as a way to find the answer to a multiplication combination that they might have forgotten.

$$
\begin{array}{ccc}
7 & 6 & 9 \\
\times 6 & \times 8 & \times 5 \\
\hline
\end{array}
$$

$$8 \times 5 = \qquad\qquad 3 \times 9 =$$

Frequent use should be made of this "multiplying twice" procedure, since it is an important foundation for and a check of multi-digit multiplication.

The associative property of multiplication

The binary operation of multiplication requires some means of multiplying three or more factors. This is accomplished by the use of the associative property. Thus, $8 \times 3 \times 5$ becomes $(8 \times 3) \times 5$ and can be associated to $8 \times (3 \times 5)$.

Pupils and teachers often see little mathematical power in the associative property. Therefore, it is important that an introductory situation be developed in which the associative property presents a definite aid to computation.

The teacher began by asking, "What is the product of $2 \times 9 \times 6$?" Pupils multiplied 2×9 and then 18×6. The teacher recorded the students' thinking as $(2 \times 9) \times 6$. She then asked, "Is there another or possibly an easier way of arriving at the answer?" Pupils suggested multiplying 9×6 and then the product by 2. The multiplication was recorded as $2 \times (9 \times 6)$. Pupils verified $(2 \times 9) \times 6 = 2 \times (9 \times 6)$ and then worked several other exercises of a similar type to verify that the procedure was effective.

Another use of the associative property can be made in conjunction with renaming. If a pupil forgets a multiplication combination such $7 \times 8 = \square$, he may rename 8 as (4×2) and then use the associative property. Thus, $7 \times 8 = 7 \times (4 \times 2) = (7 \times 4) \times 2$. After pupils have a wide variety of experience using the associative property, they can generalize the property using frames $[(\triangle \times \bigcirc) \times \square = \triangle \times (\bigcirc \times \square)]$ and give the property a name.

MULTI-DIGIT MULTIPLICATION

Multi-digit multiplication can begin with a problem situation such as "How many green stamps will Jane need to fill her book if there are 3 empty pages and each page holds 30 green stamps?"

A suggestion to write the number question, to solve the problem, and to show that the answer is correct normally results in the following responses: How many are three 30's? $3 \times 30 = N$.

(a)

```
  30
  30
+ 30
─────
  90 stamps
```

(b)

90 stamps

(c)

$3 \times 30 =$

3×3 tens $= 9$ tens $= 90$

90 stamps

(d)

```
3 tens          30
 × 3           × 3
─────         ────
9 tens          90
90 stamps
```

(e)

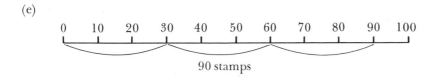

90 stamps

(f)

tens	ones

90 stamps

A discussion of the solutions should lead class members to formulate a generalization such as "To multiply tens, you multiply the number of tens that you have (30 = 3 tens) by the multiplier and then you write a zero in the ones place to show that your product is tens." (3×4 tens = 120)

The next logical step is the multiplication of a two-digit number by a one-digit number in a situation that does not involve renaming (carrying). Pupils can figure out the following solutions to $3 \times 23 = \square$.

(a)   23
       23
      +23
      ———
       69

(b)   2 tens   3 ones   Twenty-three is 2 tens and 3 ones. Three groups
    ×   3   of 3 ones equals 9 and 3 groups of 2 tens equals
      ——————————————   6 tens or 60. Adding these I got an answer of 69.
       6 tens   9 ones
          69

(c)

tens	ones

(d)

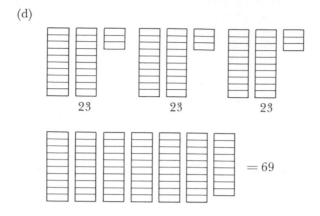

(e) I made use of the "multiplying twice" (distributive principle) that we have used to check multiplication combinations.

$$3 \times 23 = 3 \times (20 + 3) = (3 \times 20) + (3 \times 3) = 60 + 9 = 69$$

(f) An array could be drawn.

(g) The number line could be used.

Class discussion of the various approaches verified that the "multiplying twice" approach was the most effective, particularly when the computational short-cut was used. This short-cut was stated as

$$\begin{array}{r} 32 \\ \times\ 3 \\ \hline 6 \end{array} \qquad \begin{array}{r} 32 \\ \times\ 3 \\ \hline 96 \end{array}$$ "Think of 32 as 30 plus 2. Multiply 3 times 2; write the 6 in the ones place of the product. Think 3 times 30 equals 90; write 9 in the tens place of the product."

Renaming

Renaming is one of the more important understandings necessary to success with multiplication. Renaming was introduced in one classroom with the following problem: "Alice was asked by the girl scout troop to bake 8 dozen cookies. Remember there are 12 cookies in one dozen. How many cookies will she need to bake? Write the number question and solve the problem in as many ways as you are able." The pupils reported the following means of working the problem:

(a) $12 + 12 + 12 + 12 + 12 + 12 + 12 + 12 = 96$.

(b) $8 \times 12 = 8 \times (10 + 2) = (8 \times 10) + (8 \times 2) = 80 + 16 = 96$

(c) $8 \times 10 = 80$ and $8 \times 2 = 16$; the $80 + 16 = 96$.

(d) Draw an 8 by 12 array. Then you can fold the array to make combinations that you know. For example,

$$8 \times 8 \qquad 8 \times 10$$
$$\text{and} \quad \text{or} \quad \text{and}$$
$$8 \times 4 \qquad 8 \times 2$$

(e)
$$\begin{array}{r} 10 + 2 \\ \times\, 8 \\ \hline 80 + 16 \end{array} \qquad \begin{array}{r} 80 \\ \times\, 16 \\ \hline 96 \end{array}$$

(f) Draw a number line.

   The teacher discussed the various approaches with the class members. The group decided that form (c) was actually using the same principle as form (b). Next, the array pattern was discussed. The majority of the class felt that the most efficient folding of the array would involve 8 by 10 with 8 by 2. It was also agreed that form (e) made use of the same principle (distributive) as forms (b) and (c), but the class felt that it was more compact.

   During the next class period work continued on multiplication problems and examples that needed to be renamed. At the close of the period that teacher asked, "Have any of you found a shorter method for writing your computation?" The following forms were suggested:

(a)	(b)	(c)
$\begin{array}{r} 10+2 \\ \times\,8 \\ \hline 16 \\ 80 \\ \hline 96 \end{array}$	$\begin{array}{r} 12 \\ \times\,8 \\ \hline 16 \\ 80 \\ \hline 96 \end{array}$	$\begin{array}{r} \overset{1}{12} \\ \times\,8 \\ \hline 96 \end{array}$

   Class members could readily see the logic of forms (a) and (b), but questions were raised concerning form (c). To explain the procedure one of the pupils said, "I multiplied $8 \times 2 = 16$; this is 1 ten and 6 ones. I wrote the 6 in the ones place and the 1 ten above the tens place in the multiplicand. Then I multiplied 8×1 ten $= 80$, plus the 10 I had "carried" equals 90. Write the 9 in the tens place of the answer." Several other examples were tested using this method. The teacher suggested that for the remainder of the multiplication exercises the class should try the short form, checking it by one of the longer methods. Any pupil experiencing difficulty was told to use a form that he found understandable. Pupils were encouraged to remember rather than to write the numeral that was "carried."

After the pupils had had experience using the shortened form of multiplication, the teacher made use of "the arithmetic theme" [2] to test pupil understanding of the procedure. Pupils who appeared to be using the "carrying" procedure mechanically were instructed to continue using one of the longer forms until they had the idea of the distributive principle firmly in mind.

Two-digit multipliers

In explaining two-digit multipliers, a teacher began by using a verbal problem that could be solved by the mathematical sentence $12 \times 28 = \square$. Pupils suggested using a 12 by 28 array and folding it in one of the following ways:

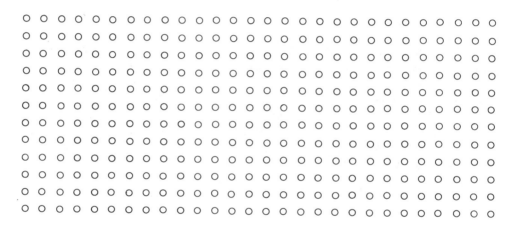

6 by 28 and 6 by 28
10 by 28 and 2 by 28
8 by 28 and 4 by 28

Other correct suggestions were also made. Also, the following algorisms were suggested: $12 \times 28 = \square$

$$
\begin{array}{ccccccc}
28 & \quad 28 & \quad 168 & \quad\quad 28 & \quad 28 & \quad 56 \\
\times 6 & \quad \times 6 & \quad 168 & \quad\quad \times 10 & \quad \times 2 & \quad 280 \\
\hline
48 & \quad \overline{168} & \quad \overline{336} & \quad\quad \overline{280} & \quad \overline{56} & \quad \overline{336} \\
120 & & & & & \\
\hline
168 & & & & &
\end{array}
$$

$$
\begin{array}{ll}
28 & \\
12 & \\
\hline
56 & (2 \times 28) \\
280 & (10 \times 280) \\
\hline
336 &
\end{array}
\qquad
\begin{aligned}
12 \times 28 &= (10 + 2) \times 28 \\
&= (10 \times 28) + (2 \times 28) \\
&= 280 + 56 \\
&= 336
\end{aligned}
$$

[2] Alan Riedesel, "The Theme in Arithmetic," *The Arithmetic Teacher*, Vol. 6, No. 4 (April 1959), pp. 154-155.

Pupils were encouraged to use the method which they found to be most under-standable. After the basic idea of the use of the distributive principle was established, the teacher developed the conventional algorism through class discussion.

REINTRODUCING MULTIPLICATION

As was true of addition and subtraction, there is a need to review multiplication that has been studied at an earlier grade level. Many "traditional" and "modern" mathematics programs present this reintroduction or review in a manner that is very similar to its original presentation. Thus, many students are not challenged, and even those who have a very poor grasp of the material do not vigorously attack the topic because they feel, "We're just doing the same old thing that we learned at an earlier grade." The suggestions that follow are designed to provide a novel setting for reintroducing topics in multiplication.[3]

Finger multiplication (grade five).   Even today some peasants in central France don't learn the multiplication table above 5. If they wish to multiply 9×8, they bend down 4 fingers on the left hand (4 is the difference between 9 and 5) and 3 fingers on the right hand ($8 - 5 = 3$). The number of bent fingers give the tens of the result ($4 + 3 = 7$ tens). The product of the unbent fingers give the units ($1 \times 2 = 2$).[4] A teacher instructed a class to watch the following demonstration:

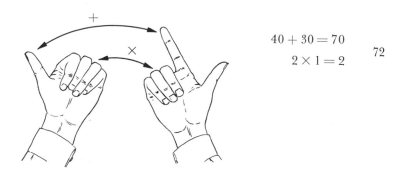

$$40 + 30 = 70$$
$$2 \times 1 = 2 \qquad 72$$

The teacher then said, "Now see if you can try it out with $8 \times 7 = \square$." The class members tried out various multiplication combinations using the finger method. One pupil asked if the procedure would work with combinations such as 6×6. It was suggested that he try the method out on 6×6. The pupil found that the procedure worked, but it was necessary to add $20 + 16$.

[3] For sources from which ideas for reintroduction of topics may be obtained, consult the bibliography on p. 169.
[4] Tobias Dantzig, *Number, the Language of Science* (New York: Macmillan, 1941), p. 11.

The class was assigned several practice exercises of multiplication combinations and directed to use "finger multiplication" to check their results. The teacher challenged the pupils to discover why the procedure worked.

A similar procedure for finger multiplication is bending the fingers that equal the difference between the number multiplied and ten.

Thus, to solve $8 \times 8 = \square$, the thinking is $10 - 8 = 2$; bend down 2 fingers; $10 - 8 = 2$; bend down 2 fingers; the standing fingers have a value of 10 each, and the bent fingers are multiplied.[5]

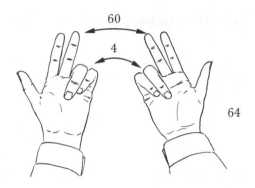

Reintroduction of multiplication combinations

Patterns (grade five).   The lesson was opened with the statement, "A director of a marching band numbered each member of his 100 piece band. There were 8 players in each row."

The teacher wrote the numerals from 1 through 8 on the board and then wrote 9 above the 1 and 10 above the 2. Then she asked, "What numeral should be written above the 6? _____ 14 _____ right. Above the 8? _____ 16 _____ right.

9	10	11	12	__	__	__	16
1	2	3	4	5	6	7	8

The band director numbered the rest of the 100 members in the same way.

"The director enjoyed quizzing the players to check them on their movements for various marching formations. Can you figure out the player movements? The director wrote 12 ↑. To what position would the player go? _____ 20 _____ right. 26 ↑↑ _____ 42 _____ right. See if you can figure out the moves on the sheet I'm giving you."

$$14 \uparrow\uparrow\uparrow = \square \qquad 29 \downarrow\downarrow\downarrow = \square$$
$$33 \uparrow\uparrow\uparrow\uparrow = \square \qquad 78 \rightarrow \downarrow\downarrow\downarrow$$

[5] For a detailed explanation of the rational of finger multiplication see Catherine Stern, "New Experiments with Multiplication," *The Arithmetic Teacher*, Vol. 7, No. 8 (December 1960), pp. 387–388.

Example of 8

41	42	43	44	45	46	47	48
33	34	35	36	37	38	39	40
25	26	27	28	29	30	31	32
17	18	19	20	21	22	23	24↑
9	10	11	12	13	14	15	16↑
1	2	3	4	5	6	7	8↑

8↑↑↑

Students quickly discover that the fastest method of solving a situation such as 6 ↑↑↑↑ is to multiply 4 × 8 and add this to 6. Thus. a great deal of computational practice with multiples of 8 is obtained. If work is desired with 6, 7, or 9, the number in the first row may be changed to 6, 7, or 9.

Reintroduction of multi-digit multiplication

Gelosia or lattice multiplication[6] (grade five).   One of the older methods of multiplying is called the Gelosia method by the Italians and the lattice method by the English.

The lattice is made up of a rectangle cut into squares according to the number of digits in the multiplier and multiplicand. Study the diagrams.

$34 \times 26 = \square$

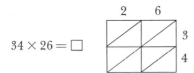

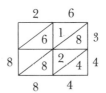

One factor is written across the top of the lattice and the other factor is written along the right-hand edge. The product of each combination of factors is written in its proper box with the diagonal line dividing two-digit products. The digits in each diagonal are added, and the sum is written below each diagonal column. If the sum is larger than ten, it is carried to the next column.

Larger multi-digit numbers can be multiplied by increasing the number of boxes in the lattice.

Sacchero multiplication (grade six). The teacher said, "The exercise I have written on the chalkboard appeared in an Italian arithmetic book in 1478 and is called Sacchero multiplication. See if you can figure out how they multiplied large numbers."

```
      9 3 4
    3 7 3 6 /
      9 3 4 /
    2 8 0 2 /  314
    2 9 3 2 7 6
```

```
      9 3 4
    × 3 1 4
```

[6] D. E. Smith, *History of Mathematics* (New York: Dover Publications, 1953), pp. 114-116.

After a discussion cleared up any difficulties that pupils had in under-standing the method, they were directed to work a number of exercises in the regular manner and to use the Sacchero system to check their answers.

Duplation (grade six). The teacher stated, "Early in the middle ages multi-plication exercises were worked by doubling. Study the example on the board. Why does it work?" [7]

$$31 \times 42 = \square$$

$$
\begin{array}{rl}
1 \times 42 = & 42 \\
2 \times 42 = & 84 \\
4 \times 42 = & 168 \\
8 \times 42 = & 336 \\
16 \times 42 = & 672 \\
\hline
31 & 1302
\end{array}
$$

"Work the multiplication exercises in your book and check by the duplation method."

Enrichment and remedial work. In addition to the suggestions made in chapter 3, the following materials are suggested. The teacher may develop remedial and enrichment programs (see chapter 16 for construction sugges-tions) such as the one illustrated below.

ENRICHMENT PROGRAM—GRADE FIVE

Roger liked to show off his arithmetic ability to other members of his class. One day he said, "I can multiply any number between 10 and 100 by 11 in five seconds or less and without using paper and pen-cil. Just write the number you want multiplied by 11 on the board or on a sheet of paper, and I'll give you the an-swer immediately." Roger then worked several examples rapidly. His friend Gene then said, "Please show me how you are able to work those examples that quickly." Roger said, "All right, but I want you to figure this out for yourself. I'll only help by asking some questions." Look at these examples:

---

[7] Note: It is necessary to select the factors in the left-hand column whose sum is equal to the multiplier.

34 multiplicand $34 \times 11 = 374$
$\times 11$ multiplier $11 \times 45 = 495$
‾‾‾‾
34                  $11 \times 23 = 253$
34                  $11 \times 14 = 154$
‾‾‾‾
374 product

(1) What is true of the number in the ones place of the product?

(1) It is the same as the ones number in the multiplicand.

(2) Study carefully the number in the tens place of the product. Then study the multiplicand. What is the relationship between these numbers?

(2) The tens number in the product is the sum of the numbers in the multiplicand.

(3) Now look at the hundreds number in the product. Then study the multiplicand. What do you see?

(3) The hundreds number in the product and the tens number in the multiplicand are the same.

(4) How would you solve the example below by using the ideas you have worked on? $11 \times 27 =$

(4) 2 7 + 2 7
      297
      ‾‾‾

(5) How should a rule for this rapid multiplication by 11 be written?

(5) The product is formed by placing the sum of the numbers in the multiplicand between the numbers in the multiplicand. (Any similar rule can be considered to be correct.)

Work the following examples using Roger's method for multiplying by 11. They should help you to improve your skill in this rapid multiplication.

Multiply each of these numbers by 11.

(6) 36 _____   (8) 72 _____

(7) 62 _____   (9) 44 _____

(6) 396   (8) 792

(7) 682   (9) 484

(10) 90 _____　　　　(12) 51 _____　　　　(10) 990　(12) 561

(11) 34 _____　　　　(13) 25 _____　　　　(11) 374　(13) 275

(14) Roger wasn't through showing off. He said, "O. K., Gene, you did a good job on those examples. Now I want to see if you can think out the answer to some harder ones. Try this one."
$11 \times 47 =$

(14) 517

(15) What do you get for an answer in the above example when you add the two numbers of the multiplicand?

(15) 11

(16) Can you write this in the tens place?

(16) No

(17) What must you do if you can't write the number in the tens place?

(17) Carry the 1.

(18) What is the middle term of the product?

(18) 1

(19) What is the number in the hundreds place of the product?

(19) 5

(20) Is this the same as the tens number in the multiplicand?

(20) No

(21) Why?

(21) It is necessary to carry the 1.

(22) How can you change your original rule for multiplying by 11 rapidly to take into account these larger numbers?

(22) If the sum of the numbers in the multiplicand is larger than 9, the ones number in this sum is used for the middle digit in the product and the ten digit is carried.

The following examples will give more practice in multiplying by 11 rapidly.

Multiply each of these numbers by 11.

(23) 67 _____   (26) 75 _____   (23) 737   (26) 825

(24) 59 _____   (27) 87 _____   (24) 649   (27) 957

(25) 19 _____   (28) 93 _____   (25) 209   (28) 1023

The next day Gene said, "I've practiced so that I can quickly multiply any number up to 100 by 11. Is there a quick way to multiply numbers larger than 100 by 11?" Roger wasn't sure but suggested that the two of them try to figure out a way to quickly multiply large numbers by 11. They started with the example: $11 \times 234 = 2574$. Study it carefully.

(29) Could they get the ones number in the product in the same way they previously did?

(29) Yes

(30) How could they get the tens number (which is 7 in the example above)? Study the multiplicand carefully.

(30) By adding the ones number and the tens number in the multiplicand. ($4 + 3 = 7$)

(31) How could they get the hundreds number in the product (which is 5 in the example above)?

(31) By adding the tens number and the hundreds number in the multiplicand. ($3 + 2 = 5$)

(32) How could they get the thousands number in the product?

(32) It will be the same as the first number in the multiplicand.

(33) You should now be able to work the following example using the method Roger and Gene developed. Test your skill with this example:
$11 \times 321 =$

(33) 1
$1 + 2 = 3$
$2 + 3 = 5$
   3
Answer: 3531

REMEDIAL PROGRAM—GRADE FIVE

(1) Jean worked the multiplication question 4×17 in the following manner:

$$\begin{array}{r} 1 \text{ ten} \quad 7 \text{ ones} \\ \times \quad 4 \text{ ones} \\ \hline \underline{}\text{tens } 28 \text{ ones} \end{array}$$

(1) 4

(2) How many tens and ones in twenty-eight?

_____tens   _____ones

(2) 2 tens   8 ones

(3) 4 tens + 2 tens and 8 ones =

(3) 68

Jean finished the multiplication exercise in the following manner:

$$\begin{array}{r} 1 \text{ ten} \quad 7 \text{ ones} \\ \times \quad 4 \text{ ones} \\ \hline 4 \text{ tens } 28 \text{ ones} \\ 40 + 28 = 68 \end{array}$$

Use Jean's method to work the following exercises:

(4)   16
     $\times 6$

(4)   1 ten   6 ones
        $\times$ 6 ones
    6 tens   36 ones
    60 + 36 = 96

(5)   23
     $\times 4$

(5)   2 tens   3 ones
        $\times$ 4 ones
    8 tens   12 ones
    80 + 12 = 92

(6)   13
     $\times 7$

(6)   1 ten   3 ones
        $\times$ 7 ones
    7 tens   21 ones
    70 + 21 = 91

Randy said that he had a faster way of working this type of multiplication. He wrote

$$\begin{array}{r} 2 \\ 17 \\ \times 4 \\ \hline 68 \end{array}$$

(7) He said, "I wrote down the 8 from the product of 4×7. What number did I carry?"_____

(7) 2

(8) Next I multiplied the 1 by 4 and added the 2 that I had carried. How much does this give me for the tens place?_____

(8) 6

(9) Randy asked, "What value did the 2 that I carried have?"_____

(9) It is really 2 tens or 20.

(10) The following exercises will help you improve in your ability to multiply in situations where you have to carry. Use Randy's method to find the answer and then check by using Jean's method.

Randy's Method	Jean's Method
1	2 tens 6 ones
26	$\times$ 3 ones
$\times 3$	
78	6 tens 18 ones
	$60 + 18 = 78$
34	
$\times 3$	

(10)
$$\begin{array}{r} 1 \\ 34 \\ \times 3 \\ \hline 102 \end{array}$$
3 tens   4 ones
$\times$ 3 ones
9 tens 12 ones
$90 + 12 = 102$

(11)   17
      $\times 2$

(11)
$$\begin{array}{r} 1 \\ 17 \\ \times 2 \\ \hline 34 \end{array}$$
1 ten   7 ones
$\times$ 2 ones
2 tens 14 ones
$20 + 14 = 34$

(12)   25
      $\times 5$

(12)
$$\begin{array}{r} 2 \\ 25 \\ \times 5 \\ \hline 125 \end{array}$$
2 tens   5 ones
$\times$ 5 ones
10 tens 25 ones
$100 + 25 = 125$

(13)   33
      $\times 5$

(13)
$$\begin{array}{r} 1 \\ 33 \\ \times 5 \\ \hline 165 \end{array}$$
3 tens   3 ones
$\times$ 5 ones
15 tens 15 ones
$150 + 15 = 165$

(14)   26
      ×3
      ———

(15)   53
      ×8
      ———

(16)   39
      ×7
      ———

(17)   53
      ×6
      ———

                                    1
(14)   26   2 tens   6 ones
      ×3   ×   3 ones
      ———   ——————————————
      78   6 tens 18 ones
            60 + 18 = 78

                                    2
(15)   53   5 tens   3 ones
      ×8   ×   8 ones
      ———   ——————————————
      424   40 tens 24 ones
            400 + 24 = 424

                                    6
(16)   39   3 tens   9 ones
      ×7   ×   7 ones
      ———   ——————————————
      273   21 tens 63 ones
            210 + 63 = 273

                                    1
(17)   53   5 tens   3 ones
      ×6   ×   6 ones
      ———   ——————————————
      318   30 tens 18 ones
            300 + 18 = 318

Check your skill. Find the products when each number written below is multiplied by 6. Write the answer on your answer pad and compare with the answers given at the right.

Multiply each of these numbers by 6.

(18) 3 _____   (22) 5 _____   (18) 18   (22) 30

(19) 7 _____   (23) 4 _____   (19) 42   (23) 24

(20) 9 _____   (24) 8 _____   (20) 54   (24) 48

(21) 6 _____   (25) 2 _____   (21) 36   (25) 12

Think the product of 7 and each number in the sets of numbers written below.

Multiply each of these numbers by 7.

(26) 3_____	(30) 5_____	(26) 21	(30) 35
(27) 7_____	(31) 4_____	(27) 49	(31) 28
(28) 9_____	(32) 6_____	(28) 63	(32) 42
(29) 8_____		(29) 56	

Study the multiplication example that Bill wrote.

$$\begin{array}{r} 281 \\ \times 6 \\ \hline 1686 \end{array}$$

(33) How did Bill get the 8 that he wrote in the tens place?_____

(33) He multiplied 6 × 8 tens and got 48 tens. He carried the 4 (hundreds) and wrote the 8 (tens) in the tens place.

(34) Why did he show 16 hundreds in his product? How did he get the 16 hundreds in his product?_____

(34) He multiplied 6 × 2 (hundreds) and got 12 hundreds. Then he added the 4 hundreds he had carried and got 16 hundreds.

STUDY SUGGESTIONS

1. Carefully compare the suggestions made in the teacher's manual of an elementary school arithmetic when multiplication is first introduced with the suggestions made in the School Mathematics Study Group materials.
2. Discuss the advantages and/or disadvantages of using the series of additions idea in the initial phase of whole number multiplication.
3. Develop a set of twenty verbal problems that could be used in the multiplication foundation program.
4. Use an array pattern to solve one of the first five problems on page 144.
5. It has been suggested that the terms multiplier and multiplicand be eliminated from the elementary school mathematics vocabulary and that they should always be called factors. Discuss whether or not there are situations in which the terms multiplier and multiplicand are helpful.
6. Develop a set of remedial materials for a pupil who is experiencing difficulty learning to multiply combinations such as 304×4609 which have internal zeros.
7. Develop an arithmetic bulletin board to be used with a class that is beginning a study of the distributive principle.
8. Develop a set of multiplication exercises that you would orally present to sixth-grade students.

SUGGESTED REFERENCES

An asterisk (*) indicates sources that are helpful in studying the basic ideas of multiplication.

Banks, J. Houston, *Learning and Teaching Arithmetic,* 2nd ed. (Boston: Allyn and Bacon, 1964), pp. 181–271.
*Boyer, Lee, Brumfiel, C., and Higgins, W., "Definitions in Arithmetic," *Instruction in Arithmetic,* Twenty-fifth Yearbook of the National Council of Teachers of Mathematics (Washington, D. C.: The Council, 1960), p. 267.

*Buckingham, B. R., *Elementary Arithmetic, Its Meaning and Practice* (Boston: Ginn, 1953), p. 64.

*Gibb, E. G., Jones, P. S., and Junge, C. W., "Number and Operation," *Growth of Mathematical Ideas,* Twenty-fourth Yearbook of the National Council of Teachers of Mathematics (Washington, D. C.: The Council, 1959), p. 23.

Gibney, T. C., "Multiplication for Slow Learners," *The Arithmetic Teacher,* Vol. 9, No. 6 (February 1962), pp. 74–76.

Grossnickle, Foster E., and Brueckner, Leo J., *Discovering Meanings in Elementary School Mathematics* (New York: Holt, Rinehart and Winston, 1963), pp. 160–211.

Hannon, Herbert, "A New Look at the Basic Principles of Multiplication with Whole Numbers," *The Arithmetic Teacher,* Vol. 7, No. 7 (November 1960), pp. 357–361.

Hervey, Margaret A., "Children's Responses to Two Types of Multiplication Problems," *The Arithmetic Teacher,* Vol. 13, No. 4 (April 1966), pp. 288–292.

*Mueller, Francis J., *Arithmetic: Its Structure and Concepts* (Englewood Cliffs, New Jersey: Prentice-Hall, 1956), p. 69.

———, *Arithmetic: Its Structure and Concepts,* 2nd ed. (Englewood Cliffs, New Jersey: Prentice-Hall, 1964), pp. 82–112.

*Peterson, John A., and Hashisaki, Joseph, *Theory of Arithmetic* (New York: Wiley, 1963), p. 92.

*School Mathematics Study Group, *Mathematics for the Elementary School, Teacher's Commentary, Grade 4 (preliminary ed.) (Part 1),* The Board of Trustees of the Leland Stanford University, 1962, pp. CAE-104, 1–25.

Smith, David E., *History of Mathematics* (New York: Dover, 1953), Vol. II, pp. 101–128.

Spitzer, Herbert F., *The Teaching of Arithmetic,* 3rd ed. (Boston: Houghton Mifflin, 1961), pp. 121–142.

Stern, Catherine, "New Experiments with Multiplication," *The Arithmetic Teacher,* Vol. 7, No. 8 (December 1960), pp. 381–388.

*Swain, Robert L., *Understanding Arithmetic* (New York: Holt, Rinehart and Winston, 1957), pp. 53, 80–88.

Van Engen, Henry, The Reform Movement in Arithmetic and the Verbal Problem," *The Arithmetic Teacher,* Vol. 10, No. 1 (January 1963), pp. 3–6.

USE OF SUGGESTED REFERENCES

1. Work several multiplication examples using the "every-day arithmetic" presented by Banks.

2. Review Gibney's multiplication materials for slow seventh-grade students. How could such procedures be used for fifth- and sixth-grade students? Develop a set of similar exercises for fifth-grade students.

3. Compare the suggestion of Grossnickle and Brueckner that multiplication be introduced with combinations such as 2×3 with the suggestions made in this book.

4. Develop a lesson that makes use of Hannon's three-dimensional array in developing understanding in multiplication.

5. What implications for introducing multiplication can you draw from Hervey's research concerning the equal addition and Cartesian product ideas?

6. How does Mueller use array patterns to develop the associative property of multiplication? Use his ideas in developing a lesson for fourth- or fifth-grade pupils.

7. Use one of the historical methods of multiplying presented by Smith to develop a reintroduction lesson at the fifth-grade level.

8. Study carefully the exercises and materials for teaching multiplication suggested by Spitzer.

9. Compare Stern's use of the dual board with Cuisenaire rods and the tens board of the Greater Cleveland Mathematics Program.

10. Solve several multiplication situations using the scratch method as shown by Swain (page 82).

11. Van Engen suggests that multiplication should be developed as "mapping." How does his approach compare with the author's?

7

Division
of whole numbers

WHAT IS DIVISION?

Division is usually the most difficult operation for pupils to under-stand and for teachers to teach. This is not surprising because division, as the inverse of multiplication, can be viewed in several ways. Besides being familiar with the various interpretations of division, a child must also understand addition, subtraction, and multiplication and be able to estimate an answer before he can handle all of the whole number division situations. Several means of viewing division follow:

1. The division of whole numbers is the inverse of the multiplication of whole numbers. If a and c are identified in the expression $a \times b = c$ and if they uniquely determine b, the operation of "finding" b is called division. Thus, if $3 \times b = 12$, then

$$
\begin{array}{ccc}
\text{dividend} & \text{divisor} & \text{quotient} \\
12 \quad \div & 3 \quad = & b
\end{array}
$$

However, if $12 \times b = 3$, then b must equal $\frac{1}{4}$ and thus the division operation cannot be performed by using whole numbers alone. The student must re-member that any time two whole numbers were combined by the operation of multiplication, the result (the product) was a whole number. This is not true for division. Thus, for the set of whole numbers, division is not *closed;* that is, division of one whole number by another whole number does not always result in a whole number quotient; it may produce a fraction.

2. The addition of whole numbers and the multiplication of whole numbers may be related because the multiplication of whole numbers may be viewed as a special case of addition with the addends being of equal size. Division may be related to subtraction because the division of whole numbers may be considered as a series of subtractions in which the subtrahend is the same size. For example, $12 \div 4 = \square$ can be considered $12 - 4 = 8$; $8 - 4 =$

171

4; $4 - 4 = 0$; three subtractions have been made; therefore, $12 \div 4 = 3$. This thought process lends itself well to the question, "How many 4's equal 12?"

3. As with multiplication, division may be viewed as finding the missing part of a ratio. In divison, the student is searching for the number that is contained in the dividend as many times as unity is contained in the divisor. Taking the same example $12 \div 4 = \square$, by using the ratio idea the pupil is looking for a number that has the same ratio to 12 as 1 has to 4. $\dfrac{12}{\square} = \dfrac{4}{1}$; $\square = 3$. The ratio $\dfrac{12}{4} = \dfrac{\square}{1}$ may also be used to define division. In this case, the number that has the same ratio to unity as the dividend has to the divisor is being sought.

It is essential that the first two definitions of division be developed for the understanding of physical world problem situations by using whole numbers that require division. The ratio definition could be developed with whole number division, but it is not essential that it be so introduced, since its major use will be found in the division of fractions.

FOUNDATION EXPERIENCES

Many elementary school mathematics programs do little to develop any understanding of division until the formal introduction, which usually occurs in third grade. This practice is to be questioned. A recent yearbook of the National Council of Teachers of Mathematics stresses the idea that the development of an understanding of fundamental mathematical ideas is a continuous process and is facilitated by a continual development of a topic from grade to grade.[1] To implement this procedure, foundation work in division should begin in kindergarten and grade one.

Foundation work in division makes use of orally presented problem situations which can be solved by the use of counting, the number line, sets, subtraction, addition, and manipulative materials. Many situations that use division concepts may be developed through entire class consideration. The three problems that follow are illustrative of the type used in a foundation program.

1. Nancy is going to paste 9 pictures on sheets of construction paper. If she pastes 3 on each sheet, how many sheets of paper will she need? (The problem can be solved with the actual sets of pictures, or with drawings.)

[1] National Council of Teachers of Mathematics, *The Growth of Mathematical Ideas, Grades K-12* (Washington, D.C.: The Council, 1959).

2. Three girls are going to share equally 12 pieces of candy. How many pieces of candy will each girl receive? (The problem can be solved by taking 12 objects and "counting them out" to 3 girls.)

3. How many pupils do we have in our class?——30——right. How many cars will we need for our science trip to the weather station if we put 6 of you in each car? (The problem can be solved by the class counting off by 6's, by the class forming in groups of 6 each, or by class consideration of the number line.)

MEASUREMENT AND PARTITION DIVISION

Subtraction has three definite types of physical world situations, "take-away," "comparison," and "how many more are needed." Division has two, measurement and partition. What are measurement and partition division? Does the division algorithm differ for each? The differences between these two division situations can most easily be described by an analysis of two division problem situations which make use of these concepts.

Measurement. A store owner states, "I wll give 6 roses free to each customer until I have given away 24 roses. How many customers will receive roses?"

Partition. A store owner states, "I will give the first 4 customers free roses." If he gives away 24 roses, how many will each customer receive?

The two situations above make use of the same numbers; however, analysis will indicate that different concepts of division are involved.

The measurement problem can be solved in several ways.

By drawings

By a series of subtractions

```
    24
  −  6   1
    ──
    18
  −  6   2
    ──
    12
  −  6   3
    ──
     6
  −  6   4
    ──
     0
```

By use of the number line

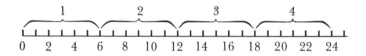

By the division algorithm $24 \div 6 = 4$

The partition problem does not lend itself to many solutions. It may be solved by use of a drawing, a number line, or a division algorithm. The drawing represents a different type of action and is quite similar to dealing out cards.

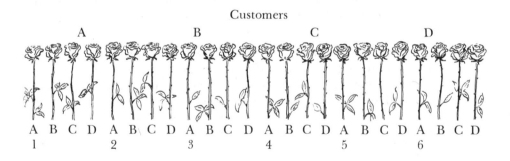

Customers

or, associate a number with each rose.

	Customers		
A	B	C	D
1	2	3	4
5	6	7	8
9	10	11	12
13	14	15	16
17	18	19	20
21	22	23	24

In the measurement situation, a set has been separated into subsets of a given size. The essential mathematical question becomes, "How many equal sets of 6 equal 24?" In the partition situation, a set has been separated into a given number of equal subsets to find how many elements each subset contains. The essential mathematical question becomes, "How many elements in each of 4 subsets when the total set has 24 elements?"

If the inverse relationship between multiplication and division is considered, a basic reason for these two problem types becomes evident. If division is considered to be the finding of the missing factor, then measurement or partition situations are dependent upon which factor is missing, the multiplier or the multiplicand. Consider $5 \times \square = 20$ and $\square \times 4 = 20$. In the first situation the fact that 5 groups of a given size equal 20 is known, but the size of each group (a partition situation) is not. In the second situation, the size of each group (4) is known, but the number of groups (a measurement situation) is not.

In the suggestions for teaching that follow, measurement situations will always be used for introductory work. There are several reasons for this selection:

1. Measurement situations allow for a wide variety of solutions. This is in keeping with a discovery approach in which pupils are challenged to think through problem situations and to figure out solutions for themselves. Greater opportunity for individual thinking is thus provided.

2. Studies[2] of pupil work in division have demonstrated that partition division is much more difficult for pupils to understand.

3. Partition situations require some knowledge of fractional concepts, as well as a knowledge of division. In the previous problem, each customer receives $\frac{1}{4}$ of the roses. The problem can be thought of as, "What is $\frac{1}{4}$ of 24?" Following introductory work with measurement situations and development of the concept of division, the partition idea is introduced.

Discovering the basic division facts

The teacher began the formal study of division by giving each pupil a set of several measurement division problems with the following directions: "Study the problem. Try to determine the mathematical questions involved. Then find an answer to each problem. If you can, try to use different methods in solving each of the problems. I'll read the first problem and you can follow along. 'Jim raised Indian Corn to sell for fall decorations. If he tied 4 ears together, how many bunches could he make from 12 ears of corn?' "

The teacher observed as the pupils worked on the problems. She suggested the use of drawings to those pupils who were experiencing difficulty with the problems. When all class members had finished at least one problem, some of the pupils were asked to put their solutions on the board and to explain how they had worked the problems. The solutions are shown below.

[2] For a recent study see Marilyn J. Zweng, "Division Problems and the Concept of Rate," *The Arithmetic Teacher*, Vol. II, No. 8 (December 1964), pp. 547–556.

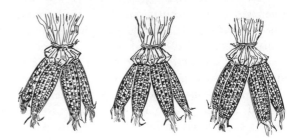

Charlie: I drew a picture to show what happened.

Lucy: I drew an array like we use in multiplication. I drew 4 dots, then 4 more, then 4 more—12 dots in all.

Linus: I used the number line. Also, you could start at 12 and move back by 4's.

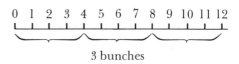

0 1 2 3 4 5 6 7 8 9 10 11 12

3 bunches

Vicki: I used popsicle sticks and counted off by 4's.

3 bunches

Pete: I started with the 12 ears and subtracted 4 for each bunch. I had to make 3 subtractions to get all of the ears in bunches.

$$
\begin{array}{r}
12 \\
-\ 4 \quad (1) \\
\hline
8 \\
-\ 4 \quad (2) \\
\hline
4 \\
-\ 4 \quad (3) \quad \text{3 bunches} \\
\hline
0
\end{array}
$$

Joe: I started with one bunch of 4 and then kept adding 4's until I reached 12. I had 3 bunches.

$$
\begin{array}{r}
4 \\
+\ 4 \\
\hline
8 \\
+\ 4 \\
\hline
12
\end{array}
$$

After a discussion of the methods, the teacher said, "I asked you to think of the mathematical question asked by the problem. What is it?" The pupils responded that the question was, "How many 4's equal 12?" "How many 4's are contained in 12?" "How many 4's are in 12?" (Note that these closely tie division to multiplication.) and "Twelve can be broken into how many sets of 4?"

The teacher noted that all of the mathematical questions were representative of the situation. Then she said, "Let's see if we can write a mathematical sentence (equation) which represents the problem." The sentence $\square \times 4 = 12$ was suggested to replace "How many 4's equal 12?" The teacher suggested, "We have written addition and subtraction sentences, and you just wrote a multiplication sentence for the problem. Is this the same type of situation we have usually found in multiplication?" The class agreed that it was different in that they were actually separating a set of 12 into 3 equal sets of 4 each.

Then the teacher stated, "The problem situations we have been dealing with are called *division* problems. We can write the mathematical sentence as 12 divided by $4 = 3$. Just as we have symbols to represent the operations of addition, subtraction, and multiplication, we have a division symbol. We can write $12 \div 4 = 3$." The division sentence $15 \div 5 = \square$ was written on the board, and the questions "How would you read this mathematical sentence?" and "What does it mean?" were asked.

The pupils replied that it would be read, "Fifteen divided by 5 equals what number?" and that it asked, "How many groups of 5 equal 15?"

During the remainder of the period, the class members solved verbal problems that were concerned with division situations. In each case they wrote the mathematical sentence that represented the problem, solved the problem, and showed the answer to be correct by solving the problem by a different method.

The next day the class discussed various procedures for solving mathematical sentences that involved division for the purpose of arriving at efficient procedures. The two most frequently suggested were to use a series of subtractions or to try to think of a related multiplication combination. The use of the related multiplication combination was explained in the following manner: "If I have a division question such as $15 \div 5 = N$, I can think 'five times what number equals 15, or $5 \times N = 15$.'"

In the days that followed, the class solved mathematical sentences which related multipication and division (see below) and studied the relationship by using a multiplication table.

$$18 \div 3 = N \qquad 9 \times N = 27 \qquad N \times 5 = 15$$
$$9 \div 3 = N \qquad 10 \div 2 = N \qquad 4 \times N = 12$$

The computational form of the division algorithm $4\overline{)\,12}$ was also introduced.

The pupils who found the answer by using a series of subtractions used these forms of computation:

Example A records the subtraction above and makes some use of place-value aspects, which are helpful in later division work.

Example A

```
      3
      1
      1
      1
4) 12
   4
   8
   4
   4
   4
```

Example B handily records the count of the subtractions at the right of each subtraction.

Example B

```
4) 12
   4   1
   8
   4   1
   4
   4   1
       3
```

For early work, either form is acceptable and pupils should probably have experience in using both forms.

On their own or in response to questions asked by the teacher, the pupils quickly discover that it is not necessary to complete the entire series of subtractions. They note that in situations such as $24 \div 4 = N$, procedures A_1 and A_2 are more efficient than procedures B_1 or B_2.

```
     A₁          A₂          B₁          B₂

  4)24           6        4)24          6
    16   4       2          4   1       1
     8           4         20           1
     8   2    4)24          4   1       1
         6      16         16           1
                 8          4   1       1
                 8         12           1
                            4   1    4)24
                            8           4
                            4   1      20
                            4           4
                            4   1      16
                                6       4
                                       12
                                        4
                                        8
                                        4
                                        4
                                        4
```

When the teacher is confident that the pupils are understanding division, the terminology of division may be introduced. A logical way may be to develop these terms in relation to multiplication by related multiplication and division combinations. For example, how many 7's equal 14?

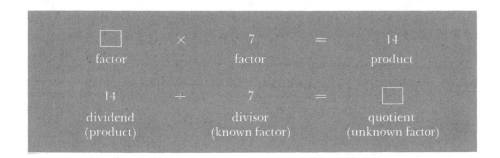

When the majority of the pupils were progressing well in division, the teacher introduced the partitioning concept using problems such as "Mark, Ken, Bill, and Gene plan to share equally 12 pieces of candy. How many pieces will each boy receive?"

The pupils thought of several procedures for solving the problems. Examples appear below.

Henry: I used 12 sticks to represent the candy. I wrote the name of each boy on my paper and then gave each a stick in turn. It's like dealing cards. Each boy would receive 3 pieces of candy.

Mark	Ken	Bill	Gene
1 5 9	2 6 10	3 7 9	4 8 12
/ / /	/ / /	/ / /	/ / /

Mary: I drew a picture of 12 pieces of candy. Then I listed the boys. I then drew lines from the candy to the boys.

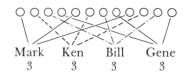

Mark Ken Bill Gene
 3   3   3   3

Lois: I used the number line and the boys' initials. I listed the initials in order and then counted to see how many pieces each received.

```
0  1  2  3  4  5  6  7  8  9 10 11 12
|__|__|__|__|__|__|__|__|__|__|__|__|
   M  K  B  G  M  K  B  G  M  K  B  G
```

The next problem stated, "Aunt Kay has 8 pencils to divide evenly between Nancy and Jim. How many pencils will Nancy receive?" The teacher asked the pupils to try to identify the mathematical question involved in the problem. At first the children were somewhat puzzled. Then one suggested that Nancy actually would receive one-half of the pencils so that the mathematical question could be, "What is one-half of eight?" Further study revealed that "one-half of eight" could be found by using the division sentence $8 \div 2 = N$. A lengthy discussion concerning the difference between the type of division question just posed and that previously posed developed the following generalizations:

Type I (measurement)	Type II (partition)
a. We try to find "how many sets" when the number in each set is known.	a. We try to find "how many in each set" when the number of sets is known.
b. The divisor and dividend are the same "material" (for example, pencils and pencils).	b. The quotient and dividend are the same "material" (for example, pencils and pencils).
c. In terms of multiplication we know the multiplicand. We also know the product. We are looking for the multiplier.	c. In terms of multiplication we know the multiplier. We know the product. We are looking for the multiplicand.

Study procedures similar to those suggested for multiplication were used to study division combinations.

Analysis

As in the case of the other basic operations, a guided discovery procedure was used to introduce the material. (See chapter 6.) Little stress was placed on mastery of the combinations in the early stages. Since division involves many features which add difficulty, it is suggested that the pupils encounter a wide range of division situations before practice for mastery begins. As suggested previously, there is little reason to limit early work to a few basic combinations. The typical instructional pattern presents readiness for division in grade two, a study for mastery of easy division facts in grade three, and a study for mastery of the remainder of basic division facts in grade four. The author feels that pupils will be better challenged and also more "comfortable" with division if readiness begins in grades one and two, if all division combinations are introduced in grade three, and if a study for mastery is undertaken in grade four.

The role of zero and one in division

The 100 basic addition facts, the 100 basic subtraction facts, and the 100 basic multiplication facts have been discussed. There are not 100 basic division facts, however; there are 90. Why? The classroom procedure that follows provides an answer.

When the class was relating division and multiplication, one pupil suggested that the multiplication table should be a help in seeing relationships, just as the addition table helped with subtraction. The pupils noted that the products represented the dividends and that the factors could be used to indicate divisors and quotients. The discussion moved along smoothly until the teacher asked, "What do you notice about the zero facts? Use the left-hand column as your divisor and see what you find out. What are the mathematical division sentences involving zero?"

The pupils wrote all of the division sentences involving zero on the board.

x	0	1	2	3	4	5	6	7	8	9
0	0	0	0	0	0	0	0	0	0	0
1	0	1	2	3	4	5	6	7	8	9
2	0	2	4	6	8	10	12	14	16	18
3	0	3	6	9	12	15	18	21	24	27
4	0	4	8	12	16	20	24	28	32	36
5	0	5	10	15	20	25	30	35	40	45
6	0	6	12	18	24	30	36	42	48	54
7	0	7	14	21	28	35	42	49	56	63
8	0	8	16	24	32	40	48	56	64	72
9	0	9	18	27	36	45	54	63	72	81

Group A

$0 \div 1 = 0$
$0 \div 2 = 0$
$0 \div 3 = 0$
$0 \div 4 = 0$
$0 \div 5 = 0$
$0 \div 6 = 0$
$0 \div 7 = 0$
$0 \div 8 = 0$
$0 \div 9 = 0$

The pupils noted that Group A made sense. There are no groups of one in zero, no groups of two in zero, etc. The teacher suggested that they check to see if the related multiplication sentence made sense. It did: $1 \times 0 = 0$ or $0 \times 1 = 0$. Then the teacher asked, "What about a situation such as $6 \div 0 = N$; $7 \div 0 = N$; or $5 \div 0 = N$?" One pupil thought that the answer should be 0; another thought that the answer should be 6; still another thought that there were an unlimited number of zeros in 6. At that point a class member suggested, "Let's look at the related multiplication question and see if this helps." The multiplication questions were written: $N \times 0 = 6$; $N \times 0 = 7$; $N \times 0 = 5$. The pupils noted that it was not possible to find a replacement

Group B

$0 \div 0 = 0$
$0 \div 0 = 1$
$0 \div 0 = 2$
$0 \div 0 = 3$
$0 \div 0 = 4$
$0 \div 0 = 5$
$0 \div 0 = 6$
$0 \div 0 = 7$
$0 \div 0 = 8$
$0 \div 0 = 9$

for N. Then the teacher said, "You've noted an interesting feature of division. Because we cannot replace for N, mathematicians do not allow division by zero. Division by zero is said to be undefined."

Pupils noted that the varying answers for $0 \div 0$ (Group B) didn't make sense because $0 \div 0$ apparently could equal any number, so the teacher suggested that they discuss the situation. After some discussion, the class decided that $0 \div 0$ would not really fit into the system since in all other cases there was only one number which could answer an addition, subtraction, multiplication, or division question. Further discussion and exercises stressed this principle: $0 \div N = 0$ is a perfectly correct operation in which the quotient will always equal 0, but $N \div 0 =$ is undefined.

Next the pupils considered the role of one in division. From a study of the multiplication-division table the pupils made this generalization: "When 1 is the divisor, the dividend is the same as the quotient. This is because of the role of 1 as the identity element for multiplication."

MULTI-DIGIT DIVISION

Before all of the basic division facts have been introduced, division involving multi-digit dividends is usually introduced. The teacher can effectively introduce this phase of division in the following manner: "A set of 48 special electronic transistors was manufactured for use in experimental rockets. If each rocket needs 4 such electronic transistors, how many rockets will the 48 electronic transistors equip? Write the mathematical sentence you can use to solve the problem and then solve the problem in as many ways as you can. You will see an array diagram of the transistors on the top of the duplicated sheet that I've given to each of you. This may help with the problem." After a few moments the teacher said, "I see that most of you have identified the mathematical sentence. What is the mathematical sentence? —— Yes, $48 \div 4 = N$. Some of you seem to be having trouble starting out on the problem. How can you always solve a division problem? —— Right, use subtraction. Go ahead and try to find an answer." While the pupils worked, the teacher moved about the room asking questions and giving aid. As the pupils completed various solutions to the problem, the teacher asked class members to illustrate their solutions on large sheets of lined paper (24 inches × 30 inches) with magic-markers or crayons. When discussion began, the pupils explained their methods of solving the division problem. The teacher began with students who used the less mature solutions and ended with students who used the more mature solutions. The children's solutions and explanations appear below.

```
4) 48
   4    1
  ──
  44
   4    1
  ──
  40
   8    2
  ──
  32
   8    2
  ──
  24
   8    2
  ──
  16
   8    2
  ──
   8
   8    2
  ──   ──
   0   12
```

Lyle: I know that we can solve any division situation by a series of subtractions. I started to find "how many 4's equal 48" by subtracting 4's. Then I shortened it some by subtracting 2 groups of 4.

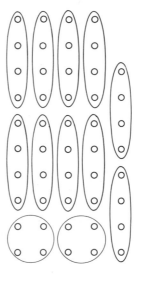

Joan: I studied the array patterns and then circled groups of 4 in the pattern.

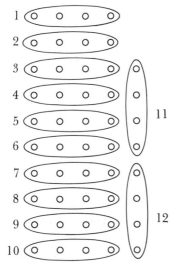

Mike: I also used the array pattern, but I shortened it some. I could see that by counting the row I could find the 4's in 40. Then I partitioned the 8 into 2 groups of 4.

$$\begin{array}{r} 12 \\ \underline{2} \\ 5 \\ \underline{5} \\ 4\overline{)\,48} \\ 20 \\ \underline{20} \\ 28 \\ 20 \\ \underline{20} \\ 8 \\ 8 \\ \underline{} \end{array}$$

Ann: I used subtraction. I know 5 sets of 4 equal 20, so I recorded 5 and subtracted 20. I still had another group of five 4's, so I subtracted another 20. Two 4's equal 8, so I recorded the 2.

$$\begin{array}{r} 4\overline{)\,48} \\ 20 \quad 5 \\ \underline{} \\ 28 \\ 20 \quad 5 \\ \underline{} \\ 8 \\ 8 \quad 2 \\ \underline{} \\ 12 \end{array}$$

Charlie: I used the same procedure but a different form.

$$\begin{array}{r} 12 \\ \underline{2} \\ 10 \\ 4\overline{)\,48} \\ 40 \\ \underline{40} \\ 8 \\ 8 \\ \underline{} \end{array}$$

Nancy: I shortened the procedure they used. I know that ten 4's equal 40 so I subtracted 10 groups of 4. I also know that two 4's equal 8.

$$40 \div 4 = N$$
$$(40 + 8) \div 4 = N$$
$$(40 \div 4) + (8 \div 4) = N$$

$$\begin{array}{cc} 10 & 2 \\ 4\overline{)\,40} & 4\overline{)\,8} \\ 40 & 8 \\ \underline{} & \underline{} \end{array}$$

$$10 + 2 = 12$$

Ned: I used the idea of "a number has many names." I renamed 48 as 40 + 8 and worked from there. I know that ten 4's equal 40 and that two 4's equal 8. I think I used a procedure similar to the distributive property we used in multiplication.

The representative procedures used by the pupils illustrate the wide diversity of approaches that may be used in division situations. The approaches taken by Nancy and Ned are quite mature in their development and might well have occurred on the third day of study of multi-digit division rather than on the first. Once the division situation has been made clear, the class may be challenged to "see if you can find the *best* method of solving these division situations." It is to be expected that slower learners will remain with the more concrete approaches, such as those taken by Joan, Mike, and Lyle, for a rather long period. As they gain further insight into division, they will simplify their procedures. A significant point to remember is that it is important for a slow learner to understand the situations because he often has a poor memory and will rather rapidly forget a rote computational pattern.

Source: Still Photo Services U.D.I.S., Pennsylvania State University

Discussion of the reasons for various methods of performing the division algorithm helps children to understand division.

In the days that followed the teacher continued to stress the relationship between multiplication and division, the use of the array in using the distributive property of division over multiplication, and the usefulness of the relationship between subtraction and division.

To develop the relationship between multiplication and division further, a chart such as the following was developed as an exercise.[3]

Mathematical sentence (division)	Number in each whole set	Number in each subset	Number of subsets	Remainder	Mathematical sentence (multiplication)
$35 \div 7 = N$	35	7	5	0	$5 \times 7 = 35$
$42 \div N = 6$	42	(?)	6	0	$6 \times 7 = 42$
$53 \div 8 = N$	(?)	(?)	(?)	5	(?)
$N \div 7 = 8$ rl	57	(?)	8	(?)	$(7 \times 8) + 1 = 57$

Further discussion and exploratory work helped the children to develop generalizations concerning the division of a multi-digit dividend (product). Emphasis was placed upon finding the multiples of 100 and 10 that could be subtracted from the dividend (product). The teacher was able to analyze each pupil's thinking by use of a mathematics theme in which each child was asked to explain the "how" and "why" of working a division situation. The selection below is representative of an acceptable development.

$$5 \overline{) 582}$$

$$(500 + 82) \div 5 = N$$

$$\begin{array}{r} 116 \\ \hline 6 \\ 10 \\ 100 \\ \hline 5 \overline{) 582} \\ 500 \\ \hline 82 \\ 50 \\ \hline 32 \\ 30 \\ \hline 2 \end{array}$$

What is the first step in finding "how many 5's equal 582?" I have to think of renaming 582 so I can divide each addend by the known factor (5). I also want to use as large a multiple of 5 as I can. Looking at 582 I think that 500 can be used because it is the smallest multiple of 5×100 that can be used.

Now I need to find the number of 5's equal to 82. Using a multiple of 10 I know that $5 \times 10 = 50$, so I use this.

The next question is, "How many 5's equal 32?" or 5 times what number equals 32? I know from basic multiplication and division facts that $5 \times 6 = 30$. I continue to work. I subtract 30 from 32. My remainder of 2 cannot be divided by 5. My answer is 116 r2.

[3] School Mathematics Study Group, *Mathematics for the Elementary School, Grade Four, Part I* (New Haven: Yale University Press, 1963), p. 361.

Multi-digit divisors

The multi-digit phase of division was introduced with the following statement, "Look at the division problems and exercises on the duplicated sheet. The first problem says, 'Packing material for electronic missile parts comes off the assembly line in sections that contain 168 small parts. (See the array pictured.) How many sections that hold 12 parts each can be made from the section that contains 168 parts? Use the array and other means to solve the problem. First identify the mathematical sentence that is needed to solve the problem.'"

The work of the pupils on the problem revealed several solutions.

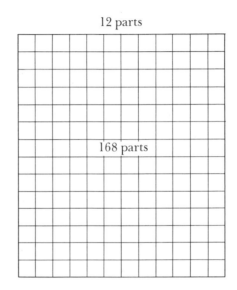

12 parts

168 parts

Nan: $168 \div 12 = N$. I knew there were 12 elements in each row, so I counted the number of rows—14. This is the same as subtracting 12 from 168—14 times.

$$
\begin{array}{r}
12\overline{)\,168} \\
60 \quad 5 \\
\hline
108 \\
60 \quad 5 \\
\hline
48 \\
24 \quad 2 \\
\hline
24 \\
24 \quad 2 \\
\hline
14
\end{array}
$$

Phil: $168 \div 12 = N$

I used subtraction. I knew there were at least five 12's. Then I took 5 more, 2 more, and 2 more.

$$
\begin{array}{r}
14 \\
4 \\
\hline
10 \\
12\overline{)\,168} \\
120 \\
\hline
48 \\
48 \\
\hline
\end{array}
$$

Jean: I thought, "How many sets of $12 = 168$? Are there 10? Yes, $10 \times 12 = 120$. How many more? 2. Yes, more than 2. 4? Yes, exactly $4 \times 12 = 48$."

$$168 + 12 =$$
$$(100 + 68) + 12$$

```
        8
 3     12) 68 + 4
 5
12) 100                    6
 60                        1
 ──                        5
 40                    12) 72
 36                        60
 ──                        ──
  4                        12
```

Jim: I renamed 168 as 100 + 68. This didn't work out as well as it does sometimes.

$$8 + 6 = 14$$

Then, to direct pupil thinking toward ways to solve such division situations efficiently, the teacher used the following guided questions:

Teacher	Pupil

Let's look at this division situation.

$$22) \overline{568}$$

Teacher	Pupil
Will the quotient be in the 100's?	No, $100 \times 22 = 2,200$
Will it be more than 10?	Yes, $10 \times 22 = 220$
How about 20?	Yes, 20×22 would be $220 + 220$ or 440.
We'll try 20 as a starter. What next?	Let's try 5.
How does 5 turn out?	$5 \times 22 = 110$. Good.
Now what?	There will be no more sets of 22. Our answer is 25 r18.

```
    25 r18
     5
    20
22) 568
   440
   ───
   128
   110
   ───
    18
```

OTHER DIVISION RELATIONSHIPS

As the inverse of multiplication, division possesses several other properties which lead to exploration by pupils. With the use of directed questions by the teacher, children can discover the following relationships:

1. There are twenty-eight pairs of division facts in which each pair has the same dividend. For these pairs, the quotient of one equals the divisor of the other. Examples:

$$\begin{array}{r} 5 \\ \hline 7)\,35 \end{array} \qquad \begin{array}{r} 7 \\ \hline 5)\,35 \end{array}$$

2. For division facts having dividends that are squares (such as 36, 49, etc.) the quotient and the divisor are the same if the divisor is the square root of the dividend. Thus, $36 \div 6 = 6$.

3. Multiplying or dividing the divisor and the dividend by the same number produces no change in the quotient. Thus, $3)\,\overline{9}$, $9)\,\overline{27}$, and $27)\,\overline{81}$ all have the same quotient.

4. For any even division situation, the dividend contains a factor which is divisible by the divisor. In such instances, the following procedure may be used:

$$3)\,\overline{63} \qquad 3)\,\overline{9 \times 7} \qquad 3)\,\overline{9 \times 7} \qquad \begin{array}{r} 3 \\ \hline 3)\,9 \end{array} \begin{array}{l} \times 7 \\ \\ = 21 \end{array}$$

5. Multiplying the dividend by a number changes the quotient in the same proportion.

$$\begin{array}{r} 4 \\ \hline 4)\,16 \end{array} \qquad \begin{array}{r} 8 \\ \hline 4)\,32 \end{array} \qquad \begin{array}{r} 2 \times 16 = 32 \\ 2 \times 4 = 8 \end{array}$$

6. The distributive property allows the dividend to be expressed as a sum. The quotient is the sum of the "partial quotients." Examples:

$$8)\,\overline{96} \;=\; 8)\,\begin{array}{l} \overline{10 + 2} = 12 \\ 80 + 16 \end{array}$$

$$5)\,\overline{125} \;=\; 5)\,\begin{array}{l} \overline{20 + 5} = 25 \\ 100 + 25 \end{array}$$

$$6)\,\overline{638} \;=\; 6)\,\begin{array}{l} \overline{100 + 6} + \text{r2} = 106\ \text{r2} \\ 600 + 38 \end{array}$$

The above generalizations are important principally because they exhibit the relationship between multiplication and division, allow for pupil insight into the structure of division, provide opportunity for pupil thinking and discovery, and allow simplification in learning some of the basic division facts.

Inexact division

Many physical world situations arise in which the division is not exact. For example, "If 4 boys are asked to share equally 10 cookies, how many cookies will each boy receive?" In that case, the boys could each take 2 cookies and leave 2 cookies on the plate. This probably would not occur. The boys probably would break the 2 remaining cookies in half and each eat $2\frac{1}{2}$ cookies.

Inexactness in division is another stumbling block to understanding. Too often in the past teachers have followed the procedure of having all leftover parts expressed as remainders in the early grades. In the later grades, the leftover part was always expressed as a fraction. An analysis of problem situations requiring division reveals that the above procedure can be misleading. The leftover part should be expressed in keeping with the problem situation. The problems illustrated below require a specific decision concerning the leftover part.

1. "The pencils in a store were labeled 3 for 10¢. How much would one pencil cost?" The answer is not 3¢ with a remainder of 1. Nor is it $3\frac{1}{3}$¢. Any time a purchase involves division, the "remainder" is rounded up. One pencil would cost 4¢.

2. "Mrs. Ronald buys 10 yards of curtain material on sale. How many curtains can she make from the piece of cloth if each curtain requires 3 yards of cloth?" In this setting Mrs. Ronald will be able to make only 3 curtains, not $3\frac{1}{3}$. The answer could be expressed as 3 curtains with 1 yard of cloth left over.

3. "How long will each board be if I cut a 14-foot board into 3 parts? (Do not consider the saw cuts.)" The answer of 4 feet with a remainder of 2 feet is meaningless and therefore incorrect. In this case, the only logical answer is $4\frac{2}{3}$ feet or 4 feet 8 inches.

The problems above point up the difficulty of deciding what to do with the leftover part. The alert teacher will take advantage of problem situations such as those mentioned above to discuss with the class the need for interpreting the leftover part in terms of the problem.

Another questionable practice also occurs in dealing with remainders. Teachers often say, "You should have a fractional remainder." Actually when the leftover part is expressed as a fraction, it becomes an integral part of the quotient and should be considered to be a part of the quotient. The answer to problem (3) above is $4\frac{2}{3}$ feet, not 4 r$\frac{2}{3}$.

In many classes, the teacher may be able to use fractions to express leftover parts at a much earlier grade level than is common. Most third graders will give an answer of $2\frac{1}{2}$ to the orally stated question, "If I divide 5 pieces of candy equally between two persons, how many pieces will each person receive?"

Short division versus long division

Prior to 1925 the majority of textbooks presented all early work with one-digit divisors in short division form.

	Long Division		Short Division

$$
\begin{array}{r}
253 \\
3\overline{)\,759} \\
600 \\
\hline
159 \\
150 \\
\hline
9 \\
9 \\
\hline
\end{array}
\qquad \text{or} \qquad
\begin{array}{r}
253 \\
3\overline{)\,759} \\
6 \\
\hline
15 \\
15 \\
\hline
9 \\
9 \\
\hline
\end{array}
\qquad
\begin{array}{r}
253 \\
3\overline{)\,759}
\end{array}
$$

Studies by Grossnickle[4] and others indicate that short division is less accurate for elementary school pupils and also more difficult because unseen numerals are involved. Short division is still used with basic facts because they involve no unseen numerals, but it does not often appear for other division work.

Pupils do have some direct uses for short division once computation with fractions begins. It is somewhat useful in work with addition and subtraction of fractions and becomes of increased value once multiplication of fractions is introduced.

$$
\begin{aligned}
\frac{5}{3} &= \frac{10}{6} \\
\frac{2}{3} &= \frac{4}{6} \\
+\quad \frac{1}{3} &= \frac{2}{6} \\
\hline
&\frac{16}{6}
\end{aligned}
\qquad\qquad
\begin{aligned}
3\tfrac{1}{2} \times 6\tfrac{1}{4} &= \\
\frac{7}{2} \times \frac{25}{4} &= \frac{175}{8}
\end{aligned}
$$

Estimating quotients

A relatively long period of time should be spent in allowing pupils to explore efficient methods of estimating the quotient to division situations. When the teacher feels that pupils have quite a good grasp of division, she may then begin to develop the more standard means of estimating the quotient.

The three procedures for estimating the quotient have several names. The most common method used in textbooks of the 1960's is called the "round-down" or "apparent" method. In addition to the "apparent" method, the "round-up" and the "two-rule" procedures find favor with many writers on the teaching of elementary school mathematics.

Each of these three rather standard means of estimating the quotient is discussed below. Then a suggested teaching procedure is developed.

Round-down or apparent method. The round-down or apparent method follows the procedure of using the digit to the left in the divisor as the "guide digit." In the division $24\overline{)\,464}$ the round-down thinking would be, How many 2's equal 4? or the more meaningfully, How many 20's equal 400? This procedure always produces a correct estimate or an estimate that is too large and

[4] Foster E. Grossnickle and Leo J. Brueckner, *Discovering Meanings in Elementary School Mathematics* (New York: Holt, Rinehart and Winston, 1963), pp. 190-191.

therefore needs to be reduced. Also, because the tens digit of the divisor is always used to make the estimate, the guide-digit is always visible.

Round-up or increase-by-one method.   The round-up method increases the left-hand digit in the divisor by one. In the division $24\overline{)462}$ the round-up thinking would be, How many 3's equal 4? or more meaningfully, How many 30's equal 400? This round-up plan has the advantage of fitting well into the series of subtractions pattern that has been established earlier, because the estimate will never be too large. It also eliminates the need to erase. This aids the teacher in analyzing pupil errors. If an estimate of the quotient is too small, it still may be used and another division used. For example,

$$
\begin{array}{r}
32 \\
\hline
1 \\
1 \\
10 \\
20 \\
21\overline{)685} \\
420 \\
\hline
265 \\
210 \\
\hline
55 \\
21 \\
\hline
34 \\
21 \\
\hline
13 \\
\end{array}
$$

A disadvantage of this procedure is that the guide-digit is not written down but must be remembered.

Two-rule procedure.   The two-rule procedure makes use of both the round-down method and the round-up method. In using the two-rule pattern, a pupil rounds the divisor to the nearest multiple of 10 or 100 or 1000 as the case may be. Thus 54 becomes 50, 56 becomes 60, 453 becomes 500. For divisors ending in 5, the pupil determines whether to round up or down by the quotient. The two-rule procedure results in fewer occasions on which an inexact estimate is made. However, it requires a greater amount of mathematical proficiency than either of the other two methods.

A suggested sequence.   The question of which of the three procedures shall be used does not really arise, because in most cases the average and above average pupil will discover the two-rule procedure. Those who do not figure the two-rule procedure out for themselves are probably better off remaining with a procedure they understand.

Since the round-up procedure is in keeping with an understanding of the series of subtractions approach to division, it can be taught as a natural outgrowth of this procedure.

One teacher started to develop the round-up method by stating, "Some of us have been going through a rather long procedure in solving division questions. This is perfectly all right mathematically, but it is time consuming. Let's see if we can develop some faster procedures. Look over the division exercises I've given to you and see if you can estimate the quotient without performing the division." A portion of the exercise sheet appears below.

$$4)\overline{16} \qquad\qquad 5)\overline{35}$$

$$3 \text{ tens})\overline{12 \text{ tens}} \qquad 5 \text{ tens})\overline{20 \text{ tens}} = 50)\overline{200}$$

$$30)\overline{120} \qquad\qquad 37)\overline{8000}$$

$$29)\overline{1200} \qquad\qquad 18)\overline{200}$$

The pupils experienced little difficulty with the division involving even tens as the divisor. There was less certainty on the situations such as $1200 \div 29$. The teacher suggested that they approximate the number of tens in the divisor and in the dividend to make their estimate. In the above example, the pupils suggested that an estimate for $1200 \div 29$ could be obtained by asking the question, "How many 3 tens equal 120 tens? _____ approximately 40." This estimate was used and the division problem completed. The procedure continued with emphasis upon rounding the divisor upward to the next ten.

After some further work the following day, the class formulated a procedure for estimating the quotient. They suggested, "If the divisor is an even ten such as 50, we think, 'how many sets of 5 tens?' If the divisor is tens and ones such as 36, we think the next tens number or 4 tens." It should be noted that during this time pupils having difficulty shortening the division procedure by estimating were allowed to work by using a less accurate procedure they had learned in the past such as the following:

231 r29	Are there one hundred 37's?	Yes
$\overline{\quad 1}$	Another 100?	Yes
10	Another 100?	No
20	About how many tens?	I'll try 2 tens.
100	Any more tens?	One ten
100	Now what?	One group of 37.
37)$\overline{8576}$		
3700		
$\overline{4876}$		
3700		
$\overline{1176}$		
740		
$\overline{\quad 436}$		
370		
$\overline{\quad\quad 66}$		
37		
$\overline{\quad\quad 29}$		

Divisibility

In some situations it is valuable to know by inspection when a number can be exactly divided by another number. A grandmother may wish to purchase a large bag of marbles that can be divided evenly among her 5 grandchildren. How can she look at the numeral stamped on a bag of marbles and quickly tell if it is exactly divisible by 5? To develop a generalization for divisibility by 5 a teacher may present the problem above and then suggest that the pupils take a number of possible quantities to represent the contents of the bag of marbles.

24	48	100	164
25	64	125	175
50	65	144	

The teacher posed the question, "Which of these numbers is exactly divisible by 5? Study the results you get and see if you can find a general rule concerning numbers that can be exactly divided by 5." The pupils worked for a few minutes and then discussed the numbers which were divisible by 5. The majority of the pupils had "discovered" that any of the numbers ending in 5 or 0 were divisible by 5. The teacher then asked, "Although we've dealt with only two-digit and three-digit forms, would this also be true of larger numbers?" Several larger numbers were analyzed. The generalization still worked.

It was suggested that the group attempt to "discover" the reason for the rule. The following discussion occurred:

Teacher	Pupils
Let's try one example and analyze it. How could we write 365 in expanded notation?	$300 + 60 + 5$
Good, let's further break down the notation. What does 300 mean?	(3×100)
What does 60 mean? Write this by using parentheses.	(6×10)
What about divisibility by 5 of the hundreds and the tens place?	(5×1) or (5) $(3 \times 100) + (6 \times 10) + (5)$ Even; hundreds place should always be divisible by 5 because 100 is divisible by 5. Even; tens should be divisible by 5.

What about the ones place?

If 0 is in the ones place, the number should be divisible by 5 because it is an even ten. If 5 is in the ones place, the number should be divisible by 5 because we know that the other places are divisible by 5 and that 5 is divisible by itself.

This directed question procedure will vary with the ability of the class group. However, with most classes the teacher can use this type of technique rather than a "show-and-tell" method.

A similar questioning procedure can be used to develop the following divisibility rules.

Divisibility by 2.   A number is divisible by 2 if the units digit is even. (Every number in the tens digit and each succeeding digit is divisible by 2.) Therefore, if the number of the units digit is divisible by 2, the entire number is divisible by 2.

Divisibility by 3.   A number is divisible by 3 if the sum of the digits is divisible by 3. For example, 567 is divisible by 3 because $5 + 6 + 7 = 18$. 18 is exactly divisible by 3.

Divisibility by 4.   A number is divisible by 4 if the last two digits represent a number that is divisible by 4. For example, 756 is divisible by 4 since 56 is divisible by 4. Note: Because 4 is divisible by 2, every number that is divisible by 4 will have an even ones digit in its numeral.

Divisibility by 6.   A number is divisible by 6 if it is divisible by both 2 and 3.

Divisibility by 8.   A number is divisible by 8 if the last three digits represent a number that is divisible by 8.

Divisibility by 9.   A number is divisible by 9 if the sum of its digits is divisible by 9. (Reference to checks of nines can be a useful method of developing this generalization with pupils.)

CHECKING DIVISION

The close relationship between division and the other fundamental operations allows for a variety of procedures for checking. A good procedure is to make use of different checks during the elementary school program, thus allowing "something new" to occur in each grade.

Inverse relationship check (grade three).   The most common check for division is based upon its inverse relationship with multipication. Thus to check $44 \div 5 = N$, the inverse relationship $5 \times N = 44$. In the case above, $N = 8$ with a remainder of 4. The check is performed by multiplying $5 \times 8 = 40$ and then adding 4, because 4 has not been divided. If the answer is given as $8\frac{4}{5}$, then $5 \times 8\frac{4}{5} = 44$. This format may also be used: $5\overline{)44}^{\,8\,r4}$ $5 \times 8 = 40 + 4 = 44$.

Partial dividend check (grade four).   The partial dividend check makes use of the principle that the sum of the numbers subtracted from the dividend (plus the remainder) should equal the dividend. It should be noted that this check actually checks only the correctness of the subtraction.

$$
\begin{array}{r}
630 \\
\overline{30} \\
600 \\
9\,\overline{)\,5673} \\
5400 \\
\overline{273} \\
270 \\
\overline{3}
\end{array}
\qquad
\begin{array}{r}
\text{check} \\
5400 \\
270 \\
\overline{3} \\
5673
\end{array}
$$

Reversing divisor and quotient (grade five).   Rather than multiplying the divisor by the quotient, the quotient may be used as the divisor in checking division. If the new quotient is equal to the original divisor and the remainder (if any) is the same, the problem has been solved correctly.

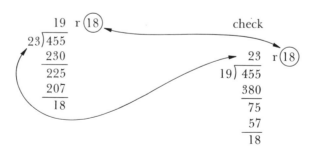

This check also has the advantage of affording further practice in division.

Casting out nines (grade six).   The excess of 9's is found for each of the numbers in the same manner as for the other operations in the casting out nine's check (by summing the digits). The fact that the dividend equals the product of the divisor and the quotient (plus the remainder) is used, with this fact applied to the excess.

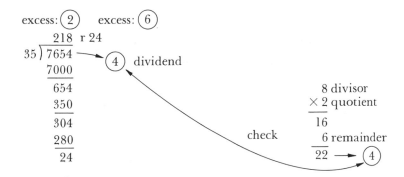

Casting out elevens (enrichment).   Remember the excess of 11's found by subtracting the sum of the even-order digits from the sum of the odd-order digits. (Remember to add 11 if a subtraction cannot be completed.) Then the check is performed in the same manner as the check of nines.

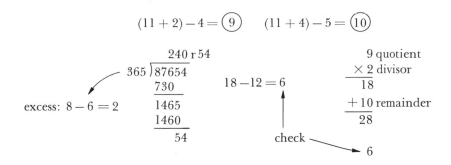

REINTRODUCTION OF DIVISION IN THE UPPER GRADES

The teaching of all of the major concepts that are concerned with whole number division occupies portions of several years of the elementary school curriculum. Therefore, the need for new settings to reintroduce is less acute than was true for the other operations. Because of this fact, only a few other approaches are suggested. They may be used for either reintroductory work or for enrichment.

The numerical array.   Another use of the numerical array suggested in chapter 6, page 158 is useful in the reintroduction of basic division facts. In this situation the teacher began with the array started below as follows: "In which row and above which numeral in the first row will 23 appear?

$$\uparrow \quad \uparrow \quad \uparrow \quad \uparrow \quad \uparrow \quad \uparrow$$

Row 2	7	8	9	10	11	12
Row 1	1	2	3	4	5	6

Try to find an answer without completing the array. Raise your hand when you have an answer and check with me. If you can't figure out a method for finding the answer, you may complete the array."

The typical solution discovered by the pupils involved thinking, "Twenty-four will be above the 6 because it is a multiple of 6. Twenty-four will be in the fourth row. So will 23. Twenty-three will be above the 5."

Then the teacher asked in which row and above which numeral 32 will appear. Many pupils used the same solution; however, several suggested, "I

divided 6) 32   Five 6's equal 30, this will be the end of the fifth row. I

5 r2.
30

have a remainder of 2, so I move into the sixth row two places, which is above the 2." A short discussion was needed to clarify the reason for 32 appearing in the sixth row rather than in the fifth. Once that difficulty was disposed of, the class used the division algorithm to find the location of other numbers.

The array procedure can be used to review any division involving one-digit divisors. For example, to work with 7 as the divisor, 7 is used as the last numeral in the bottom row.

In addition to providing a novel setting for the reintroduction of division, the array reintroduction allows pupils to

1. Discover patterns found in arrays.

2. Use alternate procedures to solve the mathematical questions.

3. Count and draw a chart.

4. Develop background for later study of modular systems and numeration systems with bases other than 10.

The pyramid of multiplication and division.   The teacher may use the pyramid to study multiplication-division relationships and patterns. She may use questions such as "What do you notice concerning the column circled in black?"

$$1$$

$$2 \quad \tfrac{2}{4}$$

$$3 \quad \tfrac{2}{6} \quad \tfrac{3}{9}$$

$$4 \quad \tfrac{2}{8} \quad \tfrac{3}{12} \quad \tfrac{4}{16}$$

$$5 \quad \tfrac{2}{10} \quad \tfrac{3}{15} \quad \tfrac{4}{20} \quad \tfrac{5}{25}$$

$$6 \quad \tfrac{2}{12} \quad \tfrac{3}{18} \quad \tfrac{4}{24} \quad \tfrac{5}{30} \quad \tfrac{6}{36}$$

$$7 \quad \tfrac{2}{14} \quad \tfrac{3}{21} \quad \tfrac{4}{28} \quad \tfrac{5}{35} \quad \tfrac{6}{42} \quad \tfrac{7}{49}$$

$$8 \quad \tfrac{2}{16} \quad \tfrac{3}{24} \quad \tfrac{4}{32} \quad \tfrac{5}{40} \quad \tfrac{6}{48} \quad \tfrac{7}{56} \quad \tfrac{8}{64}$$

$$9 \quad \tfrac{2}{18} \quad \tfrac{3}{27} \quad \tfrac{4}{36} \quad \tfrac{5}{45} \quad \tfrac{6}{54} \quad \tfrac{7}{63} \quad \tfrac{8}{72} \quad \tfrac{9}{81}$$

$$10 \quad \tfrac{2}{20} \quad \tfrac{3}{30} \quad \tfrac{4}{40} \quad \tfrac{5}{50} \quad \tfrac{6}{60} \quad \tfrac{7}{70} \quad \tfrac{8}{80} \quad \tfrac{9}{90} \quad \tfrac{10}{100}$$

$$11 \quad \tfrac{2}{22} \quad \tfrac{3}{33} \quad \tfrac{4}{44} \quad \tfrac{5}{55} \quad \tfrac{6}{66} \quad \tfrac{7}{77} \quad \tfrac{8}{88} \quad \tfrac{9}{99} \quad \tfrac{10}{110} \quad \tfrac{11}{121}$$

$$12 \quad \tfrac{2}{24} \quad \tfrac{3}{36} \quad \tfrac{4}{48} \quad \tfrac{5}{60} \quad \tfrac{6}{72} \quad \tfrac{7}{84} \quad \tfrac{8}{96} \quad \tfrac{9}{108} \quad \tfrac{10}{120} \quad \tfrac{11}{132} \quad \tfrac{12}{144}$$

$$13 \quad \tfrac{2}{26} \quad \tfrac{3}{39} \quad \tfrac{4}{52} \quad \tfrac{5}{65} \quad \tfrac{6}{78} \quad \tfrac{7}{91} \quad \tfrac{8}{104} \quad \tfrac{9}{117} \quad \tfrac{10}{130} \quad \tfrac{11}{143} \quad \tfrac{12}{156} \quad \tfrac{13}{169}$$

$$14 \quad \tfrac{2}{28} \quad \tfrac{3}{42} \quad \tfrac{4}{56} \quad \tfrac{5}{70} \quad \tfrac{6}{84} \quad \tfrac{7}{98} \quad \tfrac{8}{112} \quad \tfrac{9}{126} \quad \tfrac{10}{140} \quad \tfrac{11}{154} \quad \tfrac{12}{168} \quad \tfrac{13}{182} \quad \tfrac{14}{196}$$

$$15 \quad \tfrac{2}{30} \quad \tfrac{3}{45} \quad \tfrac{4}{60} \quad \tfrac{5}{75} \quad \tfrac{6}{90} \quad \tfrac{7}{105} \quad \tfrac{8}{120} \quad \tfrac{9}{135} \quad \tfrac{10}{150} \quad \tfrac{11}{165} \quad \tfrac{12}{180} \quad \tfrac{13}{195} \quad \tfrac{14}{210} \quad \tfrac{15}{225}$$

$$16 \quad \tfrac{2}{32} \quad \tfrac{3}{48} \quad \tfrac{4}{64} \quad \tfrac{5}{80} \quad \tfrac{6}{96} \quad \tfrac{7}{112} \quad \tfrac{8}{128} \quad \tfrac{9}{144} \quad \tfrac{10}{169} \quad \tfrac{11}{176} \quad \tfrac{12}{192} \quad \tfrac{13}{208} \quad \tfrac{14}{224} \quad \tfrac{15}{240} \quad \tfrac{16}{256}$$

$$17 \quad \tfrac{2}{34} \quad \tfrac{3}{51} \quad \tfrac{4}{68} \quad \tfrac{5}{85} \quad \tfrac{6}{102} \quad \tfrac{7}{119} \quad \tfrac{8}{136} \quad \tfrac{9}{153} \quad \tfrac{10}{170} \quad \tfrac{11}{187} \quad \tfrac{12}{204} \quad \tfrac{13}{221} \quad \tfrac{14}{238} \quad \tfrac{15}{255} \quad \tfrac{16}{272} \quad \tfrac{17}{289}$$

$$18 \quad \tfrac{2}{36} \quad \tfrac{3}{54} \quad \tfrac{4}{72} \quad \tfrac{5}{90} \quad \tfrac{6}{108} \quad \tfrac{7}{126} \quad \tfrac{8}{144} \quad \tfrac{9}{162} \quad \tfrac{10}{180} \quad \tfrac{11}{198} \quad \tfrac{12}{216} \quad \tfrac{13}{234} \quad \tfrac{14}{252} \quad \tfrac{15}{270} \quad \tfrac{16}{288} \quad \tfrac{17}{306} \quad \tfrac{18}{324}$$

$$19 \quad \tfrac{2}{38} \quad \tfrac{3}{57} \quad \tfrac{4}{76} \quad \tfrac{5}{95} \quad \tfrac{6}{114} \quad \tfrac{7}{133} \quad \tfrac{8}{152} \quad \tfrac{9}{171} \quad \tfrac{10}{190} \quad \tfrac{11}{209} \quad \tfrac{12}{228} \quad \tfrac{13}{247} \quad \tfrac{14}{266} \quad \tfrac{15}{285} \quad \tfrac{16}{304} \quad \tfrac{17}{323} \quad \tfrac{18}{342} \quad \tfrac{19}{361}$$

$$20 \quad \tfrac{2}{40} \quad \tfrac{3}{60} \quad \tfrac{4}{80} \quad \tfrac{5}{100} \quad \tfrac{6}{120} \quad \tfrac{7}{140} \quad \tfrac{8}{160} \quad \tfrac{9}{180} \quad \tfrac{10}{200} \quad \tfrac{11}{220} \quad \tfrac{12}{240} \quad \tfrac{13}{260} \quad \tfrac{14}{280} \quad \tfrac{15}{300} \quad \tfrac{16}{320} \quad \tfrac{17}{340} \quad \tfrac{18}{360} \quad \tfrac{19}{380} \quad \tfrac{20}{440}$$

$$21 \quad \tfrac{2}{42} \quad \tfrac{3}{63} \quad \tfrac{4}{84} \quad \tfrac{5}{105} \quad \tfrac{6}{126} \quad \tfrac{7}{147} \quad \tfrac{8}{168} \quad \tfrac{9}{189} \quad \tfrac{10}{210} \quad \tfrac{11}{231} \quad \tfrac{12}{252} \quad \tfrac{13}{273} \quad \tfrac{14}{294} \quad \tfrac{15}{315} \quad \tfrac{16}{336} \quad \tfrac{17}{357} \quad \tfrac{18}{378} \quad \tfrac{19}{399} \quad \tfrac{20}{420} \quad \tfrac{21}{441}$$

$$22 \quad \tfrac{2}{44} \quad \tfrac{3}{66} \quad \tfrac{4}{88} \quad \tfrac{5}{110} \quad \tfrac{6}{132} \quad \tfrac{7}{154} \quad \tfrac{8}{176} \quad \tfrac{9}{198} \quad \tfrac{10}{220} \quad \tfrac{11}{242} \quad \tfrac{12}{264} \quad \tfrac{13}{286} \quad \tfrac{14}{308} \quad \tfrac{15}{330} \quad \tfrac{16}{352} \quad \tfrac{17}{374} \quad \tfrac{18}{396} \quad \tfrac{19}{418} \quad \tfrac{20}{440} \quad \tfrac{21}{462} \quad \tfrac{22}{484}$$

$$23 \quad \tfrac{2}{46} \quad \tfrac{3}{69} \quad \tfrac{4}{92} \quad \tfrac{5}{115} \quad \tfrac{6}{138} \quad \tfrac{7}{161} \quad \tfrac{8}{184} \quad \tfrac{9}{207} \quad \tfrac{10}{230} \quad \tfrac{11}{253} \quad \tfrac{12}{276} \quad \tfrac{13}{299} \quad \tfrac{14}{322} \quad \tfrac{15}{345} \quad \tfrac{16}{368} \quad \tfrac{17}{391} \quad \tfrac{18}{414} \quad \tfrac{19}{437} \quad \tfrac{20}{460} \quad \tfrac{21}{483} \quad \tfrac{22}{506} \quad \tfrac{23}{529}$$

$$24 \quad \tfrac{2}{48} \quad \tfrac{3}{72} \quad \tfrac{4}{96} \quad \tfrac{5}{120} \quad \tfrac{6}{144} \quad \tfrac{7}{168} \quad \tfrac{8}{192} \quad \tfrac{9}{216} \quad \tfrac{10}{240} \quad \tfrac{11}{264} \quad \tfrac{12}{288} \quad \tfrac{13}{312} \quad \tfrac{14}{336} \quad \tfrac{15}{360} \quad \tfrac{16}{384} \quad \tfrac{17}{408} \quad \tfrac{18}{432} \quad \tfrac{19}{456} \quad \tfrac{20}{480} \quad \tfrac{21}{504} \quad \tfrac{22}{528} \quad \tfrac{23}{552} \quad \tfrac{24}{576}$$

$$25 \quad \tfrac{2}{50} \quad \tfrac{3}{75} \quad \tfrac{4}{100} \quad \tfrac{5}{125} \quad \tfrac{6}{150} \quad \tfrac{7}{175} \quad \tfrac{8}{200} \quad \tfrac{9}{225} \quad \tfrac{10}{250} \quad \tfrac{11}{275} \quad \tfrac{12}{300} \quad \tfrac{13}{325} \quad \tfrac{14}{350} \quad \tfrac{15}{375} \quad \tfrac{16}{400} \quad \tfrac{17}{425} \quad \tfrac{18}{450} \quad \tfrac{19}{475} \quad \tfrac{20}{500} \quad \tfrac{21}{525} \quad \tfrac{22}{550} \quad \tfrac{23}{575} \quad \tfrac{24}{600} \quad \tfrac{25}{625}$$

Egyptian division. The Egyptians used a form of duplation (doubling) the divisor until the next double would be larger than the dividend. Then the partial products were added until the dividend was reached. This type of division can be introduced by stating, "I've written an example similar to division that the Egyptians used many years ago. See if you can find out the procedure they used. How is it like our division? How is it different?"

$$297 \div 27 = N$$

27	1′		297	
54	2′		216	8
			81	
108	4′		54	2
			27	
216	8′		27	1

11 answer

The following format may also be used:

$$146 \div 12 = N$$

$12 \times 1 = 12$
$12 \times 2 = 24$ (found by
$12 \times 4 = 48$ doubling)
$12 \times 8 = 96$

$$
\begin{array}{r}
146 \\
- 96 \quad \leftarrow 8 \\
\hline
50 \\
48 \quad \leftarrow 4 \\
\hline
2 \quad\quad 12 \ r2
\end{array}
$$

Early American textbook method. The teacher said, "I've duplicated a page from the *Arithmetic* by Isaac Greenwood, copyrighted in 1729 and used in many colonial schools. How is this division similar to the type we use? How is it different?"

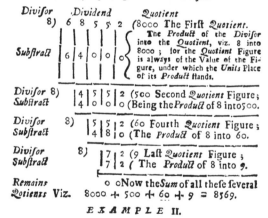

LONG DIVISION AS TAUGHT BY ISAAC GREENWOOD IN 1729

1. If you have not previously made use of the subtractive approach to division, the following divisions in base 8 will be of help to you in understanding its value in early division work. Work the following division computation using a subtractive approach.

$$7_{\text{eight}} \quad)\,\overline{65}_{\text{eight}} \qquad 6_{\text{eight}} \quad)\,\overline{140}_{\text{eight}} \qquad 5_{\text{eight}} \quad)\,\overline{223}_{\text{eight}}$$

2. Prepare a set of remedial materials for a group of sixth-grade pupils who cannot find the answer to division computations such as the two below.

$$36\,)\,\overline{2904} \qquad 201\,)\,\overline{7058}$$

3. How could the abacus be of value in division work? Study the material in Corle (see suggested readings) and decide how such a device could be helpful.
4. Develop a bulletin board that emphasizes the relationship between measurement and partition division.
5. Develop a set of first-grade problems that involve division ideas but may be solved by using sets, the number line, and counting.
6. Discuss the merits of the two forms for writing division algorithms shown below.

$$
\begin{array}{r}
32\,)\,\overline{425} \\
320 \quad 10 \\
\overline{105} \\
64 \quad 2 \\
\overline{41} \\
32 \quad 1 \\
\overline{} \quad 13
\end{array}
\qquad
\begin{array}{r}
13 \\
1 \\
2 \\
10 \\
32\,)\,\overline{425} \\
320 \\
\overline{105} \\
64 \\
\overline{41} \\
32 \\
\overline{}
\end{array}
$$

7. Write several verbal problems that illustrate measurement division. Write several that illustrate partition division.

8. Compare the approach to division with multi-digit divisors taken in a fourth-grade children's textbook copyrighted before 1958 with one copyrighted after 1963.

SUGGESTED REFERENCES

Banks, J. Houston, *Learning and Teaching Arithmetic,* 2nd ed. (Boston: Allyn and Bacon, 1964), pp. 244–270.

Corle, Clyde G., *Teaching Mathematics in the Elementary School* (New York: Ronald, 1964), pp. 147–162.

Grossnickle, Foster E., and Brueckner, Leo J., *Discovering Meanings in Elementary School Mathematics* (New York: Holt, Rinehart and Winston, 1963), pp. 167–211.

Mueller, Francis J., *Arithmetic its Structure and Concepts,* 2nd ed. (New York: Prentice-Hall, 1964), pp. 175–188.

Van Engen, Henry, and Gibb, E. Glenadine, "General Mental Functions Associated with Division," *Educational Service Bulletin,* No. 2 (Cedar Falls, Iowa: Iowa State Teachers College, 1956).

USE OF SUGGESTED REFERENCES

1. How does Banks suggest the trial divisor be developed?
2. Study Corle's use of popsicle sticks in developing an understanding of multi-digit division.
3. How does Grossnickle use the pocket chart in developing regrouping in division?
4. Study the use of array and also the distributive rationale presented by Mueller.
5. Van Engen and Gibb compared "conventional division" with "successive subtractions" for teaching division. What did they conclude?

8

Fractions
and rational numbers

The interpretation of fractions has long been a thorny problem. Historically, numbers and the symbols for numbers (numerals) were used interchangeably. The number-numeral distinction and the various possibilities of interpreting a fraction such as $\frac{3}{4}$ cause laymen and mathematics educators difficulty.

Man introduced fractions when he began to measure. The first treatment of fractions was found in an Egyptian manuscript, the Ahmes Papyrus of about 1550 B.C. The early Egyptians used only fractions with a numerator of one (unit fractions), and $\frac{3}{4}$ and $\frac{2}{3}$. This use of unit fractions caused the necessity of expressing fractions such as $\frac{2}{43}$ to be written as $\frac{1}{42} + \frac{1}{86} + \frac{1}{129} + \frac{1}{301}$. Several Egyptian notational forms follow:

$$\frac{1}{10} = \bigcirc \!\!\!\!\!\bigwedge, \quad \frac{1}{5} = \bigcirc \!\!\!\!\!\shortmid\shortmid\shortmid\shortmid, \quad \frac{1}{20} = \bigcirc \!\!\!\!\!\bigwedge\bigwedge$$

Fractions with numerators larger than one were developed by the Babylonians. They usually used fractions with denominators that were a multiple or a power of 60, which was the base of the Babylonian system.

Still other notational schemes were used by the Greeks, the Romans, and other early mathematicians. The present notation of fractions came into widespread use in the sixteenth century.

A fraction consists of an ordered pair of integers symbolized by (a, b) or more conventionally by $\frac{a}{b}$ in which the first or top integer is called the *numerator* and the second or bottom integer is called the *denominator*. The denominator may not be zero.

Ordered pairs of numbers can have several interpretations, each of which requires a different teaching emphasis for children to successfully develop understanding.

1. Ordered pairs of numbers may be treated as members of an equivalence class or a *rational number*. The rational number is an equivalence class of ordered pairs of integers, $\frac{a}{b}$, where $b \neq 0$. For example, $\{\frac{1}{2}, \frac{2}{4}, \frac{3}{6}, \frac{4}{8}, \ldots, \frac{a}{2a}, \ldots\}$. Normally the rational number is named by the "simplest" member of the equiva-

lence class, in this case $\frac{1}{2}$. The rational numbers arise from the mathematical need for an answer to the question, "If $b \cdot y = c$, what does y equal?" Thus, $b \cdot y = c$; $y = \frac{c}{b}$. For example, $5 \times y = 2$; $y = \frac{2}{5}$. This interpretation develops a multiplicative inverse for a whole number. Thus, the multiplicative inverse for 5 is $\frac{1}{5}$, since $5 \times \frac{1}{5} = 1$ (the identity element for multiplication). In a later section of the chapter, this idea will be used to develop understanding in the division of rationals.

2. Ordered pairs of numbers may be considered the quotient of a division. Use of a whole number allows for a solution to the division $4 \div 2 = \square$. However, when a situation that requires an answer to $1 \div 2 = \square$ or $15 \div 6 = \square$ arises, no whole number answer can be obtained. In such cases, a fraction provides a solution; the answer to $1 \div 2$ is $\frac{1}{2}$, which may be read "one-half" or "one divided by two"; the answer to $15 \div 6$ is $\frac{15}{6}$ or $2\frac{3}{6}$, the latter of which may be thought of as 2 and $\frac{3}{6}$ or $2\frac{1}{2}$.

Many historians believe that fractions were first developed in situations in which a whole number answer to a division problem was impossible. The division interpretation of pairs of numbers is of great importance in elementary school mathematics.

3. Ordered pairs of numbers may be considered in the traditional fraction concept. Historically, the term fraction comes from the Latin word *frangere* or *fractio*, which means "to break."

Most adults think in terms of pies, apples, or oranges when the word "fraction" is mentioned. For example, in the circular region illustrated at the left, the numerator tells "how many" (3) and the denominator tells "how large" (4ths).

Many textbooks of relatively recent vintage have placed undue emphasis upon the idea that a fraction is a part of a whole. This usage is limited because many cases arise in which a fraction such as $\frac{4}{7}$ represents four members of a set of seven objects.

Set terminology may be effectively used to develop the "parts of a group" idea. In this context, these situations may be viewed as expressing the relationship of a subset to a set.

For example, the parts of a group can be illustrated by, "Bill has $\frac{5}{8}$ of the marbles." In this case the numerator (5) expresses the number size of equivalent subsets being considered, and the denominator (8) expresses the equivalent subsets in the entire set. For fractions such as $\frac{5}{4}$ which indicate amounts greater than one, the numerator 5 tells how many equivalent subsets, and the denominator 4 indicates that one set contains 4 such subsets.

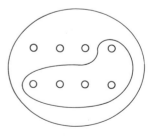

The "parts of a whole" idea can be illustrated by regions. The numerator (1) tells the number of congruent regions considered. The denominator (3) tells the number of congruent regions in a unit region.

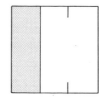

4. Ordered pairs of numbers may be considered as a "ratio" or "rate pair." In such situations an ordered pair of whole numbers indicates a rate. For example, "Claudia bought 3 pencils for 15 cents." The ordered pair of whole numbers is used to express a many-to-many correspondence. Such ordered pairs may be read as "3 for 15," or "3 to 15." This interpretation of ordered pairs is extremely useful in problem situations involving the comparison of prices and also leads to a valuable definition of percent. The teaching of ratio and percent is covered in chapter 10.

Rational numbers have the same properties as whole numbers. There are several other ideas that are important to thought concerning rational numbers.

1. The denominator may never be 0 because $\frac{5}{0}$ can be interpreted as 5 divided by 0, and division with zero as a divisor is undefined. If $\frac{5}{0} = \square$ then $\square \times 0 = 5$, and there is no unique number which will fulfill this necessary limitation.

2. The nonzero rational numbers are *closed* with respect to division. The system of integers does not provide an answer to $3 \times \square = 2$ or $2 \div 2 = \square$. Development of rational numbers allows an answer to these types of mathematical sentences because $3 \times \frac{2}{3} = 2$ and $2 \div 3 = \frac{2}{3}$.

3. If the cross-products of two fractions are equal, they are equivalent fractions (they name the same rational number). Thus,

$$\frac{3}{4} \underset{\times}{=} \frac{6}{8}$$

because $3 \times 8 = 4 \times 6$. If the numerator and denominator of a fraction are multiplied by the same whole number, the new fraction and the old fraction represent the same rational number.

4. Fractions can be renamed by multiplying the numerator and the denominator by the same whole number. Thus, $\frac{5}{5} \times \frac{3}{5} = \frac{15}{25}$; $\frac{15}{25} = \frac{3}{5}$. This is true because $\frac{5}{5}$ is another name for $\frac{1}{1}$, which is the identity element of multiplication.

5. The identity element for addition of rational numbers is zero. Zero can be named by any of the set of fractions $\{\frac{0}{1}, \frac{0}{2}, \frac{0}{3}, \frac{0}{4}, \ldots \frac{0}{n}\}$.

6. The rationals provide a *multiplicative inverse;* for example, the number $\frac{3}{2}$ is the multiplicative inverse for $\frac{2}{3}$ since $\frac{2}{3} \times \frac{3}{2} = 1$, and 1 is the identity element for multiplication.

THE FOUNDATION PROGRAM FOR FRACTIONS

If only the mathematical criterion for inclusion of a topic in the elementary curriculum were followed, the introduction of fractions would begin following all of the fundamental operations with whole numbers. In fact, this procedure was followed by most textbooks published during the nineteenth century.

However, because primary-age children have many uses for rationals and will develop concepts concerning fractions, even if they are not taught at the primary-grade level, it is important for primary teachers to begin an informal but mathematically correct development of fractional concepts early in the grades.

Children at the preschool level have heard their parents and older children make statements such as "Nick, you can have one-half of the candy bar." "Jean, you haven't finished even a quarter of your work." "Bill, give each of the children one-third of the pieces of candy." Although the meanings that children attach to such situations are varied, these experiences may be used by the teacher to develop basic ideas concerning fractions. The classroom vignettes that follow are designed to illustrate situations that provide opportunities for developing the meaning of fractions.

Early instruction

One teacher began the development of rational numbers by saying, "The directions for mounting leaves given in my science book say, 'Begin with one-half of a sheet of paper.' How can we each cut a sheet of paper into halves?" Several sheets of paper were on a table at the front of the room and several pupils demonstrated to their classmates methods of obtaining one-half of a sheet of paper. (See illustration below.) Then the teacher said, "What do we mean by one-half?" Discussion brought out the idea that the sheet of paper was being divided into parts of the same size.

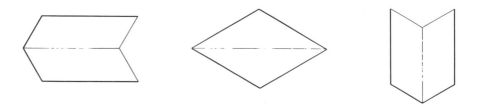

The association of one-half with the idea of region was begun by asking, "If we consider this piece of paper as a region, what has cutting the paper in half done to the region? What does the one-half mean?" The pupils suggested that the region had been divided into two regions of the same size and that one-half of a region could refer to either of the parts of a region which is split into two congruent parts.

During the next few days the teacher presented problem situations that required separating a whole into halves and identifying halves. Four such problems are presented below.

1. Jerry covered half of his kite with white paper and the other half with gray. Which picture shows the kite painted the way Jerry colored his kite?

2. Jill was asked to cut this candy bar in half. Mark off the candy bar where she could cut it.

Pupils illustrated the following cuts:

3. The directions for a science experiment indicate that a glass should be filled one-half full with water. Show how full the glass should be.

4. Jim, Jane, and Mary were arguing as to who had correctly shaded one half of the drawing. Draw a ring around the correct drawing.

| Jim | Jane | Mary |

Another interpretation of a fraction was introduced by the question, "The principal brought in this set of 6 tennis balls. We're to keep half of them and give the other half to the other first grade. How many should we keep?" The children quickly answer that each room would get 3 of the tennis balls. The teacher asked one of the children to represent the situation on the flannel board. She then asked, "How could we describe the meaning of one-half of this set?" After a short time for thought and some discussion the class agreed that one-half of the set referred to one of two subsets of the same size.

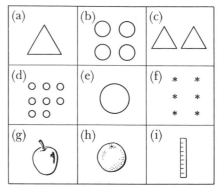

Several other problems involving the partitioning of sets or regions into halves were used. The pupils were given the worksheet shown at the right. They were directed to partition each region or set into halves.

A similar development was used for teaching the concept of one-fourth and one-third. The meaning of $\frac{2}{3}$ and $\frac{3}{4}$ was taught through the use of problems such as the following.

1. Notice the picture. Ken gave one-third of his marbles to his little brother, Mike. What fraction of the marbles did Ken keep for himself?

Ken's   Mike's

2. Nancy and her friends ate the portion of the cake that is shaded. What fraction of the cake did they eat?

Directed questions were used to develop the idea that $\frac{2}{3}$ of an object (set) means 2 parts of an object that has been divided into 3 parts of the same size or 2 subsets of a set that has been grouped into 3 subsets of the same size.

To develop fifths, one teacher said, "Yesterday you told me that his diagram could be used to show three-fourths.

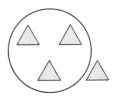

See if you can use the ideas you've learned concerning fractions to answer this question. Alice wanted to tell her mother the fraction of pages in her workbook assignment that she had finished. She had this many pages to work (holds up five pages) and had finished this many (points to three completed pages). What fraction of the five pages has she worked?"

Pupils reasoned that because 3 subsets of a set of 4 objects was stated as three-fourths, 3 subsets of a set of 5 objects probably would be stated as three-fifths. The teacher agreed with this statement and suggested that they study the objects shown on a duplicated sheet and be ready to give each a fractional name.

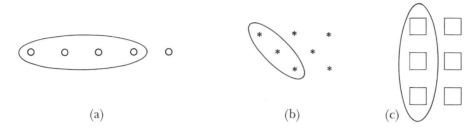

(a)   (b)   (c)

Diagrams (a) and (b) were readily identified as representing four-fifths and three-sevenths. The children generalized that to give a name to a fractional diagram, a person should first state the number of subsets indicated and then state the number of subsets in the set, adding a *th*. Thus ⊂* * *⊃* * * * indicated three-sevenths. Some pupils were somewhat unsure as to the name of (c). Several suggested that they had previously identified a similar diagram as representing one-half. Others agreed but suggested that in keeping with the handling of four-fifths and three-sevenths that (c) should be thought of as representing three-sixths. One pupil suggested that because a whole number could have more than one name, quite possibly fractions could also have more than one name. The teacher said, "Let's look at several other situations and see if it is possible for two fractions to represent the same idea."

Several geometric representations were drawn on the chalkboard and pupils were asked to think of the possible names for the fractional ideas indicated by the drawings. A portion of the drawings and the children's remarks are reproduced below.

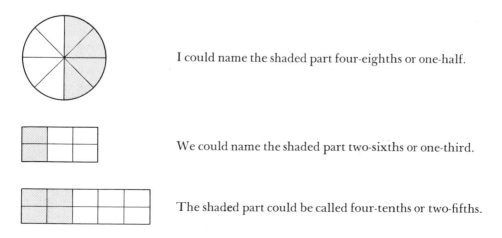

I could name the shaded part four-eighths or one-half.

We could name the shaded part two-sixths or one-third.

The shaded part could be called four-tenths or two-fifths.

Pupils generalized ideas such as "Three-sixths means the same as $\frac{1}{2}$; $\frac{5}{8}$ means the same as $\frac{10}{16}$; etc." The teacher then referred the pupils to the number line to note the location of named sets of fractions such as $\{\frac{3}{4}, \frac{6}{8}, \frac{9}{12}, \frac{12}{16}, \ldots\}$. The pupils found that each set identified the same point on the number line.

The teacher then said, "When fractions are names for the same point on the number line, they name a *rational number*. These fractions are called *equivalent* fractions."

Writing fractions

The writing of symbols for rational numbers can be readily developed as an outgrowth of previous work. When the teacher feels that the pupils can readily identify the fractional idea from diagrams and drawings, the development of the fractional symbol can begin.

The teacher began by saying, "We have shown what we mean by five-sixths of a region. Can we invent a symbol to represent this?" The pupils experimented with various possibilities for writing fractional numerals. Several pupils suggested that five-sixths might well be written as 5, 6. Others suggested 5-6. The majority of the pupils had seen numerals of the type $\frac{5}{6}$ and suggested that method. The teacher informed the class that they could use (5,6) but that the most common form is $\frac{5}{6}$. Further discussion stressed the idea that the fractional numeral represented *ordered pairs* of numbers. The pupils illustrated that $\frac{3}{4}$ and $\frac{4}{3}$ did not represent the same mathematical idea.

As work in fractions continued, the pupils discovered the concept that a fraction may be considered to indicate a division. Examples such as $\frac{6}{2}$ were used in this development. Pupils also noted that $\frac{9}{1} = 3$; $\frac{5}{1} = 5$; etc.

Further work on equivalent fractions

The skill to convert a fraction to an equivalent form is a necessary prerequisite for all but the most simple computation involving fractions. It is a useful skill in its own right when a pupil wishes to compare two fractions with different denominators to see which represents the larger number. A use situation such as the question that follows provides a motivation for this. "Fred and Bill were arguing as to whose seeds had grown the most during a science experiment. Each boy measured his seedlings one evening and brought the results back to the class. Fred reported that his seedling was $\frac{5}{8}$ in. and Bill reported his seedling to be $\frac{11}{16}$ in. Which boy's seedling was taller?"

Pupils challenged to find an answer to the problem posed above may determine that to answer the question one of two routes must be taken. Either both heights must be expressed with the same denominator or they must be marked off on the same ruler. Use of the ruler or number line indicates that $\frac{5}{8}$ can be named $\frac{10}{16}$ and thus Bill's seedling is taller.

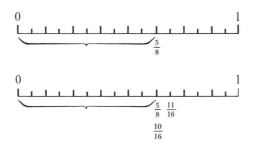

Pupils should have many opportunities to use sets and objects divided into regions of the same size to identify names for the same rational number. Several of the questions that can be used in connection with this work are listed below.

1. There are 16 ounces in a pound. Eight ounces is $\frac{8}{16}$ of a pound. What are three fractions equivalent to $\frac{8}{16}$?

2. There are 12 inches in a foot. Four inches is_____of a foot. What are three fractions equivalent to $\frac{4}{12}$?

3. What fraction of a yard is 1 foot? What are two other equivalent fractions that could be found by using inches in a foot and inches in a yard?

After pupils have become "comfortable" in deriving equivalent fractions using drawings and diagrams, the class should consider other ways in which other names for a rational number can be found. The following development can be used effectively. "Yesterday you were asked to find four equivalent fractions that are other names for $\frac{1}{2}$. You made use of drawings and the number line.

Let's look at the various names for one-half (page 212) and see if those names could be obtained more quickly.

Study the names for $\frac{1}{2}$ carefully and see if you can obtain any pattern. If you find a procedure, test it out by finding four different names for $\frac{1}{3}$." The teacher observed the students at work and mentally selected several approaches that he observed. He then asked those pupils to suggest methods of quickly finding a number of equivalent fractions.

The first student suggested that it was possible to find other names for $\frac{1}{3}$ by continued doubling of both the numerator and the denominator. His set of equivalent fractions was $\frac{1}{3}$, $\frac{2}{6}$, $\frac{4}{12}$, and $\frac{8}{24}$. The class members agreed that this method could be used, but several suggested that this did not produce all of the equivalent fractions. For example, while $\frac{3}{9}$ is another name for $\frac{1}{3}$, the doubling process will not produce $\frac{3}{9}$.

The next student suggested that in his experimentation he noticed that all the various names for $\frac{1}{2}$ could be found by multiplying both the numerator and the denominator by the same whole number. Thus

$$\frac{1 \times 2}{2 \times 2} = \frac{2}{4}, \frac{1 \times 3}{2 \times 3} = \frac{3}{6}, \frac{1 \times 8}{2 \times 8} = \frac{8}{16}, \text{etc.}$$

$\frac{1}{2} = \frac{2}{4}$ $\frac{1}{2} = \frac{5}{10}$

$\frac{1}{2} = \frac{3}{6}$ $\frac{1}{2} = \frac{6}{12}$

$\frac{1}{2} = \frac{4}{8}$ $\frac{1}{2} = \frac{7}{14}$

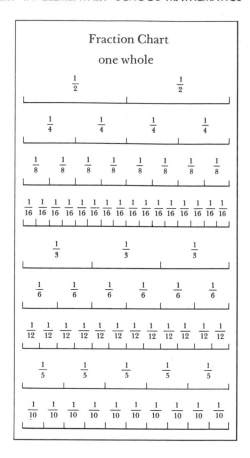

After testing several examples, the pupils were fairly confident that this procedure was effective.

Then the teacher asked, "Why do you think multiplying the numerator and denominator by the same whole number will give an equivalent fraction? Think about this and then try to write a statement explaining the reason for this 'rule.' It may help to think of the ideas of whole number multiplication."

The next day the teacher asked several pupils to read their explanations of the "rule." One pupil stated: "To find an equivalent fraction, it is possible to multiply both the numerator and denominator by the same whole number. It could look like this:

$$\frac{3 \times 2}{4 \times 2} = \frac{6}{8}\text{."}$$

Drawings and diagrams were then used to help verify the findings. (In whole number multiplication any number can be multiplied by one without changing its value.)

Further work can be given in developing sets of equivalent fractions by having pupils generate sets of equivalent fractions in the form

$\{\frac{2}{3}, \underline{\hspace{1cm}}, \underline{\hspace{1cm}}, \underline{\hspace{1cm}}, \ldots\}$. Pupils should also be given the opportunity to discover that to change the name of a fraction to that of a given denominator, for example, $\frac{2}{7} = \frac{?}{21}$, one can think, "What number was 7 multiplied by to change it to 21?——by 3——therefore, I have to multiply 2 by 3 to produce an equivalent fraction." Later the pupils discover that the number that both terms of the fraction are multiplied by may be found by dividing. Thus, $\frac{2}{5} = \frac{?}{20}$ may be found by thinking, "If $20 \div 5 = 4$, the 5 has been multiplied by 4. The 2 must also be multiplied by 4."

Often it is helpful to express a fraction in its lowest terms. (The lowest-terms form means that the numerator and denominator have no common factors other than one.) Thus, $\frac{6}{8}$ is not in lowest terms, while $\frac{3}{4}$ is in lowest terms. This process is often called reduction, which is a misnomer because the number is not changed. Directed questions can lead pupils to discover that fractions can be simplified by dividing both the numerator and the denominator by the same whole number. As the pupils become more sophisticated in the use of simplification, they can use the idea of removing common factors. In this manner

$$\frac{45}{60} = \frac{3 \times 5 \times (3)}{3 \times 5 \times (4)} = \frac{3}{4}.$$

This principle is often called the "Golden Rule" of fractions.

Care must be taken to insure that pupils understand that while

$$\frac{\cancel{2} \times 3}{\cancel{2} \times 5} = \frac{3}{5}; \frac{\cancel{2} + 3}{\cancel{2} + 5} \neq \frac{3}{5}.$$

Several examples worked during the practice time given to simplification of fractions will usually suffice to settle this point.

TEACHING ADDITION OF RATIONAL NUMBERS

Foundation work

Primary-grade pupils can readily solve problems involving the union of sets of objects that can be represented by fractions. The pupils can also make use of the number line and drawings of circular or rectangular regions to solve such problems. An example of each type of situation with typical concrete "set" solutions is provided below.

1. Bill and Nancy each received a set of pencils that contained 8 pencils. After three weeks Bill had 3 pencils left and Nancy had 4 pencils left.

    a. What part of his set did Bill have left?

b. What part of her set did Nancy have left?

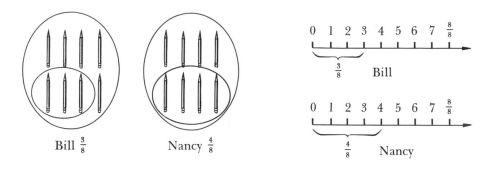

c. If the two children combined their remaining pencils, what part of a set of pencils would they have?

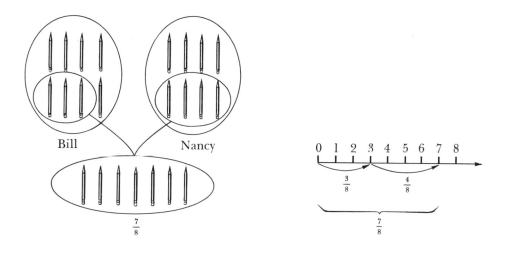

2. Joyce baked two pizzas for an evening snack. She cut both into 8 pieces. The shaded part of the drawing below shows the number of pieces left. What fraction of a whole pizza is left?

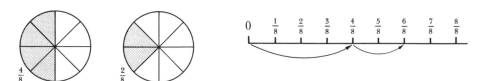

3. In baking her first cake, Kim put in $\frac{1}{8}$ of a cup of sugar and then put in $\frac{5}{8}$ of a cup more sugar. How much sugar did she put in the cake?

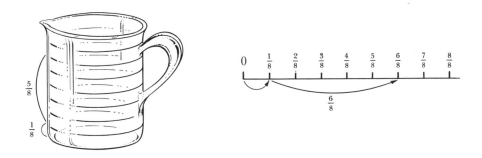

In conjunction with solving addition situations by the use of drawings and diagrams, pupils at the primary-grade level will benefit from simple problems in which they are to "think the answer" without using paper and pencil. The majority of primary-grade pupils can find the answer without pencil and paper to problems such as "Tom worked $\frac{2}{5}$ of his problems on Monday and another $\frac{2}{5}$ of the problems today. What fraction of his problems has he worked?"

Systematic development

Systematic work with addition usually occurs in the fourth or the fifth grade. The suggestions for this introduction are at variance with many present programs for teaching the addition of rational numbers; therefore, several suggestions concerning addition are given as a prelude to the teaching suggestions.

1. Often the introduction begins by dealing with fractions that have the same denominator. If a good foundation is provided in the primary grades, work with "like" fractions (fractions with the same denominator) offers little challenge to intermediate-grade pupils. Therefore, it is suggested that "unlike fractions" be used for the first critical study of addition.

2. The understanding of congruent regions is assumed. However, the name congruent is not necessary to the development.

3. Because fractions represent mathematical abstractions of physical world objects, pupils can best develop understanding if they have an opportunity to begin by dealing with physical world problem situations.

Teaching development

Previous to formal study of addition, the pupils had developed number lines (see below) which emphasized the various names for rational numbers.

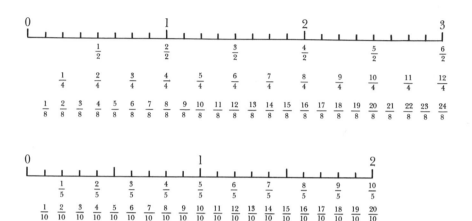

The study of addition was initiated by the pupils' consideration of the following three verbal problems.

1. Kevin lives $\frac{3}{10}$ of a mile from school. Joe lives $\frac{5}{10}$ of a mile further from school than Kevin. How far does Joe live from school?

2. To make a depot for his HO-gauge model train, Harry attached a piece of wood that was $\frac{1}{4}$-inch thick to a piece of wood that was $\frac{3}{8}$-inch thick. How thick were the combined pieces?

3. On a hike, the Girl Scouts walked $1\frac{1}{2}$ miles before a refreshment break and $\frac{3}{4}$ of a mile after the break. How far did they walk?

Problem (1) caused the pupils little difficulty. The mathematical sentence representing the problem was identified as $\frac{3}{10} + \frac{5}{10} = N$. Pupils made use of the number line, drawings, or counting by tenths, or were able to just think and answer. During the discussion of the problem, the class commented that because the denominators were the same, the addition was very similar to the addition of whole numbers. One pupil suggested, "It's just like adding ones and tens: 2 tens + 5 tens = 7 tens; 3 ones + 8 ones = 11 ones."

Problem (2) required a greater amount of pupil thought. The mathematical sentence needed was identified as $\frac{1}{4} + \frac{3}{8} = N$. Pupils suggested the following solutions:

Shirley: Use the number line that is marked in eighths and in fourths.

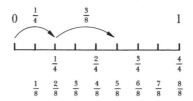

Kathleen: Use a diagram of a rectangular region or a circular region.

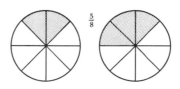

Mark: Find names for both numbers that have the same denominator.

$$\tfrac{1}{4} + \tfrac{3}{8} = N$$

$$\tfrac{2}{8} + \tfrac{3}{8} = \tfrac{5}{8}$$

In the discussion of the problem the solution suggested by Mark was considered to be the most "mathematical" one. It also provided the most economical use of time because it allowed for a solution by addition. Problem (3) was solved in a manner similar to the way in which problem (2) was solved.

During the lessons that follow the initial development, the teacher should give many problems and computational exercises that require the pupils to find equivalent fractions for performing the addition. The teacher should focus attention on addition involving fractions with the same denominator, addition involving fractions with "unlike" denominators, addition involving "mixed forms" such as $3\tfrac{1}{2} + 4\tfrac{2}{3} = N$, and methods involving renaming to obtain "like" fractions.

Properties of addition of rational numbers

After some experience with addition of rational numbers, pupils should benefit from an inquiry concerning the properties of addition. The following questions present a challenge to make mathematical generalizations.

1. Does the commutative property of addition hold true for rational numbers?
2. Does the associative property of addition hold true for rational numbers?
3. Does the addition property of zero as the identity element hold true for the addition of rational numbers?
4. When two rationals are added, can the result always be expressed as a fraction?

In answer to the questions above, the pupils should present a number of examples to verify that each of the properties work for rational numbers as they did for whole numbers. The pupils should understand that they have not mathematically proved that each property holds true. For further verification of their findings, the pupils can compare their results with an accurate textbook.

Exercises such as those suggested above should help pupils arrive at the following generalizations concerning the addition of rational numbers:

1. If two rational numbers are added, the sum is a rational number, or may be named by a fraction.

2. If 0 is added to any rational number, that rational is the sum. Members of the following set are all names for 0: $\{\frac{0}{1}, \frac{0}{2}, \frac{0}{3}, \ldots \frac{0}{n}\}$.

3. The order of addends for rational numbers does not affect the sum. (Commutative property of addition.)

4. In finding the sum of three rationals, (a) the first and the second may be added and the third added to their sum, or (b) the second and third may be added and the first added to their sum. (Associative property of addition.)

Mixed form and renaming

Any addition situations which involve mixed forms may be performed by changing the mixed forms into fraction form ($3\frac{2}{3}$ becomes $\frac{11}{3}$). However, using mixed forms, the sum of $3\frac{1}{2}$ and $2\frac{3}{4}$ is developed in (a) by using the associative and the commutative properties.

(a)

$$3\frac{1}{2} + 2\frac{3}{4} = N$$

$(3 + \frac{1}{2}) + (2 + \frac{3}{4}) = N$	
$3 + (\frac{1}{2} + 2) + \frac{3}{4} = N$	associative property
$3 + (2 + \frac{1}{2}) + \frac{3}{4} = N$	commutative property
$(3 + 2) + (\frac{1}{2} + \frac{3}{4}) = N$	associative property
$(3 + 2) + (\frac{2}{4} + \frac{3}{4}) = N$	renaming $\frac{1}{2}$
$5 + \frac{5}{4} = N$	addition
$5 + (\frac{4}{4} + \frac{1}{4}) = N$	renaming $\frac{5}{4}$
$5 + (1 + \frac{1}{4}) = N$	renaming $\frac{4}{4}$
$(5 + 1) + \frac{1}{4} = N$	associative property
$6\frac{1}{4} = N$	renaming $(5 + 1)$

In most cases, the so-called "vertical form" provides for a more efficient computation. (See (b) below.) A common error in the vertical form is to misuse the sign of equality in the manner shown; $3 + \frac{1}{2}$ does not equal $\frac{2}{4}$; it equals $3\frac{2}{4}$. The teacher should carefully avoid this tendency and discuss the misuse with pupils.

(b)

Correct

$$3\frac{1}{2} = 3 + \frac{1}{2} = 3 + \frac{2}{4}$$
$$2\frac{3}{4} = 2 + \frac{3}{4} = 2 + \frac{3}{4}$$
$$\overline{5 + \frac{5}{4} = 5 + 1 + \frac{1}{4} = 6\frac{1}{4}}$$

Incorrect

$$3\frac{1}{2} = 3 + \frac{1}{2} = \frac{2}{4}$$
$$2\frac{3}{4} = 2 + \frac{3}{4} = \frac{3}{4}$$
$$\overline{5 + \frac{5}{4} = 5 + 1 + \frac{1}{4} = 6\frac{1}{4}}$$

After an understanding has been developed, the operation may be greatly shortened by handling some of the steps mentally.

$$4\tfrac{7}{8} = 4\tfrac{7}{8}$$
$$+\ 5\tfrac{3}{4} = 5\tfrac{6}{8}$$
$$\overline{10\tfrac{5}{8}}$$

The pupil thinks: $\tfrac{3}{4} = \tfrac{6}{8}$

$\tfrac{7}{8} + \tfrac{6}{8} = \tfrac{13}{8}$ which can be renamed $1\tfrac{5}{8}$

Generalizing the addition of rational numbers through orally presented situations

The mathematical definition of addition for rational numbers is

$$\frac{a}{b} + \frac{c}{d} = \frac{(a \times d) + (b \times c)}{b \times d} \quad \text{or} \quad \frac{ad + bc}{bd}\,.$$

Numerically,

$$\frac{4}{5} + \frac{2}{3} = \frac{(4 \times 3) + (5 \times 2)}{(5 \times 3)}\,.$$

Developing an understanding of this definition is of value for two reasons: (1) such a procedure allows for a more effective approach to non-pencil and paper addition than does the method presented previously; and (2) it is the procedure that pupils will later use in algebraic work with fractions.

A teacher may use the following questioning technique to develop the definition by guided discovery:

Teacher	Pupils

We often need to add without using paper and pencil. See if you can follow me on these problems and exercises.

1. Alice has $\tfrac{3}{4}$ foot of red ribbon and $\tfrac{2}{3}$ foot of green ribbon. How many feet of ribbon does she have in all? What is the answer?

Ann: I think that the answer is $1\tfrac{5}{12}$ feet.

How did you work the problem?

Ann: In the same way I always work rational number addition. I did have a hard time remembering when I changed $\tfrac{3}{4}$ and $\tfrac{2}{3}$ to 12ths.

2. Let's look at an addition situation on the chalkboard and see if we can find a better way of adding without paper and pencil.

$$\frac{1}{2} + \frac{2}{3} = N$$

What is the quickest method of finding a common denominator when we add?

Mike: Multiply the denominators.

Is this always the simplest common denominator?

Jill: No

Is it always a correct common denominator?

Matt: Yes

Let's look at this addition. How do I change $\frac{1}{2}$ to 6ths?

Ann: Multiply the numerator by 3 and the denominator by 3.

How can I change $\frac{2}{3}$ to 6ths?

Phil: Multiply the numerator by 2 and the denominator by 2.

Can you see any method of doing this without rewriting? Try working $\frac{3}{4} + \frac{2}{3} = N$ to find a method. Work on paper and I'll come around and see how you're getting along.

Chris, would you put your method on the board and explain what you did?

Chris: $\frac{3}{4} + \frac{2}{3} = N$

I know that 4×3 will give me a common denominator.

$$\frac{3}{4} + \frac{2}{3} = \frac{}{4 \times 3}.$$

In the last problem, we worked, I noticed that we multiplied

1 × 3 and 2 × 2 to get our numerators. So I can go ahead that way.

$$\frac{3}{4} + \frac{2}{3} = \frac{(3 \times 3) + (4 \times 2)}{4 \times 3}$$

$$= \frac{9 + 8}{12} = \frac{17}{12}$$

a. "Cross multiply" and add the products to get the numerator.
b. Multiply the two denominators for the new denominator.

Other pupils worked several addition exercises to verify that Chris's method worked. The teacher then told the class that this method was correct and that it was the way in which mathematicians defined the addition of rational numbers. Periodic reviews of the ideas behind the process should occur so that the procedure does not become a mere mechanical operation.

A further look at comparing rationals

In the early stages of the study of rational numbers, pupils have had opportunities to compare rational numbers. They have determined that $\frac{2}{3} < \frac{3}{4}$ by changing the fractions to a common denominator. Soon after pupils have used the cross-products addition algorithm, the teacher can present situations in which the pupils can attempt to discover other means of comparing the size of rational numbers. The following development may be used.

Teacher	Pupils

Tom and Nancy were wondering about the size of two rationals, $\frac{15}{23}$ and $\frac{19}{27}$. Tom thought that the first was larger and Nancy thought that the second was larger. Who was right? How could we find out?

Beatrice: Because 23 is a prime number, the least common denominator (LCD) will be found by multiplying the two numbers together. I worked the problem this way.

$$23 \times 27 = 621$$

$$\frac{15}{23} = \frac{405}{621}$$

$$\frac{19}{27} = \frac{437}{621}$$

$\frac{19}{27}$ is larger. Nancy is right.

Can anyone think of a faster method of finding the answer? George?

George: I remembered that when adding by using the product of denominators for our common denominator we cross-multiplied. Because multiplying 27×15 gives us the numerator for the first fraction and multiplying 23×19 gives the numerator for the second fraction, I did that and compared numerators because the denominators will be the same. I'll show you in another example:

$$\frac{3}{5} \times \frac{4}{7} \qquad \begin{array}{l} 3 \times 7 = 21 \\ 5 \times 4 = 20 \end{array}$$

$\frac{3}{5}$ is larger.

Further discussion clarified this means of comparison and then the teacher suggested that the pupils use the method to find which was larger, $\frac{7}{13}$ or $\frac{21}{39}$. The pupils found that the cross products were equal. Further discussion and the working of examples helped the pupils to verify that if the cross products are equal, the two fractions are equivalent. The principle was generalized by the use of frames to read:

$$\frac{\triangle}{\square} = \frac{\bigcirc}{\bigcirc} \text{ if } \triangle \times \bigcirc = \square \times \bigcirc$$

Finding the least common denominator (least common multiple)

With addition, many situations arise in which it is necessary to determine the least common denominator (LCD) of two or more fractions. The LCD of fractions is analogous to the least common multiple (LCM) of whole numbers. The development up to this point has not focused on efficient ways of finding common denominators for fractions. Many modern materials that are presented to elementary school pupils focus upon this phase of fractions before addition. Such a procedure is to be questioned because the first situation in which there is an extensive need for finding the LCD of fractions occurs when the addition of rationals begins.

The teacher can begin the teaching of the LCD by presenting a situation that requires the addition of several numbers, such as $\frac{3}{4} + \frac{5}{6} + \frac{3}{8} + \frac{1}{3}$. The pupils quickly realize that none of the denominators is a common denominator and that multiplying all of the denominators together produces an extremely large denominator.

Several basic approaches to this topic can be used. The traditional elementary school mathematics program suggested a "guess and check to see if you're right" approach, which at best is inefficient. Also, teachers often suggested that the pupil double the largest denominator to see if this is the LCD. More efficient procedures are suggested below and normally would be developed in the order given.

Use of common factors. The teacher may remind the pupils that the LCD of several numbers will always have each of the numbers as a factor. Then she may suggest that the pupils factor the denominators and study their results. For the example above the pupils find that

$$\frac{3}{4} + \frac{5}{6} + \frac{3}{8} + \frac{1}{3} = \frac{3}{2 \times 2} + \frac{5}{2 \times 3} + \frac{3}{2 \times 2 \times 2} + \frac{1}{3}$$

Then the teacher may ask questions such as "Will a denominator that can be divided by 2 × 3 also be divisible by 3? Can a denominator that can be divided by 2 × 2 × 2 also be divided by 2 × 2?" Such questions cause the pupils to think of ways of reducing the number of factors needed for a common denominator. Usually pupils will suggest that because the answer to the question posed above is "yes," a common denominator for the following denominators may be found by eliminating factors that are repeated in other denominators. Thus,

$$4 = \cancel{2 \times 2}$$
$$8 = 2 \times 2 \times 2$$
$$6 = \cancel{2} \times 3$$
$$3 = \cancel{3}$$

The LCD = 2 × 2 × 2 × 3 = 24.

Another example is

$$\frac{5}{12} - \frac{7}{18}$$
$$12 = 2 \times 2 \times 3$$
$$ \rightarrow 2 \times 2 \times 3 \times 3 = 36, \text{ LCD}$$
$$18 = 2 \times 3 \times 3$$

Use of the greatest common divisor.[1]   The greatest common divisor (GCD) of two numbers is the largest number that divides both numbers. Thus 4 is the GCD of 8 and 20. The LCD or LCM can be found by dividing one of a pair of numbers by the GCD and multiplying the quotient by the other number. For example, the LCM of 8 and 20 is found by dividing 8 by the GCD (4) and multiplying the quotient (2) by 20—2 × 20 = 40. The LCM of 8 and 20 is 40.

[1] Suggested only as an enrichment topic.

This approach requires the teaching of a means of finding the GCD. The usual method of finding the GCD is to find the prime factors of the denominators, to determine the common prime factors, and to multiply the common prime factors. This approach to finding the GCD is illustrated below for the numbers 30 and 42.

$$30 \text{ prime factors} = 2 \times 3 \times 5$$
$$42 \text{ prime factors} = 2 \times 3 \times 7$$

GCD for 30, 42 is $2 \times 3 = 6$.

Thus the LCD of $\frac{5}{30}$ and $\frac{9}{42}$ may be found by dividing either 30 or 42 by the GCD, which in this case is 6, and then multiplying the quotient by the other denominator.

$$\frac{5}{30}, \frac{9}{42} \qquad 6)\overline{\frac{5}{30}} \qquad 5 \times 42 = 210$$

210 = LCD of 30 and 42.

The greatest common divisor may also be found by a process called the "Euclidean algorithm." This algorithm is a consequence of the distributive property and of the relationships between one number that "divides" another. Space does not permit a full development of the rationale of this algorithm,[2] but examples of its use are provided.

a. To find the GCD of 24 and 60 divide the smaller (24) into the larger (60). The remainder is 12. Divide the remainder into the original divisor. There is no remainder, thus 12 is the GCD of 24 and 60.

$$
\begin{array}{r}
2 \\
24\overline{)60} \\
48 \quad 2 \\
\overline{12\,)\,24} \\
24 \\
\overline{0}
\end{array}
$$

b. Find the GCD of 14 and 198. GCD of 14 and 198 is 2.

$$
\begin{array}{r}
4 \\
10 \\
14\overline{)198} \\
140 \\
\overline{58} \\
56 \quad 7 \\
\overline{2\,)\,14}
\end{array}
$$

Prime factors.   The addition of rationals also provides a "use" setting for work with factors and primes. Both are needed in working effectively with LCD. The

[2] For a more thorough treatment of the rationale of the LCM, the LCD, and the GCD see John A. Peterson and Joseph Hashisaki, *Theory of Arithmetic* (New York: Wiley, 1963), pp. 128–136; Francis J. Mueller, *Arithmetic: Its Structure and Concepts* (New York: Prentice-Hall, 1964), pp. 197–202; and Merline M. Ohmer and others, *Elementary Contemporary Mathematics* (Waltham, Mass.: Blaisdell Publishing Co., 1964), pp. 191–214.

study of factors and primes is important enough to be developed further as the student progresses in elementary school mathematics.

One teacher developed the topics by saying, "I noticed that many of you were experiencing difficulty in finding the smallest factors when we were finding the LCD yesterday. What did you notice about the smallest factors you could find for a number?——right——They were divisible only by 1 and themselves. Does anyone know what such a number is called?"

A check was made to determine the name of a number other than 1 that had only itself and 1 as factors. The pupils found that such a number was called a *prime number*. Their library work also established that a number with factors in addition to itself and 1 is called a *composite number;* and that 1 is not considered either prime or composite, but is called a unit.

The teacher suggested that it might be helpful to determine the various prime numbers less than 100 that can be used in work with the LCD. Each pupil was given a sheet of paper containing the numerals from 1 to 100 and the chance to try to find as many prime numbers as he could. The teacher said, "Think through the numbers. There are ways in which number patterns can be used to speed up this task. See if you can find some."

The pupils worked on the material for approximately fifteen minutes, after which the teacher asked, "Have any of you been able to determine methods of finding the prime number quickly?" The pupils made the following suggestions:

Ned: First I marked out 1 because we consider it as a unit, and it is neither prime nor composite. Every even number can be divided by 2, so every even number other than 2 must be a composite number. I marked out all of the even numbers except 2 on the chart. This gave me a start.

Jill: I did the same as Ned and then I decided to try the same idea with 3. Three is a prime number, and a multiple of 3 must be a composite.

~~1~~	2	3	~~4~~	5	~~6~~	7	~~8~~	~~9~~	~~10~~
11	~~12~~	13	~~14~~	~~15~~	~~16~~	17	~~18~~	19	~~20~~
~~21~~	~~22~~	23	~~24~~	25	~~26~~	~~27~~	~~28~~	29	~~30~~
31	~~32~~	~~33~~	~~34~~	35	~~36~~	37	~~38~~	~~39~~	~~40~~
41	~~42~~	43	~~44~~	~~45~~	~~46~~	47	~~48~~	49	~~50~~
51	~~52~~	53	~~54~~	55	~~56~~	~~57~~	~~58~~	59	~~60~~
61	~~62~~	~~63~~	~~64~~	65	~~66~~	67	~~68~~	69	~~70~~
71	~~72~~	73	~~74~~	~~75~~	~~76~~	77	~~78~~	79	~~80~~
~~81~~	~~82~~	83	~~84~~	85	~~86~~	~~87~~	~~88~~	89	~~90~~
91	~~92~~	~~93~~	~~94~~	95	~~96~~	97	~~98~~	99	~~100~~

The pupils took the lead from Jill and Ned and suggested, "The next prime number on the list is 5. Let's go through and mark out every multiple of 5 except 5 itself." The same line of thinking continued. The next day the completed charts were discussed. The pupils had found that it was necessary to strike out all multiples of 7, but that all of the remaining numbers were primes. There were 25 primes in all. The teacher directed the pupils to reference books in which they found that the class had "discovered" a method of finding prime factors that had been developed by Eratosthenes and called the *Sieve of Eratosthenes*. Note: The use of a reference source *after* pupils have had an opportunity to develop a procedure is a sound use of the guided discovery approach to mathematics teaching.

Sieve of Eratosthenes

2   3   4   5   6   7   8   9   10

11 12 13 14 15 16 17 18 19 20

21 22 23 24 25 26 27 28 29 30

31 32 33 34 35 36 37 38 39 40

41 42 43 44 45 46 47 48 49 50

51 52 53 54 55 56 57 58 59 60

61 62 63 64 65 66 67 68 69 70

71 72 73 74 75 76 77 78 79 80

81 82 83 84 85 86 87 88 89 90

91 92 93 94 95 96 97 98 99 100

The pupils can find the prime factors of a number by a series of factorings. For example,

$$27 = 3 \times 9 \qquad\qquad 40 = 5 \times 8$$
$$\text{or}$$
$$= 3 \times 3 \times 3 \qquad\qquad = 5 \times 2 \times 4$$
$$= 5 \times 2 \times 2 \times 2$$

As work continues with rationals, the teacher can provide further work with factors and primes. By the use of leading questions she can guide the pupils to discover the following generalizations:

1. If a prime number divides a product of two whole numbers, then it divides at least one of the numbers. (Prime-product theorem.)

2. Any common multiple of a pair of numbers is also a multiple of their lowest common multiple.

3. Every composite number can be expressed uniquely as a product of primes. (The fundamental theorem of arithmetic.) This theorem verifies that there is only one way to completely factor a given number.

TEACHING SUBTRACTION OF RATIONAL NUMBERS

Previously it was suggested that the subtraction of whole numbers should begin several days after the addition of whole numbers. In the case of rational numbers, subtraction may well be introduced the same day as addition. This is because pupils at this level should have a good understanding of the relationship between addition and subtraction, and the techniques involved in addition and subtraction of rational numbers are very similar.

The foundation work in subtraction goes hand in hand with that of addition. Emphasis should be placed upon the three types of subtraction situations, take-away, comparison, and how many more are needed.

If the additive type of renaming situation is used in whole number work, it should be continued in work with rationals. The illustration below compares additive thinking with take-away thinking.

Take-away	Additive
$17\frac{1}{2} = 17\frac{6}{12} = 16\frac{18}{12}$	$17\frac{1}{2} = 17\frac{6}{12} = 17\frac{18}{12}$
$-5\frac{2}{3} = 5\frac{8}{12} = 5\frac{8}{12}$	$-5\frac{2}{3} = 5\frac{8}{12} = 6\frac{8}{12}$
$11\frac{10}{12} = 11\frac{5}{6}$	$11\frac{10}{12} = 11\frac{5}{6}$

The teacher can also develop a process for non-pencil and paper computation with rationals by using the same format as that for addition. The algorithm for subtraction becomes the following:

$$\frac{2}{3} - \frac{3}{5} = \frac{(2 \times 5) - (3 \times 3)}{3 \times 5} = \frac{10 - 9}{15} = \frac{1}{15}$$

or

$$\frac{a}{b} - \frac{c}{d} = \frac{(a \times d) - (b \times c)}{(b \times d)} = \frac{ad - bc}{bd}$$

Subtraction such as $\frac{1}{2} - \frac{3}{4} = \square$ is not usually taught in the elementary school. However, it can be developed intuitively with the number line and verbal problem situations.

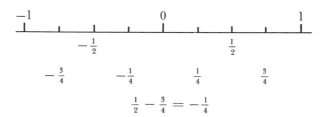

MULTIPLICATION OF RATIONAL NUMBERS

Multiplication is the simplest of the fundamental operations with rational numbers if the major criterion is the ability to perform computation. The definition of the product of two rational numbers is

$$\frac{a}{b} \times \frac{c}{d} = \frac{ac}{bd},$$

which is also the form used for the typical algorithm. This apparent simplicity is misleading for two reasons.

1. The several fractional and mixed forms have different physical world interpretations. They are illustrated by: (a) $5 \times \frac{2}{3} = N$; (b) $\frac{2}{3} \times 5 = N$; (c) $\frac{2}{3} \times \frac{4}{5} = N$; (d) $1\frac{1}{2} \times 6 = N$; (e) $4 \times 1\frac{3}{8} = N$; (f) $4\frac{1}{2} \times \frac{3}{4} = N$; (g) $\frac{1}{2} \times 2\frac{1}{2} = N$; (h) $2\frac{3}{4} \times 5\frac{2}{3} = N$. Although (a) and (b), (d) and (e), and (f) and (g) are applications of commutativity, they still do not fit the same physical world situation.

2. While a series of additions interprets all physical world situations dealing with whole number multiplication, this is not true for work with rationals. The multiplication of $\frac{1}{2} \times 4$ or $\frac{1}{2}$ of 4 is closely related to partition division. Instead of taking the multiplicand a number of times, the problem is to find a part of the multiplicand. The form $\frac{2}{3} \times \frac{3}{4}$ is also not related to a series of additions but may be better considered in terms of arrays or areas.

Effective understanding requires that the pupil have a good grasp of three of the forms above: $4 \times \frac{1}{2} = N$; $\frac{2}{3} \times \frac{1}{2} = N$; $\frac{1}{2} \times 4 = N$. It is suggested that multiplication of rational numbers be taught in this order. With this understanding and further work, the other forms can be understood. An introductory lesson for each of the three types is provided to illustrate the guided-discovery procedure for multiplication and to aid the reader in analyzing the different interpretations.

Finding products like $5 \times \frac{2}{3} = N$

Multiplication involving the form $5 \times \frac{2}{3} = N$ was introduced with the following statement: "Write a mathematical sentence that illustrates each of the problems on the duplicated sheet and then solve the problems. Try to verify your answer to each problem by working it in a different way. The first problem is, 'Ann was asked to bake 5 batches of cookies for a club bake sale. If each batch requires $\frac{2}{3}$ cup of sugar, how much sugar will she need for the 5 batches of cookies?' "

Pupils were encouraged to use as many methods as possible to solve the problems. Several pupils were asked to put one of their solutions on overhead projector mounts. (The chalkboard could have been used). Their methods and explanations follow.

Hoyt: The mathematical sentence was $5 \times \frac{2}{3} = N$. I decided that I could find 5 groups of $\frac{2}{3}$'s by adding.

$$\begin{array}{r} \frac{2}{3} \\ \frac{2}{3} \\ \frac{2}{3} \\ \frac{2}{3} \\ \frac{2}{3} \\ \hline \frac{10}{3} \end{array} = 3\frac{1}{3} \text{ cups}$$

Joyce: I wrote the same mathematical sentence and then used the number line to solve the problem.

$3\frac{1}{3}$ cups

Kit: I rewrote the mathematical sentence to read 5×2 thirds $= N$. I worked the problem as we have tens and ones. So, 5 times 2 thirds $= 10$ thirds or $3\frac{1}{3}$.

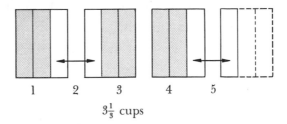

Scott: I used a drawing of
a rectangular region.

$$3\tfrac{1}{3} \text{ cups}$$

I've also shown how a circular region could be used.

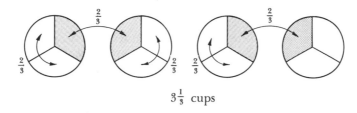

$$3\tfrac{1}{3} \text{ cups}$$

May: I used the number line first and then studied the mathematical sentence, $5 \times \tfrac{2}{3} = N$. I decided that I could find the answer by multiplying the numerators and then dividing by the denominator.

The class accepted all of the solutions as being logical. They preferred the use of addition and the number line to represent the situations. The multiplication method suggested by May was considered to be the most efficient. The next day the pupils used the method suggested by May to work a number of multiplication exercises and a drawing, adding, or the number line to verify their answers.

Analysis. The process of development described above has several features: (1) the multiplication of $5 \times \tfrac{2}{3} = N$ can be closely identified with whole number multiplication and is thus understandable for the large majority of pupils; (2) The use of the verbal problems provides a setting which points out the need for multiplication and also allows the pupils to abstract from a physical world setting; (3) the use of multiple solutions allows for individual creativity and confidence.

Finding products like $\tfrac{1}{2} \times \tfrac{3}{3} = N$

The study of this multiplication type was introduced with directions to write the mathematical sentence and to solve the problem that follows in as many ways as pupils could develop.

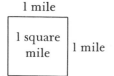

Land is often divided into square regions that are 1 mile by 1 mile. The park is to occupy a portion of a 1-square mile section which is $\tfrac{1}{2}$ mile wide and $\tfrac{2}{3}$ mile long. What fraction of a square mile will the park occupy?

Drawings were typically used by the pupils to find an answer to the mathematical sentence, which they identified as $\frac{1}{2} \times \frac{2}{3} = N$. Two solutions provided by pupils are shown below.

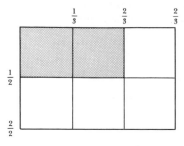

Ralph: I made a drawing of the square region. The park occupies 2 out of 6 parts of the square mile. The answer is $\frac{2}{6}$ or $\frac{1}{3}$ of a square mile.

Perry: I worked the problem the same way and then went back and looked at the mathematical sentence $\frac{1}{2} \times \frac{2}{3} = N$. I notice that by multiplying numerators by numerators and denominators by denominators the result is the correct answer, $\frac{2}{6}$. I want to explore this further.

During the next few days the pupils worked problems and exercises involving the multiplication of a fraction times a fraction. Their study verified that the product of a fractional multiplication could be found by multiplying the numerator by the numerator and the denominator by the denominator. The pupils generalized their "rule" by the use of frames and letters to

$$\frac{\square}{\triangle} \times \frac{\bigcirc}{\triangle} = \frac{\square\bigcirc}{\triangle\triangle}; \frac{a}{b} \times \frac{c}{d} = \frac{ac}{bd}.$$

The multiplication of fractions such as $\frac{4}{3} \times \frac{3}{2}$ causes little difficulty in computation. Such multiplications are difficult to rationalize. If we consider the park problem discussed above in terms of square regions, the problem becomes that of finding $\frac{4}{3}$ of $\frac{3}{2}$ of a region. The following diagrams illustrate this situation:

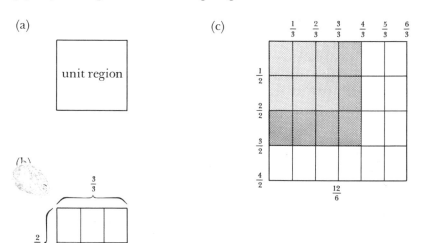

Diagram C illustrates that $\frac{4}{3} \times \frac{3}{2} = 12$ parts of a unit region that contains 6 parts. Thus, the denominator is named by the number of parts in a unit region.

Analysis.   The approach featured the use of rectangular regions to find the products. This relates this phase of rational number multiplication to the earlier work with whole number multiplication in which arrays were used to find the cross-products of sets. The use of rectangular regions is superior to the use of circles because circles cause great difficulty when fractions naming a number greater than one are used. Also circles are not as representative of physical world situations requiring multiplication in the form $\frac{a}{b} \times \frac{c}{d}$. Thus, circles do not as readily lead to pupil discovery.

Finding products like $\frac{1}{2} \times 8 = N$

This multiplication type was introduced with the following problem: A science club of 8 members was visiting the observatory. The astronomer said, "I can take only $\frac{1}{2}$ of the club at a time on the observation platform." How many members could go to the platform at a time?

When asked to write the mathematical sentence, to solve the problem, and to verify their answers, the pupils used the following procedures:

Nancy: I was to find $\frac{1}{2}$ of 8. Finding $\frac{1}{2}$ of something is breaking it into 2 equal parts. I drew a picture of the set of club members and made 2 equivalent subsets.

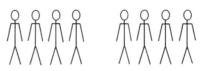

Jill: I drew 8 circles to represent the club members. Then I broke each into $\frac{1}{2}$; that is, I took $\frac{1}{2}$ of each and then I combined the one-halves. My answer is 4.

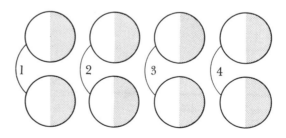

The class agreed that both situations found an answer, but that Nancy's drawing represented the physical world situation.

The pupils were not sure of the mathematical sentence involved. The majority felt that the sentence was $\frac{1}{2} \times 8 = N$. Others thought that they were really finding $8 \div 2 = N$.

Problems that used $\frac{2}{3} \times 6 = N$, $\frac{5}{6} \times 12 = N$, and $\frac{3}{5} \times 14 = N$ were given to the group. The pupils still seemed to experience some difficulty in identifying the problems as multiplication situations.

Questioning and continuing discussion during the lessons that followed helped the pupils to identify the following generalizations:

1. The multiplication $\frac{2}{3} \times 6 = N$ is the numerical equivalent of $6 \times \frac{2}{3} = N$ because of the commutative property. If $6 \times \frac{2}{3} = N$ can be thought of as $\frac{2}{3} + \frac{2}{3} + \frac{2}{3} + \frac{2}{3} + \frac{2}{3} + \frac{2}{3}$, we may think of $\frac{2}{3} \times 6$ as meaning the use of 6 as an addend less than one time. Thus we multiply by 2 and divide by 3.

2. In the lower grades, $\frac{1}{3}$ of a number is found by dividing by 3. To find $\frac{2}{3}$ of a number we can divide by 3 and then multiply by 2, or multiply by 2 and then divide by 3.

3. When we multiply by a number less than 1, we are looking for a part of a number. Problem situations for $\frac{1}{2} \times 6$ are usually stated, "Find $\frac{1}{2}$ of 6." When a fraction with a numerator of 1 such as $\frac{1}{5}$ is involved, the unit fraction is the multiplicative inverse of 5. Thus, multiplication by $\frac{1}{5}$ is equivalent to division by 5. The pupils can be aided in achieving an intuitive understanding of this concept. They are then taught that "of" means "times." An effort should be made to develop an understanding of this idea. Too often pupils multiply any time they see the word "of" in a problem.

4. Another difficulty is the need for pupils to realize that when they are multiplying rational numbers, the product is not always greater than either factor. The teacher needs to stress analysis such as $\frac{1}{2} \times \frac{1}{4} = \frac{1}{8}$. Why? Note the area of a region $\frac{1}{2}$ by $\frac{1}{4}$ units; remember that $\frac{1}{2}$ of 6 was 3. That was the same as dividing by 2. One-half of $\frac{1}{4}$ would be the same as dividing $\frac{1}{4}$ by 2.

Analysis. Basically the same format was followed as in the other forms of multiplication. It is important to remember that problems involving the form $\frac{3}{4} \times 8 = \square$ are easy to compute but hard to understand. Often many class discussions are necessary before this phase of fractional multiplication is understood.

Use of the identity element for multiplication

Pupils intuitively make use of the property of the identity element for multiplication long before a formal analysis is needed. For example, pupils multiply both the numerator and denominator of $\frac{3}{4}$ by 2 to change the fraction to $\frac{6}{8}$ before they are familiar with multiplication of rational numbers.

Soon after multiplication of rational numbers is introduced, several problem situations involving computation such as $\frac{4}{4} \times \frac{3}{4} = N$ and $\frac{3}{3} \times \frac{2}{3} = N$ may be given. Then a guided discussion can bring out the idea that a renaming has occurred because $\frac{3}{4} = \frac{12}{16}$ and $\frac{2}{3} = \frac{6}{9}$. Pupils should then be led to note that both $\frac{4}{4}$ and $\frac{3}{3}$ are other names for 1. Thus, what has occurred has been to change the name of a number by multiplying, using a form of the identity element for multiplication.

Further work should provide pupils with an opportunity to discover that both numerator and denominator can be divided by the same number to change a fraction to *lowest terms*. (A fraction is considered to be in lowest terms when the numerator and denominator of a fraction have no common factor other than 1.) Thus,

$$\frac{9}{12} = \frac{9 \div 3}{12 \div 3} = \frac{3}{4}.$$

Also, factoring may be used to change a fraction to lowest terms. For example,

$$\frac{9}{12} = \frac{3 \times 3}{3 \times 2 \times 2} = \frac{3}{4}.$$

Elementary school pupils should have many opportunities to develop equivalent fractions by using various names for 1. Three representative type exercises are shown below.

Names for Rational Numbers

(a)

| $\frac{3}{5}$ | $\frac{1 \times 3}{1 \times 5}$ | $\frac{2 \times 3}{2 \times 5}$ | $\frac{3 \times 3}{3 \times 5}$ | $\frac{4 \times 3}{4 \times 5}$ |

$\frac{3}{5}$ □ □ □

(b) $\{\frac{2}{3}, \frac{4}{6}, \underline{\quad}, \underline{\quad}, \underline{\quad}, \ldots\}$

(c) Name the points on the number line.

$$\frac{1}{4} \qquad \square$$
$$\frac{2}{8} \qquad \square$$
$$\square \qquad \square$$

Then pupils should indicate the point on a number line named by each set of equivalent fractions. Pupils then should find (by discussion and checking references) that each set of equivalent fractions names one rational number and one point on the number line. They also should find out that although each rational number has many names, the fraction in its lowest terms is usually used to name the number.

DIVISION OF RATIONAL NUMBERS

Teaching the division of rationals has always caused difficulty for teachers and students. In fact, at one time, writers who were interested principally in the social utility of arithmetic topics suggested that division using fractions might well be deleted from the arithmetic curriculum. In recent years, most authorities on the teaching of elementary school mathematics have agreed that the study of division is valuable for its mathematical contribution. Knowledge of the process is essential to the study of algebra, and it is often used in the scientific fields.

Up to 1945, many writers maintained that pupils in the upper elementary grades could not be expected to understand the rationale behind inverting the divisor in division involving fractions and therefore should be taught the rule or mechanics of this computational short-cut.[3] Research and classroom use since 1945 indicate that the inversion procedure can be justified.

As in the case of multiplication, six forms of division involve fractions, mixed forms, and whole numbers. The six forms can be illustrated by the following examples: (1) $6 \div \frac{3}{4} = \square$; (2) $\frac{3}{4} \div 6 = \square$; (3) $\frac{3}{4} \div \frac{1}{6} = \square$; (4) $6\frac{1}{2} \div \frac{3}{4} = \square$; (5) $\frac{3}{4} \div 6\frac{1}{2} = \square$; and (6) $6\frac{1}{2} \div 1\frac{1}{2} = \square$. The most universal type is that of form (3), $\frac{3}{4} \div \frac{1}{6} = \square$. If the development of computational skill in division were the only criterion, this form would be the most logical for introductory purposes, for all of the other forms can be converted to it. However, if we believe that pupil discovery and understanding of the relationship between rationals and whole numbers are important, study should begin with form (1), $6 \div \frac{3}{4} = \square$.

Two major methods of developing understanding of the inversion procedure are in use today, the common denominator approach[4] and the reciprocal approach.[5] Each procedure has its advocates and valid reasons to support it.

Because the use of multiple solutions to problems and exercises is a valuable learning procedure, it is suggested that neither the common denominator method nor the reciprocal method be discarded; both can be used in developing the process of division. The illustrative lessons that follow describe a means of making use of both procedures.[6]

Foundation work

In the primary grades the pupils should be given an opportunity to answer questions such as "Alice has 5 apples. How many pieces will she have if she divides each one into halves?" The number line, actual objects, models, drawings, and diagrams prove useful in solving such problems.

In addition to the intuitive development of ideas concerning division, a knowledge of the multiplicative inverse of a rational (the reciprocal) is useful if a guided discovery approach is to be taken. During the study of the multiplication of rationals a teacher used the following procedure:

"Before you came in this morning, I drew a picture of four rectangular regions on the board and indicated their lengths and widths. (See below.) Take a few minutes and find the area of each rectangular region."

[3] J. A. Hickerson, *Guiding Children's Arithmetic Experiences* (New York: Prentice-Hall, 1952), p. 236.
[4] H. F. Spitzer, *The Teaching of Arithmetic*, 3rd ed. (Boston: Houghton Mifflin, 1961), pp. 191–196.
[5] M. L. Hartung, H. Van Engen, L. Knowles, and E. G. Gibb, *Charting the Course for Arithmetic* (Chicago: Scott, Foresman, 1960), pp. 140–143.
[6] Part of the material that follows has been adopted from A. J. Shryock and A. Riedesel, "The Use of the Common Denominator and the Reciprocal in Dividing Fractions," *School Science and Mathematics*, Vol. LXIV, No. 1 (January 1964), pp. 53–59.

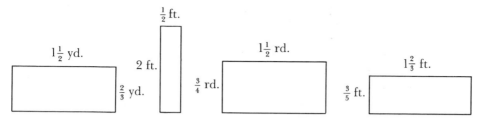

After a few minutes four pupils were asked to show their solutions on the board. After the checking of solutions, several pupils asked about the reason for each area being equal to one square unit. The teacher asked whether anyone could find a reason for this unusual result. Although several pupils immediately felt that they knew the answer, the teacher waited a few minutes to provide ample time for most of the class members to notice any similarity in the problems. Then one of the pupils explained, "In each problem such as $\frac{3}{2} \times \frac{2}{3}$ the numerator of each fraction is the denominator of the other fraction. In such cases the product is equal to 1."

By referring to a book suggested by the teacher, the class found that two rational numbers whose product equals 1 are the *reciprocal* of each other. They also found that these two numbers are considered the *multiplicative inverse* of each other because their product is always a name for the identity element for multiplication (1). Several exercises were given in which the pupils were to find the reciprocals of fractions and mixed forms.[7]

Introducing the division of rational numbers

The teacher introduced division by saying, "You each have received a sheet of verbal problems. First write the mathematical sentence that you would use in solving the problems and then use anything we've learned so far to solve the problems. When you've solved a problem, try to check your work by using another method. Try to solve each problem in as many ways as you can." The first two problems are shown below.

1. A rocket of the future is being designed to carry a pay load of 6 tons of scientific equipment. One of the present rockets carries a pay load of $\frac{3}{4}$ of a ton. How many of the old rockets are needed to carry a load equal to the experimental rocket?

2. Peg wanted to make ribbon streamers $\frac{2}{3}$ of a yard long for her bicycle handle bars. She had 6 yards of ribbon. How many streamers $\frac{2}{3}$ of a yard long could she get from 6 yards?

During the next few minutes the children worked on the problems as the teacher moved about the room and gave individual help. When a pupil had a

---

[7] Note: The above lesson may appear out of place in a development of division of fractions. However, the need for such a preliminary lesson will become evident in the material that follows.

question, the usual procedure was for the teacher to ask the child a question about a similar problem involving whole numbers. Quite often a problem that asked how many 3's equal 12 was employed. The use of the number line was also suggested. After noting that some pupils were experiencing difficulty, the teacher said, "I want to call your attention to something in the first problem. The old rockets carry $\frac{3}{4}$ of a ton. The new rocket carries 6 tons. Some of you haven't figured out the mathematical sentence that can be used to solve the problem. What is the mathematical sentence?"

The answer, "How many $\frac{3}{4}$'s equal 6, or $6 \div \frac{3}{4} = N$," was given by a pupil. As the period continued, the teacher asked several pupils to put their solutions to the problems on the board. Some of the explanations are presented below.

Bill: When you use the number line, you count $\frac{3}{4}$'s each time; and when you get to 6, you count the number of times you have the $\frac{3}{4}$.

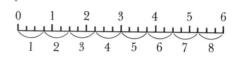

Larry: Look at the diagram. The experimental rocket will hold 6 tons. The old rocket will hold $\frac{3}{4}$ of a ton. The mathematical question is "How many $\frac{3}{4}$'s equal 6?" Each ton will hold the load of an old rocket. I have 6 tons so I count—1, 2, 3, 4, 5, 6. I have 2 groups of $\frac{3}{4}$ that I haven't used so the new rocket will hold the payload of 8 rockets of the old model.

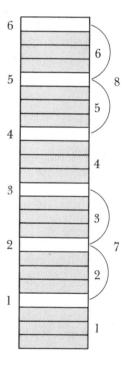

Kathy: The problem is, "How many $\frac{3}{4}$'s equal 6?" I set the problem up this way: I didn't know how to divide using a fraction and a whole number so I changed 6 to $\frac{24}{4}$ and divided $\frac{3}{4}$ into $\frac{24}{4}$. Really this is the same as 6 divided by $\frac{3}{4}$ because $6 = \frac{24}{4}$.

$$\frac{3}{4}\overline{)6} = \frac{3}{4}\overline{)\frac{24}{4}}^{\,8}$$

Matt: Kathy might have written the problem this way: 3 fourths $\overline{)\,24\text{ fourths.}}$

Janet:

①   ②   ③   ④

$\frac{3}{4} + \frac{3}{4} = 1\frac{1}{2}\,;$ $1\frac{1}{2} + \frac{3}{4} = 2\frac{1}{4}\,;$ $2\frac{1}{4} + \frac{3}{4} = 3$

⑤   ⑥   ⑦   ⑧

$3 + \frac{3}{4} = 3\frac{3}{4}\,;$ $3\frac{3}{4} + \frac{3}{4} = 4\frac{1}{2}\,;$ $4\frac{1}{2} + \frac{3}{4} = 5\frac{1}{4}\,;$ $5\frac{1}{4} + \frac{3}{4} = 6$

8 loads

The various methods used to solve the problems were discussed, and Kathy's method (the common denominator method) was used to solve a number of problems. Some time was spent discussing why Kathy's method worked. Then the teacher directed the children to work another set of problems using the method which they considered best and a different method.

Further development

The next day the teacher said, "Remember that Kathy wrote the mathematical sentence, 'How many $\frac{3}{4}$'s equal 6?' as $\frac{3}{4}\overline{)\,6}$ and $\frac{3}{4}\overline{)\,\frac{24}{4}}$. Are there other ways that we could write this mathematical sentence?"

The following ways of writing the mathematical sentence were suggested by the pupils:

$$6 \div \frac{3}{4} = \square \qquad \frac{6}{\frac{3}{4}} = \square \qquad \frac{\frac{24}{4}}{\frac{3}{4}} = \square.$$

Then the teacher said, "Let's solve $\frac{24}{4} \div \frac{3}{4} = \square$." The common solution given was $\frac{24}{4} \div \frac{3}{4} = 8$.

The teacher then asked, "What steps could we write between the $\frac{24}{4} \div \frac{3}{4}$ and the $\frac{8}{1}$?" One pupil suggested that another step could be written

$$\frac{24 \div 3}{4 \div 4} = \frac{\frac{24}{3}}{\frac{4}{4}} = \frac{\frac{24}{3}}{\frac{1}{1}} = 8$$

The teacher directed the class members to work several problems using several of the techniques. Then she called the attention of the pupils to the solutions written in the fractional form and asked, "What allowed us to solve the number question written as $\frac{\frac{24}{3}}{\frac{4}{4}}$?" One pupil said that the denominator always equaled 1.

Next the teacher directed the pupils to the problem of writing a mathematical sentence for $7 \div \frac{2}{3} = \square$, which is in fractional form. They were also to attempt to solve it by using a new approach and to check it by using one of the approaches they had learned. After she had allowed a short time for the pupils to work, she said, "What is the mathematical sentence when it is written in fractional form?" The majority of the class had written the mathematical sentence as $\frac{7}{\frac{2}{3}} = \square$. The teacher said, "Have any of you worked the problem without using the common denominator approach, subtraction, or drawings?"

First alternate procedure (If the children were not able to solve the mathematical sentence without using the previous approaches). The teacher said, "Let's look at the mathematical sentence for a minute. $\frac{7}{\frac{2}{3}} = \square$. Remember the mathematical sentence $\frac{\frac{24}{3}}{\frac{4}{4}} = \square$. Now can you think of a way that we might solve this mathematical sentence?"

One pupil suggested that if the denominator could be made 1, the mathematical sentence could be solved. Another remembered that they had multiplied numbers such as $\frac{2}{3}$ by $\frac{3}{2}$ and got an answer of 1 when they had been working with area, so he suggested that the denominator could be multiplied by $\frac{3}{2}$. Another pupil said, "If you multiply the denominator by $\frac{3}{2}$ you must also multiply the numerator by $\frac{3}{2}$."

$$\frac{7 \times \frac{3}{2}}{\frac{2}{3} \times \frac{3}{2}} = \square$$

After more discussion, several problems were worked in that manner and then checked by the common denominator method. At that time the teacher said, "Have any of you found a way to shorten this method?" Bill suggested, "In the mathematical sentence $\frac{8}{\frac{3}{4}} = \square$ I can solve the mathematical sentence by multiplying the 8 by $\frac{4}{3}$ and just forgetting the denominator."

The teacher asked, "Will Bill's method always work? Why does it work?" The pupils found that in all of the cases they tested that the procedure did give a correct answer. They reasoned that this was because both the numerator and denominator can be multiplied by the same number because it is a form of multiplication by the identity element (1). The denominator obtained after the multiplication would always be 1. Division by 1 does not change the dividend.

Several other problems and examples were worked using Bill's method. Then the teacher directed the students to look in their books and compare the suggestions with Bill's method.

Second alternate procedure (If the children did solve the problem in another way). Jack said, "I remembered that when we worked with area we had several problems in which we multiplied numbers such as $\frac{2}{3}$ by $\frac{3}{2}$ and got an answer of 1. I worked the number question $\frac{7}{\frac{2}{3}} = \square$ in the following manner: I multiplied

$\frac{2}{3}$ by $\frac{3}{2}$ and got an answer of 1. I have to also multiply the numerator by the same number to keep an equivalent fraction. The problem became $7 \times \frac{3}{2} = \square$."

After several other examples were worked in the same manner and the class had discussed the approach, the teacher said, "Turn to your arithmetic books and compare the explanation there with ours."

The pupils should not be rushed into the rule, "To divide, invert the divisor and then multiply." The below average student might just as well use the common denominator method because it is understandable. The pupils who will use inversion should spend a good deal of time writing out the complete rationale rather than using the short-cut procedure. Thus, for the first week of division the format

$$\frac{2}{3} \div \frac{5}{6} =$$

$$\frac{\frac{2}{3} \times \frac{6}{5}}{\frac{5}{6} \times \frac{6}{5}} = \frac{\frac{12}{15}}{\frac{30}{30}} = \frac{12}{15} = \frac{4}{5}$$

should be used, rather than

$$\frac{2}{3} \div \frac{5}{6} =$$

$$\frac{2}{3} \times \frac{6}{5} = \frac{12}{15} = \frac{4}{5}.$$

Several advantages of this combined approach to teaching the division of rational numbers can be noted.

1. The inherent strengths of the common denominator method are utilized.
   a. The opportunity for pupil exploration is presented so that the children may figure out relationships.
   b. Early use of the common denominator method allows children to identify rational number division with whole number division, aiding understanding of the processes.
   c. The common denominator is understandable and is a good method to use in proving that answers are correct, once inversion has been developed.
2. The strengths of the reciprocal method are utilized.
   a. Reciprocals are used to rationalize that the inversion procedure is mathematically sound and precise.
   b. The reciprocal aids the pupils to see that inversion is in the reality only a short-cut procedure.
3. The procedure described in the illustrative lessons makes use of a guided discovery scheme in which pupil participation is emphasized. In most suggested procedures for using the reciprocal method the children are told how to use it.

Because of the advantages offered by a multiple approach to the introduction of rational number division, it is suggested that teachers experiment with this procedure and develop further refinements.

Division without pencil and paper

The multiplication of rationals without pencil and paper is relatively simple. However, because of the necessity of either finding a common denominator or inverting, the division of rationals without pencil and paper is often difficult. There is a procedure which allows for ease in non-pencil and paper work with the division of fractions. Rather than invert, the pupils can take the cross-products of the number pairs. For example,

$$\frac{5}{9} \mathbin{\overset{\div}{\times}} \frac{3}{4} = N \qquad\qquad \frac{3}{5} \mathbin{\overset{\div}{\times}} \frac{8}{9} = N$$

$$\frac{5}{9} \mathbin{\overset{\div}{\times}} \frac{3}{4} = \frac{20}{27} \qquad\qquad \frac{3}{5} \mathbin{\overset{\div}{\times}} \frac{8}{9} = \frac{27}{40}$$

$$(a) \qquad\qquad\qquad (b)$$

This procedure is actually the mathematical definition of the division of rationals

$$\left(\frac{a}{b} \div \frac{c}{d} = \frac{a \times d}{b \times c} \right).$$

Pupils can normally discover this procedure if the teacher writes several division computations on the chalkboard and proceeds to write down the answers quickly. In trying to figure out why the teacher can solve the division this quickly, the pupils begin to note the cross-product relationship.

SIMPLIFICATION OF MULTIPLICATION AND DIVISION

The simplification of multiplication and division (after inversion has occurred) is usually referred to as *cancellation*. Two examples of simplification or cancellation are

$$\overset{1}{\cancel{6}} \times \frac{7}{\underset{3}{\cancel{9}}} = \frac{7}{6} = 1\frac{1}{6} \qquad\qquad \frac{\overset{1}{\cancel{2}}}{\underset{1}{\cancel{3}}} \times \frac{\overset{2}{\cancel{8}}}{\underset{4}{\cancel{8}}} = \frac{2}{4} = \frac{1}{2}$$

Pupils often indiscriminately cross out numerals in inappropriate situations, such as in division before the divisor has been inverted. Difficulties with cancellation may be caused by incomplete handling of the reason for cancellation in textbooks and by poor foundation work in multiplication of rational numbers.

A careful study of cancellation reveals that applications of the basic properties of mathematics are involved. In multiplying $\frac{2}{3} \times \frac{3}{4} = N$, it should be remembered that when the multiplication involving rationals is performed, whole numbers are used; that is,

$$\frac{2 \times 3}{3 \times 4} = \frac{6}{12} = \frac{1}{2}.$$

To simplify $\frac{6}{12}$ we have divided by a form of the multiplicative identity element 1:

$$\frac{6 \div 6}{12 \div 6} = \frac{1}{2}.$$

To cancel in the original computation, the commutative property and the property of the identity element can be used to change the form of the fractions.

$$\frac{2 \times 3}{3 \times 4} = \frac{3 \times 2}{3 \times 4} = \frac{3 \times (2 \div 2)}{3 \times (4 \div 2)} = \frac{1 \times 1}{1 \times 2} = \frac{1}{2}$$

Factoring also provides an excellent means of cancelling. It provides another look at cancellation and is also an important preparation for algebra. Factoring may be used in the following manner:

First Time: $\dfrac{2}{3} \times \dfrac{3}{4} = \dfrac{3 \times 2}{3 \times 4} = \dfrac{3 \times 2 \times 1}{3 \times 2 \times 2} = \dfrac{3}{3} \times \dfrac{2}{2} \times \dfrac{1}{2} = \dfrac{1}{2}$

Second Time: $\dfrac{2}{3} \times \dfrac{3}{4} = \dfrac{2}{3} \times \dfrac{3}{2 \times 2} = \dfrac{1 \times 1}{1 \times 2} = \dfrac{1}{2}$

To avoid many of the problems of cancellation, it is suggested that cancellation be delayed until the pupils understand operations on fractions with all of the fundamental operations. The use of cancellation may well be delayed for several months after the multiplication of fractions is introduced. Also, developing cancellation in a guided discovery manner should help pupils identify the significant aspects of the process. In conjunction with this development, the teacher can ask the pupils to make use of the basic mathematical properties to verify that cancellation is "legal."

THE MULTIPLICATION-DIVISION RELATIONSHIP

The relationship of division as the inverse of multiplication provides a ready check for division of rational numbers. Pupils should be encouraged to discover methods of checking division problems and exercises. The previous work on whole number multiplication and division should provide students with a lead in developing the idea that $8 \div \frac{2}{3} = 12$ may be checked by multiplying $12 \times \frac{2}{3} = \square$. If pupils do not discover this relationship, it may easily be developed by a series of guided questions.

STUDY SUGGESTIONS

1. Develop a set of verbal problems for use with the division of rational numbers. Identify which problems are measurement division and which ones are partition division.
2. Analyze the approach taken by three children's textbooks to the development of understanding of rational number division.
3. Prepare a statement that you could make to help a pupil who says, "I don't understand why taking $\frac{2}{3}$ of 6 is multiplying $\frac{2}{3} \times 6$. Why do I get an answer smaller than 6? I think this is division."
4. Using the Egyptian or Babylonian system of fractions prepare a set of enrichment materials for fractions. (See the reference to D. E. Smith in the bibliography).
5. Prepare a mathematics theme on "Understanding Fractions."
6. Develop a "fraction kit" for use in teaching.
7. Try to develop an abacus that could be used with fractional work.

SUGGESTED REFERENCES

Banks, J. Houston, *Learning and Teaching Arithmetic*, 2nd ed. (Boston: Allyn and Bacon, 1964), pp. 291–319.

Buckingham, B. R., *Elementary Artihmetic: Its Meaning and Practice* (Boston: Ginn, 1947), Chap. 9.

Grossnickle, Foster E., and Brueckner, Leo J., *Discovering Meanings in Elementary School Mathematics*, 4th ed. (New York: Holt, Rinehart and Winston, 1963), Chaps. 10 and 11.

Mueller, Francis J., *Arithmetic: Its Structure and Concepts*, 2nd ed. (New York: Prentice-Hall, 1964), Chap. 4.

School Mathematics Study Group, *Mathematics for the Elementary School, Teachers' Commentary, Grade Five*, Parts I and II, *Grade Six*, Parts II and III (New Haven: Yale University Press, 1963).

Spitzer, Herbert F., *The Teaching of Arithmetic*, 3rd ed. (Boston: Houghton Mifflin, 1961), Chap. 7.

USE OF SUGGESTED REFERENCES

1. How does Banks relate "Fractions" to "Rational" numbers?
2. Check Buckingham's texts for alternate solutions to operations with fractions. Also study his treatment of checking.
3. Use the text of Grossnickle and Brueckner to develop a list of teaching aids for fractions.
4. Study Mueller's treatment of a fraction as a numeral.
5. Compare the treatment given in the *School Mathematics Study Group Materials* with a textbook published before 1960; with a textbook published during the current year.
6. Use the text of Spitzer and Banks to prepare a list of common difficulties encountered in teaching fractions.

9

Decimals, exponents,
and numeration systems

DECIMALS

Modern interpretation

In the context of today's mathematics, decimals taught in the elementary school may be considered as another name for rational numbers. Thus the numeral $\frac{3}{4}$ and the decimal .75 both represent the same rational number.

Historical development

The Babylonians were the first people to develop a system of fractions which used exclusively a multiple or power of the base as the denominator. Because the Babylonians used a base of sixty, a sexagesimal (sek·sa·jes·a·mal), the denominators of their fractions were multiples of 60, such as $\frac{3}{60}$ and $\frac{45}{3600}$. The sexagesimal fraction was still used for scientific purposes during the Middle Ages. During that period, 2 hours 20 minutes 45 seconds was written $2 - \frac{20}{60} - \frac{45}{3600}$ hours, rather than $2 + \frac{1}{3} + \frac{1}{80}$ hours.[1]

The decimal method of writing fractions was developed during the Middle Ages. The Middle Eastern astronomer and mathematician al-Kashî (early 1400's) used the characters *Sah-hah* 1415926535898732. Translating the *sah-hah* gives:

Integer

3   14159....[2]

Several European mathematicians used a form of decimals in the early sixteenth century. The first published explanation of the decimal fraction ap-

[1] From *History of Mathematics* by D. E. Smith, Vol. II, p. 228. Copyright 1953 by Eva May Luce Smith. Published by Dover Publications, Inc., New York 14, N. Y. at $5.00, and reprinted through permission of the publisher.
[2] *Ibid.*, pp. 238–239.

peared in 1585 in the book *La Disme* by Simon Stevin, a Flemish mathematician. Stevin would have written 7.564 as 7 $_0$ 5 $_1$ 6 $_2$ 4 $_3$. Later writers used the following forms:

$$7, 5' 6'' 4'''; \quad 7 \overline{/ 564}; \quad 7 / \overset{123 \quad \cdots}{564}; \quad 7 / \underline{564}$$

The writing of decimals is still not standardized. The following different forms of decimals are still in use:

U.S.	7.564	France	7,564
England	7·564	Scandinavia	7,564

Extending place value

The extension of place value beyond millions is of value because it helps to develop the type of thinking necessary for success with decimals. Today, with the great distances connected with space travel and the extremely small distances involved in precision instrumentation, the reading and notation of large numbers is of real interest to the elementary school pupil. The material that follows suggests a scheme for introducing the reading of large numbers.

Illustrative Situation.   In explaining the extension of place values a teacher said, "I read in the paper that the cost of the development of a new rocket is the amount I've written on the board. ($210,564,542.) How much is this? Let's indicate the value of each digit. What is the value of the various units?" As the pupils indicated the value of the digit, the teacher wrote the value above the numeral.

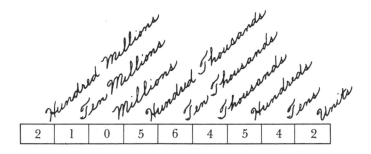

In cases where the pupils were unsure of the value, the teacher led the class to the answer with a question. If the children didn't know, the value was supplied by the teacher.

Next the teacher suggested, "Now let's read this amount. What would we have?" A student read, "2 hundred millions, 1 ten million, 0 million, 5 one-hundred thousands, 6 ten-thousands, 4 thousands, 5 hundreds, 4 tens, 2 ones."

The teacher asked, "Is the way that I had you read the numeral the way that we normally read numerals?" The pupils suggested that this method was not the usual one. They then described the procedure of reading the million only once (two hundred ten million), the thousand only once (five hundred sixty-four thousand), and the 542 as five hundred forty-two (not reading the tens and ones).

After further questioning by the teacher, the chart below was developed.

millions	thousands	ones
210	564	542

Then the pupils were asked to think out a statement concerning the reading of large numbers and to write a short statement concerning the procedure. One pupil suggested, "To read a large number, separate it into groups of three digits, starting with the ones. Name each group of three. Read the numerals in each group as though they were ones, but give the period name after each, with the exception of the ones. It's just understood that it's the ones. For example, 23,456,782 is 23 million, 456 thousand, 782."

The students then referred to their textbooks to check their comments on the reading of large numbers.

A similar development can be achieved using the size of bacteria as the example. This will result in a decimal with a large number of digits.

Foundation work with decimals

Decimals are used extensively in real world situations. Therefore, it is not difficult to develop good "use" settings for introducing decimals. In fact, the teacher should exert caution to assure that the decimal is really understood. The child's early familiarity with dollars and cents may obscure his mathematical thinking concerning the topic.

In the primary grades, pupils should have opportunities to deal with many fractions that have denominators of a power of 10. Particular emphasis should be placed upon the oral phase of this study. This fractional work will provide a helpful background of decimal development. Below are several of the comments and questions which primary-grade teachers find useful.

1. I heard on the radio that we had three-tenths of an inch of rainfall

yesterday. What does this mean? I've brought in several rulers marked in tenths. Let's look at them.

2. When we talked about rainfall and tenths of an inch, Phil used the place-value frame to show the meaning. Explain what the place-value chart indicates. How do the tallys compare in value? (From left to right, each is ten times greater in value than the tally to its right.)

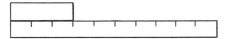

tens	ones	tenths
I	I	I

3. Alice used rods to show the value of three-tenths. Is she right?

4. How many hundredths are three-tenths?

5. Jill said that there were four and one-half inches of snow fall. How could you say this using inches and tenths of an inch?

6. Ken reported that his father told him that the right-hand column of the odometer (often incorrectly called the speedometer) measures in tenths of a mile. If the tenths column odometer was on zero when Ken's father left home, how far has he traveled?

| 2 | 6 | 5 | 3 | 8 | 7 |

7. Larry says that it's five-tenths of a mile from school to the dairy store. Orin says that Larry's wrong and that the distance is one-half of a mile. How could you settle their argument?

Reading and writing decimals

Previous everyday use and instructional background in the reading and writing of decimals should allow the teacher to begin with a situation that permits for a rather thorough analysis of the meaning of decimals. A duplicated sheet containing several situations that used decimals was given to the pupils. The pupils were then instructed, "Read these statements to yourself and be ready to discuss the value of the number involved in the statements." The first three statements are shown below.

1. The estimated budget for the National Aeronautics and Space Administration for 1970 is 7.15 billion dollars.

2. The population of the United States in 1960 was 179.323 million.

3. Jerry walked 5.6 miles on his hike.

The pupils were then asked to read the statements aloud, and the teacher asked them about the meaning of each one. Then she said, "Look at the place-value chart I've started. Let's see if you can finish the chart."

1000 (10×10×10)	100 (10×10)	10 (10)	1. (1)			
			5.	6		
			7.	1	5	3
0	1	7	9.	3	2	
thousands						▨
	hundreds				▨	
		tens		▨		
			ones			

The pupils used their reading of decimals to continue the chart. On occasion the teacher used leading questions to bring out the relationship between the whole numbers and the decimals. The completed chart follows.

1000 (10×10×10)	100 (10×10)	10 (10)	1. (1)	$\frac{1}{10}$ $\frac{1}{(10)}$	$\frac{1}{100}$ $\frac{1}{(10 \times 10)}$	$\frac{1}{1000}$ $\frac{1}{(10 \times 10 \times 10)}$
			5.	6		
			7.	1	5	
0	1	7	9.	3	2	3
thousands						thousandths
	hundreds				hundredths	
		tens		tenths		
			ones			

The following discussion took place upon completion of the chart.

Teacher	Pupils
What is the purpose of the decimal point?	*Eve:* To tell us which are decimals.
Anything else?	*Ann:* It does that but I think the main purpose is to tell us where the ones place is located. Look at the chart.
Good. How do we name the part that is on the right-hand side of the decimal point?	*Paul:* Let me try an example. .7 is called tenths; .77, hundredths; .777, thousandths. Actually the digit farthest to the right of the decimal point gives the decimal its name.
What if I want to write .534 as a fraction. How can I be sure I'm right?	*Ray:* Check on the chart. It would be $\frac{534}{1000}$.
Do you see any other pattern?	*Phyllis:* The decimal .534 has three numerals on the right-hand side of the decimal point, and there are three zeros in $\frac{534}{1000}$. The number of decimal places tells us the number of zeros in the denominator when expressed as a fraction.

In addition to verifying the suggestions made in the previous material, the following points should be developed before proceeding further into work with decimals.

1. A numeral such as 4.56 may be read in several ways—four and fifty-six hundredths, four point fifty-six, or four point five six. The use of the word "point" in the reading of a decimal has the distinct advantage of indicating the suggested decimal notation. For example, if someone reads, "seven and three-tenths," and asks for the numeral indicating this to be written, the listener does not know whether $7\frac{3}{10}$ or 7.3 is wanted. "Seven point three" indicates that the decimal form is preferred for this case.

2. The use of the "and" should be reserved for decimals. In common

usage, 149 is often read as one hundred and forty-nine. In this case no error will be made. However, it is difficult to ascertain the meaning of two hundred and twenty-eight thousandths. If the "and" is used with whole numbers as well as fractions, the pupil does not know whether the meaning is 200.028 or .228.

3. A rational number may be named by either a "fraction" or a "decimal." The term "decimal" rather than "decimal fraction" is preferred because $\frac{3}{10}$ can be considered a decimal fraction. Thus, $\frac{3}{10}$ is called a fraction, and .3 a decimal. It should be noted that there is not complete agreement among writers in mathematics education. Some will refer to decimal fractions.

4. Decimals and fractions are two types of symbolism for numbers (rational numbers). Fractions have numerators and denominators; with decimals, the denominator is not written. A number may be named either a "fraction" or a "decimal." The terms "fractions" and "decimals" for the names of numbers are preferable to the older terms of "common or vulgar fractions" and "decimal fractions." The restrictive use of the word "decimals" rather than "decimal fractions" also has the advantage of clearing up questions such as "Is $\frac{3}{10}$ a decimal fraction?"

5. It is often helpful to place a zero before the decimal point for decimals with a value less than one (0.234).

6. Pupils often read .01 as one-tenth because $\frac{1}{10}$ has two digits in the denominator. Care should be taken that this misconception is carefully discussed.

7. Emphasis should be placed upon the *ones* place as central to decimal notation. This usage emphasizes structure, balance, and symmetry. Too often the decimal point is taught as the center of the system. (See illustration.)

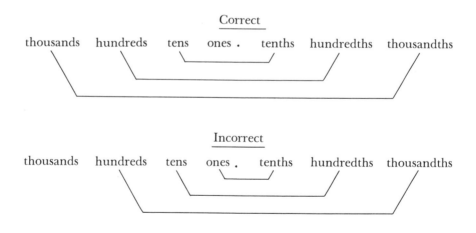

8. The steps in reading a decimal are (a) read the part of the numeral to the left of the decimal point, (b) read the decimal point as "and" or "point," and (c) read the entire part of the numeral to the right of the decimal point

as though it represented a whole number, following that statement with the place value of the digit on the far right.

Materials.   Several types of manipulative and graphical materials are depicted below. They are helpful in developing meaning concerning decimals and in later work with mathematical operations that use decimals.

The number line. (In tenths, hundredths, or thousandths)

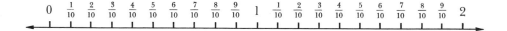

Rectangular regions. (Use the same size regions for comparative work.)

tenths

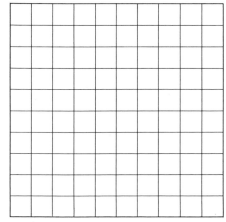

hundredths

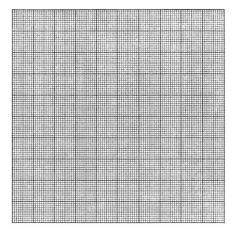

ten thousandths

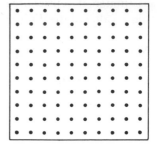

Pegboard. (Used in a manner similar to rectangular regions)

Place-value charts. (Used previously in the lessons)

thousands	hundreds	tens	ones.	tenths	hundredths	thousandths

Other materials such as rain gauges, odometers, scales (marked in tenths), calipers (marked in tenths, hundredths, and thousandths of an inch), and micrometers can be used.

Addition and subtraction with decimals

Children have many experiences adding dollars and cents in the early grades. This experience makes the addition with decimals computationally simple but may increase the difficulty of understanding addition with decimals. Because of this early experience with the addition of hundredths (cents), it is suggested that the introductory work in decimal addition begin with problems involving the addition of tenths or thousandths.

The following problem was used for introduction: "As part of a physical fitness program, the pupils of Kennedy School were to keep a record of the miles and tenths of a mile that they walked each week. Ralph walked 4.3 one day and 3.4 the next. How far did he walk on the two days?" Directions were given to write a mathematical sentence that could be used to solve the problem and to verify the answer by solving the problem in another way. The pupils were also asked to think of ways in which addition with decimals, whole numbers, and fractions differed. Some of the methods commonly used for solution by the pupils are shown below.

(a)

(b)   (c)   (d)

ones	tenths
4	3
3	4
7 .	7

$4\frac{3}{10}$ 4.3

$3\frac{4}{10}$ 3.4

$7\frac{7}{10}$ 7 . 7   7.7

(e) Commutative and Associative   (f)
            Properties

$(4 + .3) + (3 + .4) =$ 4 ones + 3 tenths

$(4 + 3) + (.3 + .4) =$ 3 ones + 4 tenths

$7 + .7 = 7.7$ 7 ones + 7 tenths

                                                7.7

In a following lesson the pupils added numbers such as 34.532 and 6.724. The following challenge was given: "Analyze your process of renaming in adding. Use expanded notation and other means to show your thinking." The pupils used a form similar to the following to illustrate their thinking.

$$34.532 = 34 + .5 \ + .03 + .002$$
$$6.724 = \ 6 + .7 \ + .02 + .004$$
$$40 + 1.2 + .05 + .006 = 41.256$$

The addition of numbers such as $3.6 + 5.8 = N$, which require regrouping, were solved by pupils in the following ways:

(a)

3 ones +   6 tenths

5 ones +   8 tenths

8 ones + 14 tenths = 8 ones + 1 one + 4 tenths = 9 ones 4 tenths = 9.4

(b)   (c)   (d)

ones	tenths
3	6
5	8
8	14 = 9.4

                             3.6 $3\frac{6}{10}$
                             5.8 $5\frac{8}{10}$
                             ‾‾‾ $8\frac{14}{10} = 9\frac{4}{10} = 9.4$
                             1.4
                             8
                             ‾‾‾
                             9.4

(e)   (f)

34.532
6.724
.006
.05
1.2
10.
30.
———
41.256

3 4 . 5 3 2
6 . 7 2 4
——————
4 1 . 2 5 6

Other examples such as .06 + .08 = N may be developed as 6 hundredths + 8 hundredths = 14 hundredths = 1 tenths, 4 hundredths = .14.

Place-value charts, pocket charts, and the abacus should be available at the mathematics table for those who need to work with concrete materials to understand the place-value concepts of decimals.

The teacher's use of leading questions should aid pupils to discover the following ideas concerning addition with decimals.

1. Although decimals and fractions name the same number, decimal addition is more closely allied to whole number addition. The significant idea to remember is that computation is most easily handled when tenths are added to tenths, hundredths to hundredths, etc. Thus, it is extremely important to keep the place value of the addends in mind.

2. If the sum of a column is ten or more, we have to rename. This is analogous to a fraction greater than one.

3. The "carrying" or renaming process works from any column to the next, not just from ones to tens or from tenths to ones. This is true because any position is ten times as great in value as the position to its right.

4. If the addends are expressed as tenths, the sum will be expressed as tenths, etc.

5. All of the basic properties of whole number addition (commutative property, associative property) and the role of the identity element (zero) hold true with decimals.

Subtraction with decimals can be generalized from addition with decimals. At this stage of their mathematical development, pupils understand the inverse relationship between addition and subtraction. Thus, they see the need for subtracting tenths from tenths, etc. They also generalize the renaming situations in the same fashion as they did in addition. Place-value frames probably provide the best means of rationalization. Pupils who use varying procedures for multi-digit subtraction (primarily additive and take-away thinking) should explore the rationale of their particular method.

Addition and subtraction with "ragged decimals"

"Ragged decimals" occur in an addition or subtraction situation in which the elements are expressed in differing decimal units; for example,

$2.34 + 3.4 + 1.564 = N$ or $3.45 - 2.3 = N$. There have been heated arguments among mathematics educators concerning the validity of using addition or subtraction of the type illustrated above. Mathematically, such computations offer no problem because, in the addition example, the addend $3.4 = 3.400$, and thus all of the addends can be easily converted to the decimal unit of the addend having the greatest number of decimal places. In this manner the addition becomes

$$
\begin{array}{ccc}
2.34 & & 2.340 \\
3.4 & \text{or} & 3.400 \\
+\ 1.564 & & 1.564 \\
\hline
\end{array}
$$

The "bone of contention" is the preciseness with which the decimals represent a physical world measurement. If the above addition involved finding the total weight of several chemicals weighed in grams, questions such as the following could be asked: Were all of the chemicals weighed with the same precision? We know that the 1.564 represents a chemical weighed to the nearest one-thousandth of a gram. Has the chemical weighing 3.4 been weighed to the nearest thousandth of a gram or only to the nearest tenth? If 3.4 has been weighed to only the nearest tenth of a gram, it may actually weigh anywhere between 3.350 and 3.449.

Some educators have argued that in no instance should pupils be exposed to computation with ragged decimals. These educators contend that situations do not exist in which persons are adding amounts measured with varying precision. Others contend that it is important to discuss a topic that will be important in scientific work—significant digits.

Significant digits as used by the scientist tell the accuracy of a measurement. The number of significant digits is equal to the number of digits of a numeral that specifies the number of units in the measurement. For example, a distance 34.5 measured to the nearest tenth of a mile has 345 tenths. Thus, it contains three significant digits. The speed of light is 186,000 miles per second. This is measured to the nearest 1,000 miles. In units, this is 186 thousands. The numeral contains three significant digits. The thickness of a piece of aircraft metal is .008. This is measured to the nearest thousandth of an inch. In units this is 8 thousandths, one significant digit.

Because of the importance that scientists place upon significant digits and because several textbooks and standardized tests imprecisely test on ragged decimals, it is suggested that the teacher use this topic for exploration. Discussion with the pupils can be developed along these guidelines:[3]

1. In textbooks and standardized tests we can assume that each of the measurements has been precisely made but recorded in terms of the simplest decimal. Thus, $3.4 = 3.40000. \ldots$ In such cases, zeros can be annexed where required so that all of the addends are expressed in the same decimal unit.

[3] Ohmer, Aucoin, and Cortez, *Elementary Contemporary Mathematics* (Waltham, Mass.: Blaisdell Publishing Company, 1964), p. 308.

2. In situations where the precision of the measurement may possibly vary, the following general principle may be employed: The precision of a sum or a difference does not exceed the precision of any of the numbers from which it is formed. (Thus, in adding $3.5 + 5.67 + 8.679$, the least precise measurement is 3.5. Hence all measurements should be rounded to the nearest tenth. The addition becomes $3.5 + 5.7 + 8.7$.)

The argument concerning significant digits and precision also occurs in the multiplication and division of decimals. In any case, the accuracy of the product or quotient does not exceed the accuracy of any of the numbers from which the product or quotient is formed and may, in fact, be less.

Multiplication with decimals

The major difficulty in teaching multiplication with decimals is determining the number of decimal places in the product. Traditional mathematics programs simply taught the following rule: "Count the number of decimal places in the factors. This is the number of decimal places that should appear in the product." At best, such a procedure produced only computational proficiency and left pupils wondering why a computation such as $3 \times .3 = N$ produced a product less than one.

The procedure that follows is designed to provide mathematical insight into the process of multiplication. Multiplication with decimals was introduced with the following problem: "The pupils in the science club are going to perform the same experiment 3 times to 'triple check' their results. If the experiment requires 3.7 grams of sulfur, how many grams of sulfur will they need for the three tests?" It was suggested that the pupils write the mathematical sentence, estimate the answer, work the problem, and verify the results.

The common solutions involved changing the decimal to a fraction and then multiplying, adding the decimals, and using the number line.

$$3 \times 3.7 = 3 \times 3\tfrac{7}{10} = 3 \times \tfrac{37}{10} = 11\tfrac{1}{10} \text{ or } 11.1 \text{ grams}$$

$$
\begin{array}{r}
3.7 \\
3.7 \\
+\,3.7 \\
\hline
11.1 \text{ grams}
\end{array}
$$

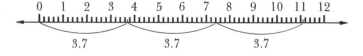

Several of the pupils had estimated the product as "a little over 10." Those pupils multiplied using the decimals and placing the decimal point from their estimate. One pupil explained, "I knew that the answer would be more than

10 but less than 15. I multiplied and got an answer of 111. I knew that this would mean that the answer should be 11.1."

Several other problems and computational exercises involving various types of decimal multiplication were given to the class. It was suggested that the assignment be worked using fractions. The pupils were also to attempt to determine a means of placing the decimal point in the product of the decimal form.

For a multiplication such as .5 × .3 the array pattern was used.

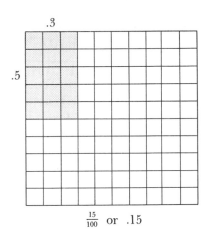

$\frac{15}{100}$ or .15

During a discussion that followed the work period, the teacher asked, "If I multiply $\frac{2}{10} \times \frac{3}{100}$, my answer will be in —— thousandths. If I multiply tenths times tenths my answer will be in —— hundredths —— right. Let's look at these ideas in decimal form. If I multiply .23 × .2 my answer should be in ——.

The pupils explained that .23 × .2 was multiplying hundredths times tenths and, therefore, the product should be expressed in thousandths. The teacher gave several other decimal multiplications and then asked if the pupils could develop an efficient means of placing the decimal point. The pupils worked out the generalization, "The product will have as many decimal places as there are in both factors. For example, .237 × .45 = N will have five decimal places in the product because the combined decimal places in the factors is five." The students then consulted references to check the validity of their statement and compared it with the statement given in the book.

The procedure detailed above is helpful in developing the decimal multiplication algorithm. As work continues on multiplication with decimals, the teacher should make use of study procedures which review and solidify the rationale of decimal multiplication. Procedures that can be used are periodic checks of decimal multiplication by fractional multiplication, mathematics themes on "How and Why I Multiply Using Decimals," and (after exponents have been introduced) the development of the rationale of decimal multiplication using the basic number properties and exponents.

Division with decimals

Division with decimals is one of the more difficult phases of elementary school mathematics because many pupils have difficulty in understanding the rationale of the process. Four types of structural situations that are taught at the elementary school level call for decimal division. They are
1. Division of a decimal by an integer.
2. Division of an integer by an integer which is not a factor of the dividend.
3. Division of an integer by a decimal.
4. Division of a decimal by a decimal.

Current children's textbooks and books on the teaching of elementary school mathematics usually introduce decimal division with situations involving the division of a decimal by an integer ($1.6 \div 4 = N$). This probably is a holdover from the time when decimal division was taught by a rather mechanical placement of the decimal point. Thus, in $4 \overline{)\ 1.6}$ the pupil placed the decimal point in the quotient directly above the decimal point in the dividend. Problem situations involving that form of decimal division are usually of the partition division variety.

It was previously emphasized that *measurement* division situations are better for introductory work than *partition* situations because the measurement type can be solved in several ways, thus providing a greater opportunity for pupil discovery. In keeping with the guided discovery principles advocated in this book, it is suggested that a measurement division problem of the type ($2 \div .4 = N$) be used for introductory purposes. This is analagous to a fractional division problem of the type $6 \div \frac{1}{2} = N$ and allows for a greater variety of pupil solutions than the division of a decimal by an integer.

An illustrative problem and several possible solutions to it are given below. As in previous introductory lessons, the use of multiple solutions of the problem should be emphasized. The teacher can also remind the pupils of the relationship between decimals and fractions. The teacher should not expect that all of the solutions described below will occur on the same day. The pupils should have a good deal of experience in using several of the approaches to assure an understanding of decimal division.

Problem. Hans, a relative from Europe was visiting John. John told Hans that they would be going on a 3-mile hike. Hans asked, "How many kilometers is that?" If a kilometer is about .6 of a mile, how many kilometers is 3 miles? (Note the problem involves measurement division because the size of each unit, .6 mile, is known.)

Solutions. The mathematical sentence needed was identified as $3 \div .6 = N$, which could be written $.6 \overline{)\ 3}$.

Herb: I used the number line to find, "How many $.6 = 3$? There are 5.

$$3.0$$
$$\underline{.6 \ (1)}$$
$$2.4$$
$$\underline{.6 \ (2)}$$

Alice: We have solved other division situations using subtraction, so I used a series of subtractions.

$$1.8$$
$$\underline{.6 \ (3)}$$
$$1.2$$
$$\underline{.6 \ (4)}$$
$$.6$$
$$\underline{.6 \ (5)}$$

Herman: I made use of the division of fractions and the common denominator. (Inversion might also have been used, but it doesn't add as much to the decimal thinking.)

$$3 \div \tfrac{6}{10} = \tfrac{30}{10} \div \tfrac{6}{10} =$$

$$\frac{5}{1} = 5$$

Cary: I used a different form of the common denominator, $3 = 30$ tenths.

$$6 \text{ tenths} \, \overline{)\, 3} \ = 6 \text{ tenths} \, \overline{)\, \overset{5}{30 \text{ tenths}}}$$

Wally: I experimented with several mathematical ideas. I found that I could use the identity element to change the problem to whole number division.

$$\frac{10}{10} \times \frac{3}{\frac{6}{10}} = \frac{30}{6} = 5$$

In the discussion that followed, all of the solutions were accepted as being mathematically correct. The pupils felt that the solutions used by Herb (the number line) and Alice (a series of subtractions) were good ways to demonstrate the thinking involved. However, the students thought that both solutions were rather cumbersome. The students felt that division using the common denominator was a very useful method, particularly when written in the form suggested by Cary (6 tenths $\overline{)\, 30 \text{ tenths}}$). Many pupils were intrigued with the method used by Wally (changing a fractional division to whole number division using the identity element).

A worksheet containing several division problems and computational exercises was then assigned to the class. It was suggested that each of the methods discussed be used and that pupils attempt to identify further improvements on the solution.

During the discussion that followed the teacher referred to the two completed division computations illustrated below and asked whether these two approaches could be combined.

$$(1)\ .4\,\overline{)\,2\,} = 4\ \text{tenths}\,\overline{)\,\overset{5}{20\ \text{tenths}}}\qquad\qquad (2)\ \frac{2}{.4} = \frac{2}{\frac{4}{10}} \times \frac{10}{10} = \frac{20}{4} = 5$$

or

$$\frac{2}{.4} \times \frac{10}{10} = \frac{20}{4} = 5$$

Class members noted that it would not be necessary to change both the divisor and the dividend to tenths. Multiplying both by 10 and making the problem a whole number division problem was effective and an application of mathematical principles (use of the identity element). The class agreed that an effective method to solve the division of decimal problems was to rename the numbers with whole numbers. As the pupils continued their work, they found that in division situations such as $2.3\,\overline{)\,5.43\,}$ the useful form of the identity element was $\frac{100}{100}$ rather than $\frac{10}{10}$. Thus the division became $230\,\overline{)\,543\,}$.

The next division problem introduced was of the type $.4 \div 2 = N$. The problem used was, "For a science experiment Nancy is to give each of 4 students an equal portion of 1.6 grams of copper sulfide. How much copper sulfide will each pupil receive?" The pupils generally wrote the division as $4\,\overline{)\,1.6\,}$ and then changed the problem to whole number division ($40\,\overline{)\,16\,}$). This created difficulties for many of the pupils. The most common solution involved writing the division as a fraction and reducing the fraction: $\frac{16}{40} = \frac{4}{10}$ $= .4$. Bill said that he had estimated that the answer would be less than 1. He then divided without thinking of the decimal point, getting an answer of 4. He reasoned that the correct answer should be .4.

Several other division computations were worked by an estimation method. During this time, several pupils noted, "When you divide tenths, the answer will be expressed in tenths. Or, you can use place value. Place the decimal point in the quotient directly above the decimal point in the divisor." For example,

$$\overset{.82}{4\,\overline{)\,3.28\,}}\qquad\qquad \text{check } 4\,\overline{)\,328\,} \begin{array}{l}\text{82 hundredths or .82}\\ \text{hundredths}\end{array}$$

$$\begin{array}{r}32\\ \hline 8\end{array}$$

After pupils have a good understanding of decimal division, they can shorten the writing required by using an arrow or a caret to indicate the multiplication they have performed. Thus, $3.4\,\overline{)\,6.25\,}$ becomes $3.\overset{\cdot}{4}\,\overline{)\,6.\overset{\cdot}{25}\,}$ or $3.4_\wedge\overline{)\,6.2_\wedge5\,}$. The use of the caret has often been criticized as being mechanical and without meaning. This is a factor of the method used in teaching division rather than of the device itself. It is strictly a computational shortcut, one that can be used instead of writing out the multiplication by the identity element.

There are methods of placing the decimal point in the quotient other than those suggested in the illustrative teaching situations. One of the more common makes use of the inverse relationship between multiplication and division. The quotient times the divisor equals the dividend, and the sum of the number of decimal places in the factors of a multiplication equals the number of decimal places in the product. Using this relationship, it follows that the number of decimal places in the quotient can be found by subtracting the number of decimal places in the divisor from the number of decimal places in the dividend. To illustrate:

1.245	3 decimal places
2.3	1 decimal place
3735	
2490	
2.8635	4 decimal places

$$2.3)\overline{2.8635} \qquad \begin{matrix}1.245\end{matrix}$$

$$1 \qquad 4 \qquad 4-1=3$$

Thus $2.36)\overline{2.36472}$ would have $5-2=$ ③ decimal places in the quotient.

$$2 \qquad 5$$

This subtractive procedure presents difficulties when the division is not exact and the person computing wishes to add several decimal places to the dividend ($.8)\overline{10}$). Problems also arise when there are more decimal places in the divisor than in the dividend, although several decimal places can be added to the dividend. ($2.06)\overline{41.2}$ can be changed $2.06)\overline{41.200}$.)

A study of the two methods of placing the decimal point—making the divisor a whole number by multiplying by a power of ten, or subtracting the number of decimal places in the divisor from the number of decimal places in the dividend—showed that (1) in general, pupils taught to make the divisor a whole number more often placed the decimal point correctly, (2) the subtractive approach was effective with above average learners, and (3) children could be taught to understand either procedure.[4]

Converting fractions and decimals

Usually pupils experience little difficulty in converting decimals to

[4] Frances Flournoy, "A Consideration of Pupil's Success with Two Methods of Placing the Decimal Point in the Quotient," *School Science and Mathematics*, Vol. LIX (June 1959), pp. 445–455.

fractions. Actually if children can read decimals, they are able to convert them to fractions with a denominator of some power of 10. After the fraction is written with a denominator as a power of ten, the only task that remains is the simplification of the fraction.

Changing a fraction to a decimal is not as simple, for to convert a fraction to a decimal, a pupil often needs to perform decimal division. Because it is sometimes necessary to convert fractions to decimals before decimal division can be taught, the teacher can use two other techniques. Early in the study of decimals, the pupils may use a table of decimal equivalents. Pupils find it beneficial to memorize several of the more common decimal equivalents such as $\frac{1}{8} = .125$, $\frac{1}{3} = .33\frac{1}{3}$, $\frac{3}{4} = .75$, etc. Later in decimal study, but before the division of decimals is studied, pupils may handle conversion as a problem in finding equivalent fractions that have a denominator of 10, 100, or 1000.

After the techniques of decimal division are mastered, the pupil can use division to find decimal equivalents. For example, to change $\frac{2}{5}$ to a decimal the pupil views $\frac{2}{5}$ as meaning 2 divided by 5 or $5\overline{)2}$. He performs the division $5\overline{)2.0}^{.4}$ and states $\frac{2}{5} = .4$. For decimals that are nonterminating, such as $\frac{1}{3} = .333 \ldots$, the pupil may round the decimal form off to the nearest hundredth. The child should realize that this means that one-third equals thirty-three hundredths to the nearest hundredth. He should not write $\frac{1}{3} = .33$.

TEACHING EXPONENTS

Foundations

The study of exponential notation allows pupils to probe further the subtleties of place value. It also allows pupils to gain insight into the place of decimals within the number system.

The study of exponents can be introduced through the contemplation of extremely large numbers. One teacher used the following procedure. She said to her class, "Yesterday I was talking with a boy who said, 'You're a teacher and supposed to know a lot about mathematics. I bet that I can stump you. Let's see you read this for me.'" (The teacher writes on board 13,000,000,000,000,000,000,000,000.) "That's the approximate weight of the earth in pounds. Can you read this number?" Several pupils made attempts but were unable to name the number. Then the teacher said, "I checked one of my old textbooks at home and found a chart. It appeared in Greenleaf's arithmetic, which was published in 1848." [5] (She gives each pupil a copy of the numeration table.)

---

[5] Note: The same chart is usually available in unabridged dictionaries.

Numeration Table

The following is the French method of enumeration, and is in general use in the United States and on the continent of Europe.

To enumerate any number of figures by this method, they should be separated by commas into divisions of three figures each, as in the annexed table. Each division will be known by a different name. The first three figures, reckoning from right to left, will be so many units, tens, and hundreds, and the next three so many thousands, and the next three so many millions, etc.

123,456,789,123,456,789,123,456,789,123,456,789,123,456,789,123,456,789,123,456,789,123

Units

Thousands

Millions

Billions

Trillions

Quadrillions

Quintillions

Sextillions

Septillions

Octillions

Nonillions

Decillions

Undecillions

Duodecillions

Tredecillions

Quattuordecillions

Quindecillions

Sexdecillions

Septendecillions

Octodecillions

Novemdecillions

Vigintillions

The value of the numbers in the annexed table, expressed in words, is one hundred twenty-three vigintillions, four hundred fifty-six novemdecillions, seven hundred eighty-nine octodecillions, one hundred twenty-three septendecillions, four hundred fifty-six sexdecillions, seven hundred eighty-nine quindecillions, one hundred twenty-three quattuordecillions, four hundred fifty-six tredecillions, seven hundred eighty-nine duodecillions, one hundred twenty-three undecillions, four hundred fifty-six decillions, seven hundred eighty-nine nonillions, one hundred twenty-three octillions, four hundred fifty-six septillions, seven hundred eighty-nine sextillions, one hundred twenty-three quintillions, four hundred fifty-six quadrillions, seven hundred eighty-nine trillions, one hundred twenty-three billions, four hundred fifty-six millions, seven hundred eighty-nine thousands, one hundred twenty-three units.

"Now can you read this numeral?" The number was identified as thirteen sextillions.

The teacher then commented, "We seldom use the period names like sextillions today, and yet we make greater use of very large numbers today than did people in the past. Today we're talking about distances in space, the number of bacteria in a particular area, and the like. How do we avoid using such large numbers?" The pupils suggested that new terms were developed, such as "light years," "astronomical" units (the distance from Earth to Sun, 93,000,000 miles), and "parsecs" (a parsec is 3.26 light years or 206,283 astronomical units).

The teacher suggested that mathematicians, other scientists, and almost all who deal with mathematics make use of another scheme. That scheme involves the idea of factors. The teacher wrote 100, 1,000, and 10,000 on the chalkboard and said, "How else could each of these be written?" The pupils suggested several methods, but the teacher focused attention on the following method:

$$100 = 10 \times 10; \ 1,000 = 10 \times 10 \times 10; \ \text{and} \ 10,000 = 10 \times 10 \times 10 \times 10.$$

Then the class was asked, "How many times is 10 used as a factor in each of those expressions?" As the pupils answered, the teacher filled in the answer on the board, as follows:

$$
\begin{aligned}
100 &= 10 \times 10 &&\rightarrow 10 \text{ as a factor 2 times} \\
1,000 &= 10 \times 10 \times 10 &&\rightarrow 10 \text{ as a factor 3 times} \\
10,000 &= 10 \times 10 \times 10 \times 10 &&\rightarrow 10 \text{ as a factor 4 times}
\end{aligned}
$$

The teacher explained, "As you've learned before, using mathematics is often a very concise way to make a statement. One of the expressions on the board is shortened to 10^3. What would this mean?" The pupils deduced that 10^3 meant $10 \times 10 \times 10$ or 10 used as a factor 3 times. The class then wrote 100 as $10 \times 10 = 10^2$; $10,000 = 10 \times 10 \times 10 \times 10 = 10^4$.

The students were asked whether they knew the name for the numeral placed above and to the right of the 10. None of them did, so the teacher identified the symbol as an *exponent*. The teacher referred the students to their chart of period names and asked, "How would you write one million by using exponents? Ten million? One billion?" The class then developed the chart below.

Decimal	Product expression	Exponent for M
1,000,000	$10 \times 10 \times 10 \times 10 \times 10 \times 10 =$	10^6
10,000,000	$10 \times 10 \times 10 \times 10 \times 10 \times 10 \times 10 =$	10^7
1,000,000,000	$10 \times 10 \times 10 \times 10 \times 10 \times 10 \times 10 \times 10 \times 10 =$	10^9

"How could you write $5 \times 5 \times 5$ by using exponents?" The pupils hesitated and then answered "5^3." The teacher asked, "What do we call the 3 in the 10^3? The 4 in the 5^4?" The students replied that they were exponents.

The teacher then said, "There is a name for the 10 and the 5 in each expression. Does anyone know what it is?" After some discussion, the numeral was identified as the *base*. The pupils were then asked to write a sentence describing the writing of expressions by using exponents. The typical sentence emphasized that a product expression in which the same number appeared as the factor could be expressed by writing the base number and then indicating the number of times that it appeared as a factor by using an exponent.

During the ensuing work with the writing and interpreting of exponents, the students were taught these additional terms:

Power. A number that can be expressed in exponent form is called a power of the number named by the base. Thus, 3^5 is read "Three to the fifth power."

Square. The second power of a number or the product of a number times itself is called the square of the number ($5 \times 5 = 5^2$).

Later a chart such as the one below was developed.

Expanded Notation

10^3	10^2	10^1	
$10 \times 10 \times 10$	10×10		1
thousands	hundreds	tens	ones
	2	4	5
3	6	7	2

$245 = (2 \times 10^2) + (4 \times 10^1) + (5 \times 1)$

$3672 = (3 \times 10^3) + (6 \times 10^2) + (7 \times 10^1) + (2 \times 1)$

Computation with exponents

The use of exponents in finding products can be taught effectively using guided discovery techniques. The vignette that follows is an example of a discovery approach.

The teacher began by saying, "Mathematicians and other scientists save a great deal of time by using exponents. They can use exponents when they are multiplying or dividing quantities that have the same base number. See if you can find an approach that uses exponents to solve the problem I'm going to read to you. Work the problem and verify your answer. If you finish early, try to develop other situations that use the basic ideas of this problem. Here's the problem: On a population map there are 10^4 dots in the state of Illinois. If each dot represents 10^3 persons, about how many persons are there in Illinois?"

All of the pupils were able to arrive at an answer to the problem. The mathematical sentence needed was identified as $10^3 \times 10^4 = N$. Bob knew that 10^3 equals 1,000 and that 10^4 equals 10,000; so he multiplied 1,000 times 10,000, finding the product to be 10,000,000 or 10^7 persons.

Jaqueline knew that $10^3 = 10 \times 10 \times 10$ and that $10^4 = 10 \times 10 \times 10 \times 10$. She then multiplied $10 \times 10 \times 10 \times 10 \times 10 \times 10 \times 10 = 10,000,000$ or 10^7 persons. She noted that she could have saved the multiplication if she had counted the factors of 10 (7 in all).

Lynn had worked the example in the same manner as Bob, but as she looked over her work she noted that $10,000,000$ was equal to 10^7. She reasoned that the product could be solved by adding the exponents; thus, $10^3 \times 10^4 = 10^7$.

The pupils felt that Lynn's method was excellent because it did not involve mutiplying the factors of 10. The pupils tested several other computations, such as $4^5 \times 4^3 = N$ and $8^2 \times 8^3 = N$, using the approach of adding exponents and then checking their work by actually performing the multiplication with all of the factors. The group noted that the addition of exponents could be used to multiply factors of the base because the exponents indicated the number of times the base was to be used as a factor. The class was then directed to mathematics reference books to check their findings with those books.

The next day the teacher presented a problem that involved $6^4 \div 6^2 = N$. The pupils were able to discover the technique of subtracting exponents to divide in much the same fashion as they had discovered the multiplication-addition relationship. The teacher presented several situations that were not appropriate to computation with exponents to emphasize that (1) the product of numbers expressed in exponential form and having the same base may be found by adding exponents, (2) the quotient of numbers expressed in exponential form and having the same base may be found by subtracting the exponent of the divisor from the exponent of the dividend, and (3) addition and subtraction may not be performed by using exponents.

Pupils are usually able to grasp readily the ideas involved with exponents. One of the more difficult aspects of the study may be the development of the proper vocabulary. The teacher should take every opportunity to emphasize words such as *base* (not to be thought of in exactly the same way as the base of a numeration system, but the factor that is to be repeated in an exponential expression), *power, repeated factor, product expression* ($27 = 3 \times 3 \times 3$), and *exponent form.*

Numbers to the zero power. After division with exponents has been developed, the teacher may introduce problem situations involving division of a number by itself, such as $10^4 \div 10^4 = N$. Pupils can use the generalization that they have developed and subtract the exponents, thus finding that the quotient is 10^0. A check by converting the numbers to whole numbers reveals that $10,000 \div 10,000 = 1$. Other examples may be used to demonstrate this.

$$2^3 \div 2^3 = 2^0 = 1 \text{ because } \frac{2 \times 2 \times 2}{2 \times 2 \times 2} = 1$$

$$6^2 \div 6^2 = 6^0 = 1 \text{ because } \frac{6 \times 6}{6 \times 6} = 1$$

After several similar examples and discussion, pupils can generalize that a number having an exponent of zero (except a numeral representing 0) is another name for the number 1. Thus, $5^0 = 8^0 = 10^0 = 1$. With this information, the charts of exponents can be completed for the ones place because $10^0 = 1$.

Negative exponents. Positive exponents indicate the number of times a number is used as a factor. The negative exponent is the multiplicative inverse of the positive exponent. Thus, the inverse of 100 or 10^2 is

$$\frac{1}{100} \quad \text{or} \quad \frac{1}{10^2}.$$

This number is represented using exponents as 10^{-2}.

The study of negative exponents should be limited to students who possess a good understanding of place value, exponents, and decimals. It can be introduced by attempting to find another name for $\frac{1}{10}$ or $\frac{1}{100}$. The teacher can call attention to the place-value chart and ask, "How could we develop a means of expressing the powers of 10 on the right-hand side of the decimal point by using exponents?"

Exponents and Their Meaning

10^3	10^2	10^1	10^0	?	?	?
$(10 \times 10 \times 10)$	(10×10)	(10)	$\frac{(1)}{10}$	$\frac{(1)}{10 \times 10}$	$\frac{(1)}{10 \times 10 \times 10}$
1000	100	10	1	$\frac{1}{10}$	$\frac{1}{100}$	$\frac{1}{1000}$
thousands	hundreds	tens	ones	tenths	hundredths	thousandths

Normally two suggestions are made by pupils. Many suggest using a notation of

$$\frac{1}{10^1} \quad \text{for} \quad \frac{1}{10} \quad \text{and} \quad \frac{1}{10^2} \quad \text{for} \quad \frac{1}{100}.$$

which is correct but cumbersome. Others will suggest the idea of negative exponents with some hesitation because they realize that they would not be the same as negative numbers. When the two suggestions described have been made, the teacher can refer the pupils to reference books to see which type of use is made of exponents. Then practice, questioning, and study can be used to develop further the concept of negative exponents.

Scientific notation. One of the very valuable uses of exponents involves *scientific notation,* which consists of expressing numbers decimally as a pair of factors. One of the factors represents a number between 1 and 10 and the other is expressed as a power of 10 by the use of an exponent. In scientific notation, 93,000,000 is 9.3×10^7 and 186,000 becomes 1.86×10^5.

The fields of astronomy and projected space travel present opportunities to use scientific notation. A statement such as the following might be made to introduce the idea of scientific notation. "A science book states that Venus is approximately 6.7×10^7 miles from the Sun. How far is this?" The pupils can work out the distance, arriving at 67,000,000 miles. Several science references that make use of scientific notation should be available in order that pupils may see how this notation is used in science.

The major purpose of introducing scientific notation to elementary school pupils is its special use of place value. Pupils are forced to give some thought to a problem such as "Light travels at about 186,000 miles per second. Express this in a scientific notation."

Some of the generalizations that pupils can develop or further extend by this study are the following:

1. To express a number in scientific notation, express the number as a decimal between 1 and 10, then multiply by the appropriate power of 10 written with an exponent.

2. To change 2,300 to scientific notation we are actually dividing 2,300 by 1,000 (10^3) to arrive at 2.3. To keep the same number, we must multiply by 1,000 (10^3). Thus $2,300 = 2.3 \times 10^3$.

3. After the decimal point is placed for scientific notation, the exponent of 10 may be found by counting the number of decimal places. That is, $36,000,000 = 3.6 \times 10^7$.

If negative exponents are studied (see previous section) pupils may make the following generalization: A number such as .000036 is expressed as 3.6×10^{-5}, which means

$$.000036 = 3.6 \times \frac{1}{10 \times 10 \times 10 \times 10 \times 10} = 3.6 \times \frac{1}{100,000} = 3.6 \times 10^{-5}.$$

NUMERATION SYSTEMS WITH BASES OTHER THAN TEN

The teaching of numeration systems with bases other than 10 has recently been reintroduced into elementary school mathematics programs.

Some books of the 1800's contained sections on duodecimals (base 12) on the basis of dozens and inches.[6] For many years the Duodecimal Society of America has advocated a change to this system.[7] Also, for the past fifteen to twenty years courses in the teaching of elementary school mathematics have devoted time to developing numeration systems with various bases to give teachers an insight into the importance of place value and to acquaint them with some of the struggles that children encounter when they work with numbers for the first time.

Some present-day teachers ask, "Isn't it a waste of time to teach children bases other than 10 unless we're going to change the base?" "What is the purpose of teaching other numeration systems?" "I have difficulty with other bases myself; isn't this topic too hard for children?" "Should I teach pupils the addition and multiplication combinations in other bases? If so, should they memorize them?" Because such questions demonstrate a certain uneasiness about other numeration systems, the several comments that follow are provided to clarify the role of numeration systems with bases other than 10.

Purposes of teaching

Numeration systems with bases other than 10 are now included in the mathematics curriculum because they have some social utility. Use is made of other bases (particularly base 12) in measuring. Electronic computers use a base of 2, and on occasion a base of 8 is used as an intermediary step between base 10 and base 2. However, the major reasons for teaching the other bases are to help pupils (1) extend their knowledge and understanding of place value, (2) understand that it is not the choice of a base of 10 but rather the basic number properties and place value that are the major factors in causing our number system to operate effectively, (3) realize that using a base of 10 was an arbitrary choice made by early peoples, probably because of their ten fingers (another base, such as 8 or 12, might be just as effective, in fact, more effective), (4) develop further insight into the fundamental operations. Operations that use another base require the pupils to think in terms of number properties.

[6] Benjamin Greenleaf, *The National Arithmetic on the Inductive System* (Boston: Robert S. Davis & Co., 1861), pp. 421–424.
[7] R. E. Andrews, *New Numbers: How Acceptance of a Duodecimal (12) Base Would Simplify Mathematics* (New York: Harcourt, Brace & World, 1935).

Source: Still Photo Services U. D. I. S., Pennsylvania State University.

The study of bases.

Numeration in base four

A teacher can introduce numeration in base 4 by using the procedures that follow. The teacher randomly placed 23 flannel representations of arrowheads on the flannel board. She said, "An Indian of early California had this number of arrowheads. How many did he have?" The pupils tried to count the number of arrowheads, but found it difficult. The count ranged from 21 to 26.

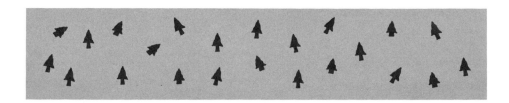

Then the teacher said, "We've had difficulty counting the number of arrowheads. How could we arrange them so that we could tell quickly how many arrowheads there are?" Several different methods of grouping were suggested:

By Tens

By Fives

By Fours

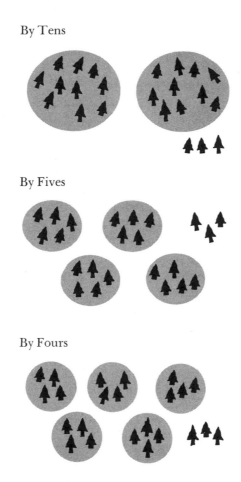

The teacher said, "Civilizations haven't always grouped by tens. The Mayan Indians of Central America grouped by twenties. Can you think why?" After a pause a student answered, "Yes, it was probably because they used both fingers and toes to count. They lived in a warm climate and didn't wear shoes of the sort we do."

The teacher added, "The Indian tribe that I mentioned in California, the Yukes, grouped by fours. Can you think of a reason for this?" None of the pupils were able to.

Therefore, the teacher explained that it is believed that they used the space between the digits on one hand as a representative group.

How would they have grouped this set of arrowheads (13)?

The pupils grouped the arrowheads into groups of fours.

How would it look on this place-value frame?

fours	ones
3	1

The pupils noted that there were 3 groups of four and 1 unit remained. The teacher suggested that as a check the students look at the meaning of the place-value frame. The pupils noted that the digit to the left of the ones place indicated the number of fours (in this case 3). Thus 3 fours and 1 can be considered to be another name for 13 in base 10.

The pupils then were given groups of sticks of varying sizes and were asked to arrange the sticks into groups of fours and ones. They then indicated the amount on the place-value frame. (All of these amounts were less than 16 base 10.) Then the teacher said, "We can write numerals in other bases without the place-value frame by indicating the base at the right and slightly below the numeral. How many objects are there in a set represented by 13? —— four ——. —— Seven —— Right, 1 four and 3 ones. Write the numeral in base 4 that represents the collections of sticks we've shown in the place-value frame." Number lines to compare base 4 and base 10 were developed by class consideration.

Base Ten

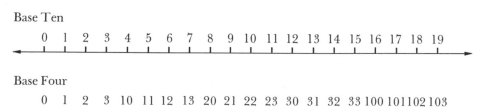

Base Four

Some difficulty was experienced in moving from 33_{four} to 100_{four}. Several pupils who suggested that 40 should follow 33_{four} were corrected by other class members who reminded them that the numeral 4 is not used in base 4. By inspecting 16 dots in groups of fours the class reasoned that 16 dots represented the base times base in a scale of 4. The teacher asked, "How do you represent the base in base 4? —— 10_{four} —— right. How would we represent the base times base?" The class agreed that to make use of place value, the base times base should be 100_{four}.

The class was challenged to indicate the number of its original set of arrowheads (23) by a base-four numeral. Several pupils mistakenly wrote the numeral as 53_{four}. However, the majority of the pupils had found methods of deriving the correct base-four numerals. Several of their methods are indicated below:

(a)

base × base sixteens	base four	ones
1	1	3

(b)

(c)

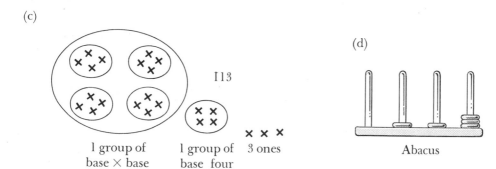

1 group of base × base   1 group of base four   3 ones

113

(d)

Abacus

The class worked further on expressing base-four and base-ten numerals and then considered the development of a place-value chart for base 4. Their completed chart is reproduced below.

Base Four

B^3	B^2	B^1	B^0
Sixty-four 4^3 ($4 \times 4 \times 4$)	Sixteens 4^2 (4×4)	Fours 4^1	Units 4^0

The pupils then worked with several other bases and developed place-value charts for them. The pupils found the chart to be helpful in converting numerals from one base to another. From the use of the chart and further discussion, the pupils formulated the following generalizations and procedures:

1. When we're working in another base we're still working with the same number, but we give the number a different name. For example, 13_{four} and 7_{ten} represent the same number but they are different numerals for this number.

2. If we understand place value we can rather easily convert a numeral in another base to base 10. For example, 233_{five} means (2 of the base $\times$ base) + (3 of the base) + (3 ones). It can be written as

25's	5's	1's
2	3	3

$$233_{five} = (2 \times 25_{ten}) + (3 \times 5_{ten}) + (3 \times 1_{ten})$$
$$233_{five} = 50 + 15 + 3$$
$$233_{five} = 68.$$

3. To convert a numeral from base 10 to another base we can develop a chart of powers of the base. Then we group in powers of the new base. For example, to convert 68_{ten} to base 5, we develop the chart and then think

$B \times B$ 5×5 25	B 5	1's
2	3	3

$$\begin{array}{r} 68 \\ - 50 \quad (2 \times 25) \\ \hline 18 \\ - 15 \quad (3 \times 5) \\ \hline 3 \text{ ones} \end{array}$$

Any groups of $5 \times 5 \times 5$ or 125's? Any groups of 5×5 or 25's? Yes. How many? Two. Two 25's = 50. Thus, we have 18 remaining. How many 5's equal 18? Three. How many ones are left? Three. $68_{ten} = 233_{five}$.

A division algorithm for converting from base 10 to another base is sometimes used. The meaning of the algorithm is often vague; therefore it is suggested for use only with people who have a great deal of insight. An example of this algorithm with an explanation of the rationale is given below.

Topics: Convert 245_{ten} to base 6.

$$
\begin{array}{rl}
& 0 \text{ R } 1 \\
\text{Step 4} \rightarrow & 6)\overline{1} \text{ R } 0 \\
\text{Step 3} \rightarrow & 6)\overline{6} \text{ R } 4 \\
\text{Step 2} \rightarrow & 6)\overline{40} \text{ R } 5 \\
\text{Step 1} \rightarrow & 6)\overline{245}
\end{array}
$$

$$1045_{six} = 245_{ten}$$

A study of the steps in order should lead to the following rationale. In Step 1 we have divided the base-ten value by 6. The remainder tells the number remaining from an even multiple of 6, or the ones in base 6. Because we have previously divided by 6 in Step 1, the second division by 6 in Step 2 divides the original number by 36. Thus the remainder indicates the number of 6^1. Step 3 divides the original number by 6^3 and the remainder indicates the left-over groups of 6^2. Step 4 divides the original amount by 6^4. Thus the remainder indicates an excess of 6^3.

Source: Publishers Newspaper Syndicate

While the principal use of the binary system is with computors, there are a number of interesting diversions in which pupils can use the system.

Binary and duodecimal notation

Although not suggested for introductory work, the duodecimal and binary systems are used more often than the other nondecimal bases. Conversion tables for the two systems are given below. As shown in the first table, T in base 12 has a value of 10 in base 10; E in base 12 has a value of 11 in base ten.

Duodecimal System

12^3	12^2	12^1	12^0	
one thousand seven hundred twenty eights	one hundred forty fours	twelves	ones	
$12 \times 12 \times 12$	12×12	12	1	Decimal (Base 10)
1728	144	12	1	Equivalent
			1	1
			2	2
			3	3
			4	4
			.	.
			.	.
			.	.
			T	10
			E	11
			10	12
			11	13
			.	.
			.	.
			.	.
		4	2	50
			.	.
			.	.
			.	.
	1	0	0	144
			.	.
			.	.
			.	.
	4	2	0	600
			.	.
			.	.
			.	.
1	1	T	8	2000

Computation in other systems

It is important to emphasize that computation in other bases is for the purpose of identifying structure in mathematics. The teacher should not require the memorization of number facts in other bases. Early computation may be performed by grouping sticks, with the number line, and by counting. After a few examples have been performed, addition or multiplication tables in various bases can be developed. Any other work with computation will make use of the table to find the basic facts.

Binary System

2^4	2^3	2^2	2^1	2^0	
sixteens	eights	fours	twos	ones	
$2 \times 2 \times 2 \times 2$	$2 \times 2 \times 2$	2×2	2	1	Decimal
16	8	4	2	1	Equivalent
				1	1
			1	0	2
			1	1	3
		1	0	0	4
		1	0	1	5
		1	1	0	6
		1	1	1	7
	1	0	0	0	8
	1	0	0	1	9
	1	0	1	0	10
	1	0	1	1	11
	1	1	0	0	12
	1	1	0	1	13
	1	1	1	0	14
	1	1	1	1	15
1	0	0	0	0	16
1	0	0	0	1	17
1	0	0	1	0	18
1	0	0	1	1	19
1	0	1	0	0	20

Base Five

+	0	1	2	3	4
0	0	1	2	3	4
1	1	2	3	4	10
2	2	3	4	10	11
3	3	4	10	11	12
4	4	10	11	12	13

$\times$	0	1	2	3	4
0	0	0	0	0	0
1	0	1	2	3	4
2	0	2	4	11	13
2	0	3	11	13	22
4	0	4	13	22	31

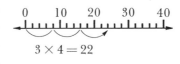

$3 \times 4 = 22$

Base Two

+	0	1
0	0	1
1	1	10

$\times$	0	1
0	0	0
1	0	1

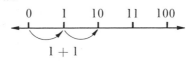

$1 + 1$

The solution of computations that require renaming provides an opportunity for pupils to gain further insight into the renaming rationale. Several
completed examples are presented below.

Addition base five   (use table).

$$\begin{array}{r} 324 \\ +\ 243 \\ \hline 1122 \end{array}$$

$4 + 3 = 12$; write 2, "carry 1."
$2 + 4 = 11$; $11 + 1 = 12$; write 2, "carry 1."
$3 + 2 = 10$; $10 + 1 = 11$; write 11.

Multiplication base five   (use table).

$$\begin{array}{r} 234 \\ \times\ 23 \\ \hline 1312 \\ 10230 \\ \hline 12042 \end{array}$$

$3 \times 4 = 22$; write 2, "carry 2."
$3 \times 3 = 14$; $14 + 2 = 21$; write 1, "carry 2."
$3 \times 2 = 11$; $11 + 2 = 13$; write 13.
Same procedure for 20×234.

Division base five   (use multiplication table).

$$\begin{array}{r} 2 \\ 30 \\ 4)\overline{233} \\ 220 \\ \hline 13 \\ 13 \\ \hline \end{array}$$

How many 4's equal 233?
Check table; three 4's = 22. Thus, by place value,
thirty 4's = 220.
How many 4's equal 13? Check table.

Older numeration systems

A study of numeration systems used by ancient peoples can be both
interesting and useful for providing insight into present-day problems. Typically, schools study the system used by the Romans because it is used on clocks,
in cornerstones on buildings, in outlines, etc. The Roman system can be of
greater value to the pupils if its structure is also studied. In addition, pupils
can benefit from studying the systems used by the Babylonians, the Egyptians,
the Mayas, the Greeks, and possibly the Chinese. Short descriptions of the
Egyptian, Babylonian, and Mayan systems are provided in the material that
follows. Also, a table showing basic numerals in several systems is presented.

Egyptian numerals.   The Egyptian system of notation is at least five thousand
years old. They developed hieroglyphic picture writing and a set of hieroglyphic numerals. The basic symbols are shown below.

Egyptian Numerals

1	10	100	1,000	10,000	100,000	1,000,000
vertical stroke	heelbone	coil of rope	lotus flower	bent line	burbot fish	man in astonishment

Note the introduction of a new symbol for each power of ten and the use of objects familiar to persons engaged in commerce along the Nile. The Egyptian system made use of two features. (1) A symbol could be repeated several times in one numeral form. Thus, ∩∩||| = 23. This is called the *repetition* principle. (2) The location of a symbol in a numeral does not affect its value. This type of system is an *additive* system *without place value*.

Note: $= 1,000 + 1000 + 10 + 10 + 10 + 10 + 10 + 1 + 1 + 1 = 2,053$

The Hindu-Arabic system uses both the principles of place value and of addition. Thus, $222 = 200 + 20 + 2$.

Babylonian numerals.   About the same time that the Egyptians were writing their numerals in stone, the Babylonians in Mesopotamia were writing numerals in clay using a stylus. The numerals were wedge-shaped (cuneiform) symbols. The system used a base of 60 (a sexagesimal system). The Babylonians were great traders and interested in astronomy. Their base of 60 was probably developed because 60 can be closely associated with 360, the number of calendar days in the Babylonian year. (Today we use 60 and multiples of 60 for time, angles, the globe, etc.) The Babylonians made some use of place value as we know it. (See below.) Also, their system made use of repetition (VVV = 3) and addition (<<< VVV = $10 + 10 + 10 + 1 + 1 + 1 = 33$).

Babylonian Numerals

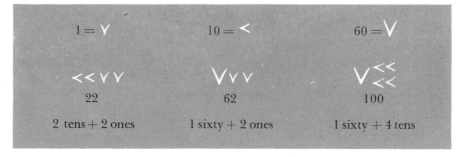

Mayan numerals. The Mayas of southern Mexico had a well-developed system of number notation. The Mayas used a base of 20 and had two numeral forms, a standard form and a hieroglyphic form used for artistic and religious purposes. It is believed that some time during the fourth century B.C. the Mayan priests for the first time in history devised a system of numeration involving position (place value) and the use of a symbol for zero. This development preceded the Hindu development of positional value and the use of zero by about one thousand years. Repetition was used in the case of the numeral for one (.) and the numeral for 5 (-). Thus, (... = 3) and ≣ = 15.

Mayan Numerals

ILLUSTRATIVE QUESTIONS

1. Which system, the Mayan, Egyptian, or Babylonian, exhibits the closest parallel to our system of place value? Why?

2. Most early notational systems were not used for computation. Why? Check references to see how computation was handled.

3. What carry-overs do we have from the Babylonian base of 60?

4. Devise a numeration system of your own. Invent symbols and a form of place value.

5. Why do you think the Mayans used ⬭ to indicate 360 rather than 400?

6. What principle of the Roman system allows us to know that XC is equal to 90, not 110?

7. What symbol in the Mayan system corresponds to zero in our system?

Hindu Arabic	Egyptian	Babylonian (base 60)	Mayan (base 20)	Greek	Chinese
1	I	V	•	A	一
2	II	V V	• •	B	二
3	III	V V V	• • •	Γ	三
4	IIII	V V V V	• • • •	Δ	四
5	III II	V V V / V V	—	E	五
10	∩ Arch	<	=	I	十
15	∩ III II	< V V V / V V	≡		
20	∩∩	< / <	⊙	K	
50	∩∩∩ / ∩∩	< < < / < <		N	
60	∩∩∩ / ∩∩∩	V	⊙	⊟	
100	☉ Coiled rope	V < < < <	⊙	P	百
360	999 ∩∩∩ / 999 ∩∩∩	V V V / V V V	⊙		
600	999 / 999	<		X	
1,000	♀ Lotus flower	< V V V <<<< / V V V		IA	千
10,000	A pointed finger			M	
100,000	A burbot fish				
1,000,000	Man in astonishment				

281

1. Explain the importance of tying to previous knowledge new skills, concepts, and generalizations related to decimals.
2. Your class questions the practicability of bases other than 10. Describe social applications that may be useful in demonstrating the use of other bases.
3. Discuss ways in which instruction in exponential notation and expanded notation aid in the understanding of a numeration system.
4. Explain how you could demonstrate the fundamental properties in bases other than 10.
5. The teaching of exponents can either precede or follow the teaching of numeration systems with bases other than 10. Discuss the reasons advanced for each of these practices.
6. Prepare a one-page letter to parents which explains why bases other than 10 are taught.
7. Develop a lesson for reintroducing decimals which uses an historical setting.

SUGGESTED REFERENCES

Allen, H. D., "Understanding Through Number Systems," *The Mathematics Teacher,* Vol. 55 (March 1962), pp. 184–188.

Banks, J. H., *Learning and Teaching Arithmetic* (Boston: Allyn & Bacon, 1964), Chaps. 10 and 11.

Grossnickle, F. E., and Brueckner, L. J., *Discovering Meanings In Elementary School Mathematics* (New York: Holt, Rinehart and Winston, 1963), Chap. 12.

Hollister, G. E., and Gunderson, A. G., *Teaching Arithmetic in the Primary Grades* (Boston: Heath, 1964), Chap. 4.

Howard, Charles F., and Dumas, Enoch, *Basic Procedures in Teaching Arithmetic* (Boston: Heath, 1963), Chap. 10, pp. 267–288.

Jamison, K. W., "An Experiment With a Variable Base Abacus," *The Arithmetic Teacher,* Vol. 11, No. 2 (February 1964), pp. 81–84.

Marks, J. L., Purdy, C. R., and Kinney, L. A., *Teaching Elementary School Mathematics for Understanding* (New York: McGraw-Hill, 1965), Chap. 10.

Mueller, F. J., *Arithmetic: Its Structures and Concepts* (Englewood Cliffs, New Jersey: Prentice-Hall, 1964), Chaps. 3, 4, 21, and 22.

Peterson, W., "Numeration—A Fresh Look," *The Arithmetic Teacher,* Vol. 12, No. 5 (May 1965), pp. 335–338.

Swenson, E. J., *Teaching Arithmetic to Children* (New York: MacMillan, 1964), Chaps. 3, and 17.

USE OF SUGGESTED REFERENCES

1. Jamison did an experiment involving the use of the abacus as an aid in teaching numeration. Peterson suggests the use of the abacus in teaching numeration. Read both articles and write a critique on the use of the abacus in instruction on numeration.

2. Contrast the approach to teaching decimals suggested by Marks, Purdy, and Kinney with the approach suggested by Grossnickle and Brueckner.

3. Compare the use of the word "and" in relation to the decimal point as presented by Banks and by Swenson. Is there a difference of opinion? Why?

4. Why would the understanding of other numeration systems be helpful to a primary teacher in teaching beginning concepts of the Hindu-Arabic system?

5. Examine the approach to teaching division of decimal fractions suggested by Howard and Dumas. Compare their handling of the topic with that of Grossnickle and Brueckner.

6. For additional information or depth of understanding read Allen's article.

7. Mueller indicates that general acceptance of the Hindu-Arabic system coincided with the early developments in modern science. What hypotheses can you draw concerning this relationship? Is there any parallel to our present use of other bases in computers?

10

Ratio, proportion,
and percent

RATIO AND PROPORTION

Pairs of numbers may be used to indicate a relationship between the numbers. One of the most useful relations is the *ratio* of one number to another. The ratio of the number 3 to the number 4 is the quotient $3 \div 4$. In early times this relationship was written 3:4 (three is to four). Today ratios are more often written in the form of a fractional numeral ($\frac{3}{4}$) or as an ordered pair (3, 4).

The concept of sets provides a helpful method of studying ratio.[1] The ratio is considered to express a numerical property that exists between two sets. For example, if apples are sold at 2 for 5¢, the relationship between sets of apples and pennies may be shown in the following manner:

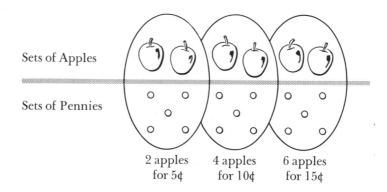

Sets of Apples

Sets of Pennies

2 apples 4 apples 6 apples
for 5¢   for 10¢   for 15¢

The ratio or the relationship illustrated exists between sets of apples and pennies. This is a modern interpretation of ratio. Some mathematicians to-

[1] Francis J. Mueller, *Arithmetic: Its Structure and Concepts,* 2nd ed. (Englewood Cliffs, New Jersey: Prentice-Hall, 1964), pp. 290–291.

day use the term "rate" or "rate pairs" to indicate the relationship between two dissimilar sets. The traditional interpretation requires that only *like* things be compared. Thus, in traditional ratio terms, apples must be compared with apples and pennies with pennies.

<table>
<tr><td colspan="2" align="center">Traditional</td><td colspan="2" align="center">Modern</td></tr>
</table>

$$\frac{2 \text{ apples}}{6 \text{ apples}} = \frac{5\cancel{c}}{15\cancel{c}} \qquad \frac{2 \text{ apples}}{5\cancel{c}} = \frac{6 \text{ apples}}{15\cancel{c}}$$

The greatest use of ratios in problem solving involves finding the equivalent ratio or *proportion*. The statement $\frac{3}{4} = \frac{6}{8}$ expresses a proportionality relationship and may be read "3 is to 4 as 6 is to 8." An infinite set of equivalent ratios such as $\{\frac{1}{2}, \frac{2}{4}, \frac{3}{6}, \frac{4}{8} \ldots \frac{n}{2n}\}$ can be generated. This set is representative of a proportionality relationship.

Such a relationship may be shown graphically. The proportionality relationship always produces a straight-line graph, but not all straight-line graphings are proportionality relationships.

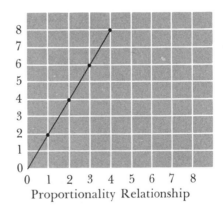

Proportionality Relationship

Illustrated procedures for teaching proportions are developed later in this chapter.

Historical development

Ratio and proportion had their origin in antiquity. Documents containing ratios and proportions and dating back to the early Egyptian and Babylonian civilizations have been found. The early Greeks made major advances in the use of ratio. Euclid treated ratios in developing a theory of music. He, along with a number of other Greek mathematicians, considered ratios as relations, rather than as numbers.

Ratio was also used extensively by the Hindus and Arabs. For example, the Hindu Al-Khowarizmi made extensive use of ratio in his algebra in A.D. 825, and the Moorish Arabs also made extensive use of ratio.[2] During the Middle Ages ratio was taught in Italy and employed in solving everyday business problems.

[2] Louis C. Karpinski, *The History of Arithmetic* (Chicago: Rand, McNally, 1925), p. 139.

Ratio was emphasized in textbooks used in the United States until the end of the nineteenth century. Textbooks of the late 1880's contained highly complex proportionality problems such as "If in 8 days 15 sugar maples, each running 12 quarts of sap per day, make 10 boxes of sugar, each weighing 6 lb., how many boxes weighing 10 lb. apiece, will a maple grove containing 300 trees, make in 36 days, each tree running 16 quarts per day? Answer, 720 boxes." [3]

Because of the extremely long and complicated problems used with ratio and proportion and the belief that a linear equation could be used more easily, early twentieth-century writers attacked the heavy emphasis given to ratio and proportion. In 1909 David Eugene Smith attacked the wide use of ratio in the elementary school.[4] He suggested the use of a simple equation or *unitary analysis*. Unitary analysis involved finding the cost of one object and then finding the total. For example, "If 2 apples cost 6 cents, how much will 5 apples cost?"

Using unitary analysis	Using a proportion
2 cost 6 cents	$\frac{2}{6} = \frac{5}{n}$
1 costs $\frac{1}{2}$ of 6, or 3 cents	$2N = 30$
5 will cost 5×3 or 15 cents.	$N = 15.$

Thus, between 1910 and 1950 there was little formal study of ratio in the elementary school mathematics program. With the reform movement in mathematics during the late 1950's and 1960's the teaching of ratio again became an integral part of the elementary mathematics curriculum.

Current issues

There are still many unanswered problems concerning ratio and the use of ratio. The three following questions are discussed in detail: (1) Are ratios rational numbers? (2) How important is the use of ratio in the schools today? (3) How early in the elementary school curriculum should ratios be introduced?

Are ratios rational numbers?   This is one of the debatable questions of mathematics education. Hartung, Van Engen, and others contend that ratios are relations, not numbers. They state:[5]

Ratios are often written with one numeral above the other as shown in the example at the right. Remember that this symbol does *not*, in this case, represent a fraction. It represents a rate. Note that in the example about the "pieces of candy" and the "cents," one cannot say that "The candy is a fraction of the money."

[3] James B. Thompson, *New Practical Arithmetic* (New York: Clark and Maynard Publishers, 1873), p. 318.
[4] David E. Smith, *The Teaching of Arithmetic* (Boston: Ginn, 1909), pp. 185–186.
[5] From *Charting the Course for Arithmetic*, by Maurice L. Hartung, Henry Van Engen, Lois Knowles, and E. Glenadine Gibb, p. 104. Copyright© by Scott, Foresman & Company, Chicago, Illinois.

The School Mathematics Study Group states:[6]

It will be recognized here that ratio is not presented as a number. . . . ratio is called a property belonging to two sets and the symbol used for ratio describes this property. The similarity of the words "ratio" and "rational" may suggest some close relation between ratios and rational numbers; such a relation does exist.

While ratios can be matched in a one-to-one correspondence to every rational number on the number line, they do not perform in the same manner as members of the number system. The essential difference between working with ordered pairs as "rate pairs" rather than as "rational numbers" is that rational numbers may be added, subtracted, multiplied, and divided. Working with rate pairs involves working with one equivalence class at a time. While operations are not usually performed on ratios, there are occasions in which a problem situation requires the combining of two ratios. For example, if Bob bought 3 pencils for 10¢ and 2 pencils for 5¢, what was the total number of pencils he purchased and the total cost? The addition $\frac{3}{10} + \frac{2}{5} = \frac{3}{10} + \frac{4}{10} = \frac{7}{10}$ would yield an incorrect result. Actually the addition would involve adding numerators to numerators and denominators to denominators: $\frac{3}{10} + \frac{2}{5} = \frac{5}{15}$—five pencils for fifteen cents. Because of the inconsistency between this example and rational number addition, it is advisable to handle the problem in two steps: (1) find the total pencils; and (2) find the total cost without writing in fraction form.

It is suggested that the teacher make use of ratios as relations and also take advantage of the fact that ratios behave in the same manner as rational numbers in terms of developing equivalent ratios. Normally the question, "Are ratios rational numbers?" does not arise in the elementary school. This is probably a fortunate circumstance because pupils need a rather sophisticated background to debate the question.

How important is the use of ratio in the elementary school today? Many problem situations involve "rate" ideas or "comparison." Such problems are solved in a more concise fashion and with good understanding if the idea of ratio is well taught. An understanding of ratio also leads to a useful means of viewing percent. These uses should make the study of ratio worthy of adequate time in the elementary school.

How early in the elementary school curriculum should ratios be introduced? From 1920 to 1957 few, if any, elementary school textbooks included the topic of ratio and proportion. This was delayed until the junior high school. At present, most commercial and "study group" materials introduce the topic of ratio at the fifth-grade level. Recent informal studies have revealed that pupils in the third and fourth grades can use ratio effectively to solve verbal problems involving relatively small quantities. Thus a foundation for the study of ratio can be laid in the primary grades, and through the use of drawings the topic can be developed thoroughly in grades five and six.

[6] School Mathematics Study Group, *Mathematics for the Elementary Grade Five Teachers' Commentary*, Part II (New Haven: Yale University Press, 1963), p. 835.

Teaching ratio and proportion

Developing ratio involves matching sets in one-to-many, many-to-one, or many-to-many correspondence. Two basic ideas, *rate* and *comparison*, may be conveyed by the matched sets. These two ideas can be understood more easily by looking at social situations that involve them. An example of a rate situation is, "Three apples cost ten cents." This rate can be expressed by two numerals, 3 to indicate the number of apples and 10 to indicate the number of cents needed to purchase the apples. An example of a comparison is, "Jill has three dolls and her sister Ann has two." The $\frac{3}{2}$ expresses the relation between Jill's dolls and Ann's dolls. The rate idea is more important to the problem-solving program of the elementary school than is the comparison idea.

Primary-grade teachers can begin to develop an understanding of ratios using sets of objects, the flannel board, and the chalkboard. Several possible situations and their representations are depicted in the following material.

We get 5 cartons of milk for 10 cents.
(Rate)

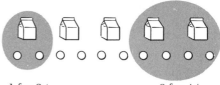

5 for 10¢

Can you tell me how much one carton of milk would cost? Two cartons?

1 for 2¢   2 for 4¢

Jim bought 3 candy bars for 9¢.
(Rate)

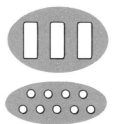

Fred

5 to 8

Fred has 5 arrowheads and Jim has 8.
(Comparison)

Jim

Ratio does not become a useful tool in mathematics until the idea of *equivalent ratios* or *proportions* is developed. Introductory problems for this concept can take the following form:

1. Jill earns 5¢ for every 3 times she makes her bed. How many times must she make her bed to earn 15¢?

2. Miss Kent bought 2 bars of soap for 15¢. At this rate how much would 6 bars cost?

If a guided discovery approach is used, with the suggestion that pupils use previous ideas concerning number pairs and develop drawings and diagrams, the following early solutions to the second rate problem will probably occur.

Mark: 6 for 45¢

Francis: I doubled the cost for 2 bars of soap. Then I could see that 2 bars cost 15¢; 4 bars cost 30¢. Then I added the cost of 2 bars and the cost of 4 bars. Six bars cost 45¢. As a ratio, 6 per 45.

2	4	6
15¢	30¢	45¢

Ken: I used the number line to indicate 2 for 15¢. I marked off another 15¢ for 2 bars more and still another 15¢ for a total of 6 for 45¢.

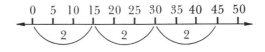

A chart of number pairs such as that used by Francis provides an opportunity to search for efficient methods to solve rate problems. One teacher handled the situation with exploration in the following manner: "Francis has shown a chart of number pairs which indicates the relationship between the number of bars of soap and the price. These number pairs or ratios are often written by using the same numeral we use with fractions. How would you interpret this pair of numerals in a rate situation — $\frac{2}{7}$ — Right; 2 for 7 or 2 per 7."

"Look at this problem. How could you write pairs of numerals to describe this situation?" (The class had previously discussed simple machines during science.) "A lever is set so that when you move the handle (effort arm)

6 feet, the resistance arm moves 2 feet. How far will the resistance arm move if the effort arm is moved 18 feet? Look at the diagram."

effort	6	18	$\frac{6}{2} = \frac{18}{N}$
resistance	2	N	$N = 6$

Pupils wrote the pairs of numerals in the notation illustrated above. The teacher asked the pupils to describe the relationship between the ratio $\frac{6}{2}$ and $\frac{18}{6}$. The pupils determined that the two ratios were equivalent.

In the lessons on ratio and problem solving that followed, the pupils learned to find the missing number in a proportion in the same manner as they had developed equivalent fractions.

The cross-products approach. Knowing that the cross-products of two equivalent ratios are equal can be a valuable tool in problem solving. In looking for an unknown such as $\frac{2}{3} = \frac{N}{21}$, the cross-products are $3N = 42$. Pupils then can find a number for N by dividing both sides of the equation by 3, because this does not affect the equality. Thus, $\frac{3N}{3} = \frac{42}{3}$; $N = 14$.

The cross-products idea can be developed in the following manner. Pupils had been working on sets of equivalent number pairs.

$$\left\{\frac{1}{2}, \frac{2}{4}, \dots, \frac{N}{2N}\right\} \qquad \left\{\frac{2}{3}, \frac{4}{\Box}, \frac{6}{\Box}, \frac{\Box}{12}\right\}$$

$$\left\{\frac{5}{9}, \frac{10}{18}, \dots, \frac{5N}{9N}\right\} \qquad \left\{\frac{3}{4}, ?, ?, ?, ?\right\}$$

They had found other members of the set by multiplying or dividing the members of the set by a form of the identity element such as $\frac{3}{3}$, $\frac{4}{4}$, etc. Then the teacher said, "Let's study a few equivalent number pairs and see if we can find any relationship between them. Look at $\frac{1}{2} = \frac{2}{4}$, $\frac{3}{4} = \frac{6}{8}$, $\frac{2}{3} = \frac{4}{6}$. Do you notice any similarities? Work with these number pairs during your spare time and see what you can discover. Test your findings on other equivalent number pairs. We'll discuss your findings tomorrow."

The next day the members of the class discussed their findings. The majority of the pupils had found that the product of numerator (first pair) times denominator (second pair) and denominator (first pair) times numerator (second pair) were equal. They had verified their findings by testing a large number of instances. The teacher said, "You've discovered a valuable tool for working with number pairs. The equality that you've just mentioned is usually stated, 'the cross-products of two equivalent number pairs are equal.'

What do we mean by cross-products?" The pupils discussed the meaning of cross-products. Then they were given several verbal problems with instructions to see if they could use the cross-products idea to solve the problems. Two of the problems and the cross-product development are recorded below.

1. The pull of gravity on the moon is $\frac{1}{6}$ the pull of gravity on the earth. A track champion can high jump 7 feet on the earth. What would be the height of a bar he could clear on the moon (all other things being equal)?

$$\text{Proportion: } \tfrac{1}{6} = \tfrac{7}{N} \qquad \text{Cross-product: } 1 \times N = 6 \times 7$$
$$N = 42.$$

2. A large gear turns 3 times while a small gear turns 15 times. How many times will the large gear turn if the small gear turns 60 times?

Proportion: $\frac{3}{15} = \frac{N}{60}$

Cross-product:[7]
$$3 \times 60 = 15 \times N$$
$$15N = 180$$
$$\frac{15N}{15} = \frac{180}{15}$$
$$N = 12$$

Analysis

Ratio and proportion can be valuable tools for verbal problem solving in the elementary school. The task for today's teachers is to establish a balance in teaching the topics, for it is possible to overdo ratio in the manner of the late 1800's. Pupils should use ratio and proportion as *one* possible tool in problem solving. The teacher should take care not to require a ratio solution of all problems. For example, "Ned has 15¢, and Art has 5¢. How many times as much money does Ned have as compared to Art?" or "Jill bought 4 stamps. Janet bought 3 times as many as Jill. How many stamps did Janet buy?" While the above problems involve comparison, they are easily handled by division in the first case (15 ÷ 5 = 3), and multiplication in the second case (3 × 4 = 12). There is little need to develop a proportion to solve either of the problems.

[7] Note: The solution of an equation such as $15N = 180$ had previously been taught. See chapter 11 for procedures.

PERCENT

Percent has been taught as another means of viewing decimals. Actually, percents were used long before decimals were developed. The term "percent" is derived from the Latin *per centum* meaning "by the hundred." Thus, the origin of percent and its major uses are more closely associated with rates and ratio than with decimals.

Many believe that the teaching of percent should cause little if any difficulty because of the close relationship of percents, ratios, and decimals. Those experienced in teaching the upper elementary grades often disagree with the conjecture. There are several reasons why the topic of percent often does confuse children and adults.

The precise language of percent

The language of percent is very precise. This precision is, in a sense, two-headed; it makes percent extremely useful, but on occasion it also causes confusion. Several common misconceptions that are found in the use of percent are analyzed below.

1. If a small-town weekly newspaper states, "Juvenile delinquency has risen by 50% this year," the population may become very upset. If, however, the paper stated, "Last year there were two cases of delinquency. This year there were three," the reaction probably would not be the same. This difficulty occurs because when some rates are converted to hundredths, they may appear to represent a larger sample than is actually the case.

2. A statement, "Forty percent of the pupils in Washington Elementary School gave to the cancer drive. Thus, 160 out of the 400 pupils donated money to the cancer drive," may be correct. If a pupil then states, "Forty percent of our class gave to the cancer drive," he may be incorrect. A rate stated for an entire population may not be true for a sample of the population.

3. A store stated, "Prices reduced 100%." Actually the store had reduced its prices 50%. An item that originally sold for $10 was on sale for $5. The store based the 100% on the sale price when it should have been based on the original price.

4. When asked, "Would you be willing to lend money at .09%?" many persons enthusiastically responded, Yes. They believed the figure to represent $9 interest per $100, when it actually represented an interest rate of 9¢ per $100.

5. A lending agency states, "We have auto loans for 5% interest." In reality, the charge is 5% of the entire loan for each of three years. Note the difference.

$1800 borrowed for three years
$50 per month paid on the principal

Regular 5% loan		Agency loan	
1st year's interest		1st year's interest	
5% of 1800 =	$90.00	5% of 1800 =	$90.00
$1800		$1800	
600 paid on principal		600 paid on principal	
$1200		$1200	
2nd year's interest		2nd years' interest	
5% of 1200 =	$60.00	5% of 1800 =	$90.00
$1200		$1200	
600 paid on principal		600	
$ 600		$ 600	
3rd year's interest		3rd year's interest	
5% of 600 =	$30.00	5% of 1800 =	$90.00
$600		$600	
600 paid on principal	$180.00 total	600	$270.00 total
0	interest	0	interest

In the above case, a policy concerning percent is implied but not stated.

Foundation work with percent

Computation with percent is not usually developed until the fifth or sixth grade. However, an understanding of the theory of percent is necessary earlier to ensure proper interpretation of social studies, science materials, and situations outside of school. The meaning of percent can be introduced effectively at the fourth-grade level by using materials from science and social studies. One teacher introduced percent by saying, "In your social studies book today you read that 8 out of 10, or 80 percent, of the population of an African country lived along the coast or along rivers. What do they mean by 80%?"

Class discussion suggested that 80% must be equivalent to 8 per 10. Also, they felt that the term "cent" must have something to do with 100. Because pupils knew that 80 per 100 and 8 per 10 were equivalent ratios, they reasoned that 80 percent meant 80 per 100.

Several other examples from science and social studies were then used for interpretation. These included: "Algae to be used as food on space expeditions is 55% protein." "Thirty-eight percent of the income from services in the United States comes from manufacturing and building." "Manned space flight represents about 65% of the NASA budget." From the discussion of these and other situations that use percent, the pupils decided that percent means per hundred or by the hundred. The pupils then checked reference books to verify their thinking. They also checked on the historical development of percent.

Since the meaning of percent should be developed before decimals are introduced, it is important to provide pupils with some form of visualizing the meaning of percent. Probably the best single device is a type of hundred board. Individual pupils can use a piece of pegboard with a width of ten holes and a length of ten holes. Using match sticks or golf tees, the students can indicate 14%, 75%, etc. This device can also be used to help children compare fractions with percents.

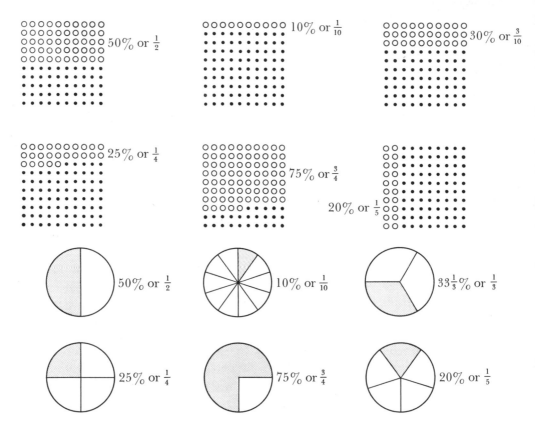

In addition to the square pattern, shaded circles may also be used. The two charts above can be constructed by the class after a need for knowing the meaning of percent has been developed.

Problems using percent

The majority of problem situations that employ percent involve three problem structures.

1. The pupils may be asked to find the percent of a number. For example, "What is 25% of 64?"

2. The pupils may be asked to find what percent one number is of another. For example, "What percent of 64 is 16?"

3. The pupils may be asked to find the total (100%) when only a percent is known. For example, "Sixteen is 25% of what number?"

Several approaches can be used to solve percent problems that occur in the literature of elementary school mathematics. Among these are (1) the decimal approach, (2) the ratio approach, (3) the unitary analysis approach, (4) the formula approach, and (5) the equation approach. Pupils' thinking in the solution of each of the three problem structures is presented for each of the approaches. Then a teaching sequence is suggested.

The following problems are solved using each approach:

1. During a sale, a 5% reduction is given on all merchandise. How much would a 40¢ item be reduced?

2. Joe won 2 games out of the 5 games that he played. What percent of the games did he win?

3. Mr. Brown sold a trailer for $150. This was 75% of the regular price. What was the regular price?

Decimal approach.   In using the decimal approach the pupil is to think, "Percent means hundredths. I change a percent to a decimal and then work the problem."

Problem 1. Pupil: I am to find 5 percent of 40. I change 5% to .05 because percent means hundredths. Then I multiply .05 × 40 to obtain the answer of 2.

Problem 2. Pupil: I am trying to find what percent 2 is of 5. This is 2 to 5. I need to change this to hundredths. Percent means hundredths.

$$\frac{.40}{5)\,\overline{2.00}}$$

Therefore .40 is 40%.

Problem 3. Pupil: Seventy-five percent means .75. To find the whole when I know a part I must divide the number by the decimal.

$$\frac{200}{.75_\wedge)\,\overline{150.00_\wedge}}$$

The ratio approach.   All problems are solved by developing a pair of equivalent ratios with a place holder representing the number which is sought.

This approach employs the idea that percent means per hundred, implying a rate.

Problem 1. Pupil: Five percent are absent, which means 5 per 100 are absent. The ratio per 40 will be equivalent to the ratio per 100. Thus I set up equivalent ratios to solve the problem.

$$\frac{5}{100} = \frac{N}{40} \qquad \begin{aligned} 100N &= 200 \\ N &= 2 \end{aligned}$$

(For the early work the student developed equivalent number pairs. Later he may use the equality of the cross-products development.)

Problem 2. Pupil: Joe won 2 games per 5 played. Now I must find out how many he would win per 100.

$$\frac{2}{5} = \frac{N}{100} \qquad \begin{aligned} 5N &= 200 \\ N &= 40 \end{aligned}$$

This means 40 per 100 or 40%.

Problem 3. Pupil: I'm to find the number of which $150 is 75%. Or, $150 is 75% of what number. I think, 75 to 100 is equal to $150 to N.

$$\frac{75}{100} = \frac{150}{N} \qquad \begin{aligned} 75N &= 15,000 \\ N &= 200 \end{aligned}$$

In order to use the ratio approach the pupils must understand ratio and proportion and be able to solve simple equations. Actually these are not difficult to understand. Pupils should be solving simple equations and working with some ratios by the fourth-grade level. If the pupils have not studied ratio by the time percent begins, it is quite possible to teach ratio and percent simultaneously. The use of ratio eliminates the need for previous study of decimal computation.

Unitary-analysis approach.   The unitary analysis approach, sometimes called the one-percent method, was once very popular in schools in the United States. It has some advantages, particularly for the slower student, because it is easily understood and requires similar thinking for all three types of problems.

Problem 1. Pupil: I want to find 5% of 40. First I'll find what 1% would be. Since 100% of the amount is 40, I can find 1% by dividing 40 by 100.

$$100\overline{)40.0}^{\,.4}$$ One percent of 40 is .4.   Five percent of 40 is $5 \times .4 = 2$.

Problem 2. Pupil: I'm finding what percent 2 is of 5.

$$5 \text{ games} = 100\% \text{ of the total.}$$
$$1 \text{ game} \ = \frac{100}{5} = 20\% \text{ of the total.}$$
$$2 \text{ games} = 2 \times 20\% = 40\%.$$

Problem 3. Pupil: I'm to find what number 150 is 75% of.

75% of the number is 150.

$$1\% \text{ of the number (} 75\overline{)150} \text{) is 2.}$$
$$100\% \text{ of the number} = 100 \times 2 = 200.$$

The solution of the above problems by unitary analysis reveals several weaknesses of the method. Solution of type-1 problems often requires rather difficult division of decimals. Also, note the cumbersome development in problems 1 and 2. Probably the chief use of unitary analysis is in type-3 problems because unitary analysis does add understanding to this problem structure.

The formula approach.   Until the past few years the formula approach was the basic approach used for the solution of problems involving percent. In the formula approach the "three parts" of percent problems are labeled. Consider this percent problem: What is 10% of 80? Answer, 8. In this case 80, (the set upon which the comparison is to be made) is called the *base*. The set compared to the base (in this case 8) is called the *percentage,* and the percent which states the ratio of the percentage to the base is called the *rate.* Using these three terms, a formula is derived. The basic formula used is percentage = rate × base, or $P = RB$.

Problem 1. Pupil: I want to find 5% of 40. Five percent is the rate. Forty is the base. Percentage = Rate × Base or $P = RB$.

$$P = 5\% \times 40$$
$$P = .05 \times 40 \text{ (5\% is equivalent to .05.)}$$
$$P = 2$$

Problem 2. Pupil: I'm to find what percent 2 is of 5. Five is the base. Two is the percentage. I'm looking for the rate. Rate $= \dfrac{\text{Percentage}}{\text{Base}}$ or $R = \dfrac{P}{B}$.

$$R = \frac{2}{5}$$
$$R = .40 \text{ (.40 is equivalent to 40\%.)}$$
$$R = 40\%$$

Problem 3. Pupil: I'm to find what number 150 is 75% of. I'm looking for the base. Base $= \dfrac{\text{Percentage}}{\text{Rate}}$ or $B = \dfrac{P}{R}$

$$B = \frac{150}{75\%}$$

$$B = \frac{150}{.75} \quad (75\% \text{ is equivalent to } .75.)$$

$$B = 200$$

The formula approach is mathematically precise and efficient. It does, however, present difficulty to the student who does not have a very firm grasp of percents. Another difficulty is that in the formula P (for percentage) represents a number rather than a percent, while R (rate) is expressed as a percent. Pupils often mistakenly consider the rate to be the percentage.

Equation approach.   The equation approach makes use of the logical thinking required for unitary analysis. It also has some of the features of the formula. The writing of the mathematical sentence required in the equation approach ties it closely to the type of mathematical thinking wanted in problem solving.

Problem 1. Pupil: The essential mathematical statement is Find 5% of 40. Or, what number is equal to 5% of 40? Now I translate the sentence into a mathematical sentence.

$$N = 5\% \times 40 \quad (5\% \text{ is equivalent to } .05 \text{ or } \tfrac{5}{100}.)$$
$$N = .05 \times 40$$
$$N = 2$$

Problem 2. Pupil: The essential mathematical question is, Two is what % of 5? I write this as a mathematical sentence.

$$2 = N \times 5$$
$$2 = 5N \quad (\text{I divide both sides of the equation by } 5.)$$
$$\frac{2}{5} = N$$
$$\frac{2}{5} = .40 = 40\% = N.$$

Problem 3. Pupil: I have to find the regular price when I know 75% of the regular price. A mathematical statement might be 75% of the number equals 150. Now I write a mathematical sentence.

$$75\% \times N = 150 \quad (75\% \text{ is equivalent to } .75.)$$
$$.75\,N = 150 \quad (\text{I divide both sides of the equation by } .75.)$$
$$N = \frac{150}{.75}$$
$$N = 200$$

The format of the equation approach becomes similar to that of the decimal approach, but the equation approach places greater emphasis upon the structure of the problem and an understanding of the rationale.

Teaching problems involving percent

Literature on the teaching of elementary school mathematics abounds with suggestions for teaching percent. Each of the approaches previously presented has its proponents. While studies are unclear as to the best single approach to teaching percent, there are indications that interrelationships between percent problems should be stressed[8] and that the use of ratio in teaching percent is of value.[9]

The suggestions that follow concerning the teaching of percent are based upon the supposition that pupils have had experience with a guided discovery approach to teaching, understand the ideas of rate and ratio, and have some acquaintance with fractions and decimals.

The teacher introduced the topic with this problem: "In the early days of the U.S. space effort, only 30% of the rocket shots were successful. At that rate, how many successful firings were made for 50 attempts?"

The pupils were instructed to state the basic mathematical question involved; to write a mathematical sentence that could be used in solving the problem; and then to try to verify the answer. Because of their previous background, a number of approaches were used with this problem. Descriptions of these approaches follow.

Nancy: I thought of 30% as being equivalent to $\frac{30}{100}$, which I wrote as a decimal. My question was, What is 30% of 50? I then wrote the mathematical sentence $N = .30 \times 50$. I multiplied $.30 \times 50 = 15$. $N = 15$.

Jack: I used the same idea as Nancy but wrote the mathematical sentence as $N = \frac{30}{100} \times 50 = 15$.

Dave: We are dealing with a rate. I wanted to find the number that would indicate the same relationship to 50 as 30 does to 100. I wrote a mathematical sentence using equivalent ratios: $\frac{N}{50} = \frac{30}{100}$. Then I used the cross-products relationship to find the missing number. $100N = 1500$; $N = 15$. I could have solved it by equivalent number pairs: $\frac{N}{50} = \frac{30}{100}$. I divided 100 by 2 to get 50; $30 \div 2 = 15$. Thus, $\frac{15}{50} = \frac{30}{100}$, $N = 15$.

Joyce: I was trying to find what number is 30% of 50. I couldn't write a very good mathematical sentence, but I worked the problem by thinking 100% of the entire rocket shots = 50. One percent of the shots would be $\frac{50}{100}$ or $\frac{1}{2}$. Then, 30% would be $30 \times \frac{1}{2} = 15$.

[8] Daniel C. Treadway, "An Experimental Study of Two Approaches to Teaching Percentage," *The Arithmetic Teacher,* Vol. 10, No. 8 (December 1963), pp. 491–495.
[9] Della McMahon, *An Experimental Comparison of Two Methods of Teaching Per Cent* (Unpublished Ph.D. dissertation, University of Missouri, 1959).

When the various approaches are studied, the features of each approach become clearer. The ratio approach used by Dave indicates a good understanding of the relationship between percents and ratio. The approach used by Nancy does not indicate the rate aspect of percent in as evident a manner as Dave's does, but the approach is very efficient. The approach used by Joyce is understandable but could be very cumbersome.

Class consideration of the approaches revealed a rather even division of class members between the approaches used by Nancy and Dave. The teacher pointed out that both of these approaches were used quite often in working with percent. The pupils were challenged to become acquainted with each and also to examine carefully the approach used by Joyce (unitary analysis).

The next day, the pupils solved type-1 problems, and the teacher introduced type-2 problems with this problem: "In a series of rocket tests, 9 of 12 test shots were considered successful. What percent were considered successful?"

Again two basic approaches were used. Several pupils considered the problem to be that of finding an equivalent ratio to $\frac{9}{12}$. They wrote the mathematical sentence $\frac{9}{12} = \frac{N}{100}$; $12N = 900$; $N = 75$. Others changed $\frac{9}{12}$ to a decimal, .75, and then changed .75 to 75%. Several of the pupils tried the unitary analysis approach but found it to be a cumbersome method of attack.

During the discussion at the end of the period, the two types of percent problems were discussed. Dave noted that if ratios were used, the format for the two problems remained similar.

When the teacher felt the pupils had a good grasp of the first two types of problems, the third type was introduced with the following problem: "Nan saw a sign in the store window saying coats on sale for $15. This is only 75% of the regular price. She wanted to know the regular price to compare it with another store. What was the regular price?" Pupil responses are indicated below.

Harry: I worked the problem into this basic question: 15 is 75% of what number. Then I wrote this mathematical sentence: $15 = 75\% \times N$. I changed 75% to the equivalent decimal .75 and stated the mathematical sentence as $.75N = 15$. Then to find N I divided both sides of the equation by .75. Division of 15 by .75 gave me the answer of $20.

Mike: We've been able to solve the percent problems by using ratios, so I tried to develop a ratio. I thought 15 is 75% of what number? Then I wrote the mathematical sentence $\frac{15}{N} = \frac{75}{100}$. Using the cross-product I computed $75N = 1500$; $N = 20$.

Cora: I remembered the method used by Joyce on another problem. I thought I'm to find the number of which 15 is 75%. I thought 75% is 15; what would 1% be? I divided 15 by 75 $(75)\overline{15.0}$ (with .2 above) and found that 1% equaled .2. Then I multiplied by 100 to get 100%. The answer is 20.

The various solutions were discussed. The equation method used by Harry proved to be the most popular. The next day a set of problems containing all three problem types was distributed, and the pupils were asked to solve each problem using at least two methods. A discussion of the problems focused on the relationship between the problem types.

As a reintroduction and review of percent, the teacher at the next grade level may employ the formula method effectively. It is not suggested for earlier use because of the ease with which the formula is learned by rote, and therefore not understood.

Percents that are greater than 100 percent or less than 1 percent

Pupils and adults are often confused by percents such as 150% and .05%. The chief suggestion that can be made to clarify the pupils' thinking regarding very large and very small percents is to present many use situations that require interpretation and discussion. In addition, the use of the hundred board is suggested.

$\frac{1}{2}\%$ 150%

Pupils may also gain insight into these percent situations by expressing the percent as a ratio. For example, 200% can be viewed as 200 per every 100, or 2 to 1; .25% can be viewed as $\frac{1}{4}$ to 100.

One teacher introduced the topic of percents that are greater than 100 and less than 1 in the following manner: "A recent issue of *Newsweek* included this material on percents: 'Consumer prices inched up another .1% in December to 127.5% of the 1947–49 average, the Labor Department reports, bringing the increase for the year as a whole to 1.5%.' What do they mean by .1%? How could we express this amount as a decimal or as a number pair?"

After discussing percents less than 1 with the class, the teacher continued by asking, "What do they mean by the statement that the prices are 127.5% of the 1947–49 average? Is it possible to have something that is more than 100% of something else? Give some other examples."

The class continued with discussion and the remainder of the period was spent in working the problems and examples on a worksheet. Later pupils developed the generalizations listed below.

1. If a number is compared to a number that is more than 100 times itself, the percent will be less than 1 percent ($\frac{1}{200} = .5\% = \frac{1}{2}\%$).

2. Percents less than 1 can be expressed in either decimal or fractional form (.5% or $\frac{1}{2}\%$).

3. When a number is compared with a smaller number, the percent will be greater than 100.

4. If two equal numbers are compared, the percent is 100.

Analysis

The suggestions for teaching percent have focused on two important ideas. The first is that the use of the mathematical sentence (an equation in this case) gives meaning to percent problems. In writing mathematical sentences, both the ratio equation and equations involving decimals were used. Second, the unitary analysis approach was presented to give meaning to type-3 percent problems.

Because research is still unclear on a single approach to problems involving percent, it is suggested that the teacher present problems that use percent to the pupils and follow the lead that they take (if it is mathematically correct). Such a procedure is in keeping with a discovery approach and also allows greater opportunity for success in handling individual dfferences.

STUDY SUGGESTIONS

1. Obtain a sixth- or seventh-grade mathematics text and work several percent problems using the various approaches described in the chapter.
2. Analyze four textbooks that have been published in the past five years to determine the approaches taken to percent.
3. Little time is devoted to percent in several of the experimental mathematics programs. Is this justified? Discuss some of the reasons for this omission.
4. Define percent and percentage.
5. Develop a set of problems by using percent based upon newspaper or magazine content.
6. Compare the emphasis given to ratio in two textbook series published before 1960 and two textbook series published after 1965.
7. Develop a lesson on ratio using content taken from elementary school science.

SUGGESTED REFERENCES

Corle, Clyde G., *Teaching Mathematics in the Elementary School* (New York: Ronald, 1964), pp. 226–238.

Crumley, Richard D., "Teaching Rate and Ratio in the Middle Grades," *School Science and Mathematics,* Vol. LX (February 1960), pp. 143–150.

Hartung, Maurice L., Van Engen, Henry, Knowles, Lois, and Gibb, E. Glenadine, *Charting the Course for Arithmetic* (Chicago: Scott, Foresman, 1960), pp. 60–63, 103–105, and 125–129.

Marks, John L., Purdy, C. Richard, and Kenney, Lucine, B., *Teaching Elementary School Mathematics for Understanding* (New York: McGraw-Hill, 1965), pp. 328–350.

Mueller, Francis J., *Arithmetic: Its Structure and Concepts,* 2nd ed. (Englewood Cliffs, New Jersey: Prentice-Hall, 1964), pp. 302–313.

Van Engen, Henry, "Rate Pairs, Fractions and Rational Numbers," *The Arithmetic Teacher,* Vol. 7, No. 8 (December 1960), pp. 389–399.

USE OF SUGGESTED REFERENCES

1. Study Corle's development of percent of increase and decrease.
2. Crumley suggested that ratio be taught in the intermediate grades. How would he develop ratio concepts with pupils?
3. How do Hartung and his associates relate percent to ratio?
4. Develop a list of aids for teaching percent from the suggestions in the chapter presented in Marks.
5. How does Mueller use sets to develop percent?
6. Study Van Engen's development of rate pairs and rational numbers.

11

Solving verbal problems

The "verbal problems" referred to in this chapter are those orally described and written quantitative situations in which a question or questions are asked without an accompanying statement concerning the mathematical operation or operations required. In this context, "How long will 6 records which last 3 minutes each take to play?" is considered to be a verbal problem, whereas "$6 \times 3 = \square$" is not.

Purposes of verbal problems

Earlier chapters have identified one important purpose of the verbal problem, that of introducing a mathematical idea in a physical world setting. This allows pupils to derive abstractions from physical world settings and apply them in the world of mathematics. These problems also demonstrate the significance of the study of a mathematical topic. A well-worded introductory problem can do much to answer the question, Why are we studying this? Also, verbal problems add interest and variety to the elementary school mathematics program.

Another reason for the study of verbal problems is that many mathematical situations that arise in the physical sciences, the social sciences, and daily life require the ability to analyze a situation, to select the proper data and computational procedure, and to arrive at a solution.

Issues in the teaching of problem solving

Probably a greater number of studies have been concerned with verbal problem solving than with any other phase of the elementary school mathematics program. At present, well over one hundred fifty studies on various phases of problem solving have been completed, and the number continues to increase each year.

The study of problem solving by researchers reveals several ideas that should be helpful to the teacher. The section that follows raises a number of basic questions on problem solving and then makes use of research findings to give some direction to the teacher.

What effect does the narrative content have upon the pupils' ability to solve the problem?   Should conventional (social settings) or more imaginative problems be used?

Teachers are often cautioned that too many verbal problems are unrealistic and they are told that children have difficulty solving unrealistic problems. Research does not completely verify this statement. Sutherland[1] and White[2] found that pupils in familiar settings answered more problems correctly than pupils who were in unusual settings. Wheat[3] and Evans[4] found that the setting was not a factor in problem success, while Welch[5] found that the pupils favored and scored better on imaginary-type problems.

Although the evidence presented in the foregoing studies indicates disagreement concerning the types of situations that are most appropriate for children, there is an indication that using material of interest to the children is advantageous. In today's rapidly changing world it seems reasonable to assume that verbal arithmetic problems cannot accurately sample situations that will be important to children while they are in school and in their post-school life. The wise teacher will use a variety of interesting problem settings and make occasional surveys of class interest in verbal problem solving.

What problem settings do pupils prefer?   Hensell surveyed the interest of children concerning problem settings and found that the following activities were consistently high in interest: (1) games, play, and organized sports, (2) movies, (3) areas of study and academic subjects, and (4) relations or activities of people. The writer[6] used a number of problem settings with sixth-grade pupils and found that they preferred problems from foreign textbooks, old American textbooks, childhood situations, and current events.

How do good problem solvers differ from poor problem solvers?   Researchers have identified eight factors that are associated with high achievement in problem solving. Conversely, the lack of those factors is associated

[1] John Sutherland, "Investigation into Some Aspects of Problem Solving in Arithmetic," *British Journal of Educational Psychology*, Vol. 11 (November 1941), pp. 215–222; Vol. 12 (February 1942), pp. 35–46.
[2] Helen M. White, "Does Experience in the Situation Involved Affect the Solving of a Problem?" *Education*, Vol. 54 (April 1934), pp. 451–455.
[3] H. G. Wheat, *The Relative Merits of Conventional and Imaginative Types of Problems in Arithmetic*, Contributions to Education, No. 359 (Bureau of Publications, Teachers College, Columbia University, 1929).
[4] John E. Evans, *A Study of the Effect of Unfamiliar Words in Problem Solving* (Master's thesis, State University of Iowa, 1940).
[5] Ronald C. Welch, *The Relative Merits of Two Types of Arithmetic Problems* (Master's thesis, State University of Iowa, 1950).
[6] C. Alan Riedesel, *Procedures for Improving Verbal Problem-Solving Ability in Arithmetic* (Ph.D. dissertation, The State University of Iowa, 1962).

with poor problem solvers. The eight traits are listed below.

1. Intelligence (1), (3), (5)
2. Computational ability (1), (3), (4), (5), (6)
3. Ability to estimate answers (6), (7)
4. Ability to analyze problems (1), (6)
5. Arithmetic vocabulary (1), (6)
6. Ability to use quantitative relationships that are social in nature (3), (6)
7. Ability to note irrelevant (superfluous) detail (2), (3), (7)
8. Knowledge of arithmetical concepts (1), (4)

(1) Alexander, Vincent E., "The Relationship of Selected Factors to the Ability to Solve Problems in Arithmetic," *Dissertation Abstracts*, Vol. 20'2, p. 1221.

(2) Beldin, Horace O., *A Study of Selected Arithmetic Verbal Problem Solving Skills Among High and Low Achieving Sixth-Grade Children* (Ph.D. dissertation, Syracuse University, 1960).

(3) Butler, Charles C., "A Study of the Relation Between Children's Understanding of Computational Skills and Their Ability to Solve Verbal Problems in Arithmetic," *Dissertation Abstracts,* Vol. 16'3, p. 2400.

(4) Chase, Clinton, "The Position of Certain Variables in the Prediction of Problem Solving in Arithmetic," *Journal of Educational Research,* Vol. 54 (September 1960), pp. 9–14.

(5) Englehardt, Max D., "The Relative Contributions of Certain Factors to Individual Differences in Problem Solving Ability," *Journal of Experimental Education,* Vol. 1 (September 1932), pp. 19–27.

(6) Hanson, Carl W., "Factors Associated with Successful Achievement in Problem Solving in Sixth-Grade Arithmetic," *Journal of Educational Research,* Vol. 38 (October 1944), pp. 111–118.

(7) Kliebhan, Sister Mary Camille, *An Experimental Study of Arithmetic Problem-Solving Ability of 6th Grade Boys* (Ph.D. dissertation, Catholic University of America, 1955).

When should instruction in problem solving begin?   The oral phase of instruction in verbal problem solving can and should begin in the kindergarten. The introduction of written verbal problems depends upon the reading comprehension level of the pupils, but usually it should begin sometime late in the first grade. It is probably better to use a good, orally presented verbal problem than a too simple problem which pupils can read.

What reading skills are important to verbal problem-solving ability? Many complex reading skills are involved in the analysis and solution of verbal problems. Research indicates that a combination of skills such as a knowledge of general and mathematical vocabularies, the ability to grasp quantitative relationships, and the capacity to draw inferences and to integrate scattered ideas are all important to problem solving.[7]

[7] David H. Russell, "Arithmetic Power Through Reading," *Instruction in Arithmetic,* Twenty-fifth Yearbook of the National Council of Teachers of Mathematics (Washington, D. C.: The Council, 1960), p. 214.

Do the mathematical operations involved in a verbal problem affect the complexity of the problem? The answer to this question would be a qualified "yes." An investigation of two-step problems revealed that:[8]

Two-Step Problem Difficulty

More difficult				Less difficult			
S	then	A	$\longleftrightarrow$	A	then	S	
A	then	M	$\longleftrightarrow$	M	then	A	A = Addition
D	then	A	$\longleftrightarrow$	A	then	D	S = Subtraction
D	then	S	$\longleftrightarrow$	S	then	D	M = Multiplication
S	then	M	$\longleftrightarrow$	M	then	S	D = Division
D	then	M	$\longleftrightarrow$	M	then	D	

What pattern can be derived from this study? Check the relationship between operations and their inverses.

Even though these differences in difficulty occur, it is advisable to mix operational types rather than to take the atomistic view of teaching a sequence of operational difficulty. If true ability to solve unique problems is desired, the student will gain little from a small-step development of problem type.

Improving verbal problem solving

Verbal problem solving has long been an area of elementary school mathematics instruction of great concern to teachers and the cause of much pupil anxiety. This situation has led to the formulation of many proposals for improving the teaching of verbal problem-solving methods. Interest in many of these proposals has waned quickly after teacher try-out or after studies to test their validity have failed to produce clear-cut evidence of the worth of the proposals. The overall result has been that during instruction on verbal problems the major portion of instructional time is devoted to the solution of the same verbal problems by all of the students in a class and by means of general or poorly defined procedures.

In 1925 Stevenson[9] described the method of problem solving used by an elementary school pupil. The pupil said, "If there are lots of numbers, I add. If there are only two numbers with lots of parts, I subtract. But if there are just two numbers and one littler than the other, it is hard. I divide if they come out even, but if they don't I multiply." On the surface this technique appears humorous. However, if the pupil had also used one other suggestion

---

[8] Gunborg Berglund-Gray and Robert V. Young. "Effect of Progress Sequence on the Interpretation of Two-Step Problems in Arithmetic," *Journal of Educational Research*, Vol. 34 (September 1940), pp. 21–29.

[9] P. R. Stevenson, "Increasing the Ability of Pupils to Solve Arithmetic Problems," *Educational Research Bulletin III* (Columbus, Ohio: The Ohio State University, October 1924), p. 270.

for problem solving, she could have scored well (if she could compute) on the majority of present-day mathematics textbook problems. This other suggestion is, if in doubt, use the operation that you've most recently studied. It is suggested that the reader study several popular textbooks and experimental curriculums to verify the situation described above.

The following suggestions are given to eliminate the type of rote thinking often used in solving verbal problems.

1. Chapter 2 emphasized the use of verbal problems in kindergarten, grade one, and grade two. This early emphasis can do much to further the entire problem-solving program of the elementary school. It also greatly eliminates the fear of and dislike for problem solving that is often found at the intermediate-grade level. When problem solving is delayed until the third-grade level, pupils have the notion that it must be hard because it hasn't been studied until now!

2. The use of multi-level problem materials, as described in chapter 3, is very important if the majority of pupils are to be good problem solvers. Problems of an inappropriate level of difficulty are puzzles, not problems, for the below average pupil, and exercises, not problems, for the above average pupil.

3. There is seldom only one correct method of solving a verbal problem. Too often pupils are given an ultimatum similar to the statement made famous by an actor who often appeared in gangster pictures. He usually said, "*Do it my way—SEE.*" Pupils should have many opportunities to apply multiple solutions to problems.

4. Developing ability in problem solving requires more than just assigning problems for pupils to solve. It is probably wiser to assign a relatively small number of problems with direction to analyze the situations and to spend time in thinking about the basic ideas of the problems than it is to give the students long lists of problems to be solved.

Procedures for improving problem-solving ability. Pupils vary in the type of experience they require to understand a given situation. Problem situations also vary in the attack required. Therefore, it is essential that the teacher use a variety of procedures and teaching techniques in developing problem-solving maturity. Several techniques and procedures are suggested in the sections that follow. Research reveals that the techniques and procedures described below are effective in improving verbal problem-solving ability.

THE MATHEMATICAL SENTENCE

Using the mathematical sentence and algebra

Early in the elementary grades pupils can learn to write mathematical sentences to express relationships, to write different names for the same number, and to indicate operations. The first grader begins the use of mathematical sentences when he abstracts $3 + 2 = \square$ from the problem "Jill had 3 dolls and her grandmother gave her 2 more. How many does she have in all?"

Mathematical sentences can be of several types: (1) $3 + 4 = 7$ is a "true sentence" and also an "equation"; (2) $3 + 4 = 8$ is a "false sentence"; (3) $3 + 4 = \square$ and $5 - 3 = N$ are "open sentences." The symbols $\square$ and N are called *place holders, pronumerals,* or *variables.* The open sentence is made true or false by the numeral used to replace the place holder. (4) In addition, sentences that indicate relationships other than equality or inequality may be written. For example, $5 > 3$; $N + 2 > 7$; and $\square - 5 < 3$. In each mathematical sentence that possesses a place holder there may be one or more than one replacement which makes the sentence a true sentence. A replacement or replacements which make a sentence true are called the *solution set* or roots of the sentence. The *solution set* for $\square - 5 < 3$ would be $\{5, 6, 7\}$ if the set of whole numbers is used as the basis for the sentence. Several other sentences and their solution set are illustrated below.

Sentence	Solution Set
$3 + 4 = \square$	$\{7\}$
$N + 2 > 7$	$\{6, 7, 8, \ldots, N\}$
$6 \times \square < 60$	$\{0, 1, 2, 3, 4, 5, 6, 7, 8, 9\}$

Solving problems by the use of mathematical sentences

At the early primary-grade level the teacher can begin the use of the mathematical sentence with the following development: "The past few days we've been working problems which I've read to you, asking you to find the answer. Today I'm going to ask you to see if you can make a mathematical sentence about the problem. Let's try one together. 'Bill bought three 4-cent stamps. How much did they cost?' Can you state in words the basic question asked?"

The pupils suggested two possibilities: (1) How many are three 4's, or three 4's equal what number? (2) How many are 4 plus 4 plus 4, or 4 plus 4 plus 4 equals what number? The teacher suggested that the questions be written in mathematical sentence form by using mathematical symbols rather than words. She quizzed the class members concerning the substitutions in symbols that could be made. The pupils suggested that 3×4 replace the three 4's; that $=$ replace the equals; and that $\square$ or N replace the what number.

Similarily, in the second case the pupils wrote the mathematical sentence as $4 + 4 + 4 = \square$.

During the remainder of the problem-solving session the teacher suggested that the pupils develop a mathematical sentence that could be used in solving the problem, solve the problem, and then verify their answers with a drawing or a diagram. On occasion, for variety, the teacher suggested that the pupils write only the mathematical sentence and not continue on to find the number for the place holder.

Soon after she introduced the mathematical sentence (when she felt the pupils understood all parts of the mathematical sentence), the teacher developed by student consideration the terms "open sentence," "equation," "solution set," and "place holder."

Later in the problem-solving program, situations will arise in which the mathematical sentences need to be rewritten. For example, the mathematical sentence for the problem "In 3 years Nancy will be 10 years old. How old is Nancy at the present time?" is $\square + 3 = 10$. The pupils should be challenged to think of a method of finding the value of the place holder. In this situation the use of a scale or some other balance device may be helpful in emphasizing that when a mathematical sentence is an equation, the two sides are equal. In such a case when a pupil suggests that $\square + 3 = 10$ may be solved by subtracting 3 from both sides, the procedure can be verified by balancing a scale with 10 blocks on each side and removing 3 blocks from each side. The scale remains balanced. The pupils also may use the addition-subtraction relationship to change $\square + 3 = 10$ to the related subtraction sentence $10 - 3 = \square$.

Several other equation types, with the procedure used to simplify the equation, are listed below. In each case the equation type should be developed by having the children abstract a mathematical sentence from a verbal problem and then logically finding a means of simplifying the equation.

$$N - 7 = 6$$ Add 7 to each side of the equation.
$$(N - 7) + 7 = 6 + 7$$
$$N = 13$$

$$3N = 15$$ Divide each side by 3.
$$\frac{3N}{3} = \frac{15}{3}$$
$$N = 5$$

$$N \div 6 = 5$$ Multiply each side by 6.
$$(N \div 6) \times 6 = 5 \times 6$$
$$N = 30$$

Combinations of the above equation types also occur.

After the pupils have had a variety of experience in abstracting mathematical sentences from verbal problems, they should attempt to verbalize procedures for solving the equations. The pupils normally will arrive at the following generalizations (often called the fundamental operational axioms involved in the solution of linear equations). These generalizations make use of the basic idea of inverse operations.

1. The same number can be added to both members of an equation.
2. The same number can be subtracted from both members of an equation.

3. Both members of an equation can be multiplied by the same number.

4. Both members of an equation can be divided by the same number, with the exception of zero.

Because of limited space, illustrative lessons on the development of generalizations for the solution of mathematical sentences are not included. This does not mean that the teacher should present the above material in an explanatory manner. Pupils can effectively discover for themselves or be led to discover the generalizations for working with equations and other types of mathematical sentences.

Multi-step problems and mathematical sentences

Pupils quickly develop skill in writing mathematical sentences for problems that require a single mathematical operation. This is not true for problems whose solutions involve several steps. Some pupils can work a multi-step problem but cannot develop the mathematical sentence that concisely describes the problem. Other pupils manipulate the numbers, hoping to arrive at some solution.

At present, few specific suggestions to use in developing pupil skill in solving multi-step problems are available to teachers. Because of this lack, two lessons that have been successfully used in fourth-, fifth-, and sixth-grade classrooms are presented.

Lesson I.   The teacher wrote this problem on the chalkboard: Jeff was collecting money to purchase groceries for a camping trip. He was to buy the following items:

> 1 tin of Spam at 45¢ a can
> 5 cans of beans at 12¢ a can
> 1 box of crackers at 24¢ a box
> 6 cans of juice at 12¢ a can
> 1 bag of potato chips at 75¢ a bag

How much money did Jeff need? (Tax was not charged on the groceries.)

The pupils were instructed to write a mathematical sentence that could be used to solved the problem.

As the faster workers finished their work, they were asked to write their mathematical sentences on the chalkboard. When most of the pupils had finished, a discussion was held to determine the best method of writing the mathematical sentence. The teacher had purposely allowed several pupils to write incorrect solutions on the board. She began with a discussion of one of the incorrect solutions.

Mel said that the problem was an addition and multiplication problem and could be written as $45 + 5 \times 12 + 24 + 6 \times 12 + 75 = 7635$¢. He computed from left to right in the following manner: $45 + 5 = 50$. $50 \times 12 = 600$. $600 + 24 = 624$. $624 + 6 = 630$. $630 \times 12 = 7560$. $7560 + 75 = 7635$. The answer was in cents, so Mel converted his answer to $76.35.

Immediately there was a stir of disapproval from class members. Jane noted that the answer was too large. A scout troop couldn't possibly pay that much for a few groceries. Another pupil noted that the multiplications should have been performed before the addition.

The class then considered other ways of writing the problem. The methods used included:

Nancy:

$$\begin{array}{r} \$.45 \\ .60 \\ .24 \\ .72 \\ \underline{.75} \\ \hline \$2.76 \end{array}$$

Howard:[10] $45 + 60 = 105 + 24 = 129 + 72 = 201 + 75 = 276\cancel{c}$

John: $45 + (5 \times 12) + 24 + (6 \times 12) + 75 = 45 + 60 + 24 + 72 + 75$
$= 276\cancel{c}$ or $\$2.76$.

The class decided that Nancy had the correct answer but hadn't shown all of her thinking. Howard's answer was also considered correct, but he, too, hadn't shown all of his thinking. Also, he had made incorrect use of the equals sign. John was asked to explain why he had used parentheses. He stated, "First, I took the 45¢ and put that down. Then, so I could show I didn't mean that $45 + 5$ was to be multiplied by 12, I enclosed the computation (5×12) in parentheses."

Special comment was then made about the possibility of working a problem incorrectly unless the work to be done was clearly indicated. The value of parentheses as an aid to showing exactly the processes involved was discussed.

Practice was then given in writing mathematical sentences for other multi-step verbal problems.

Analysis. The purpose of the lesson was to show a need for setting apart the processes involved in a multi-step problem. The pupils had an opportunity to discover the most logical use of parentheses.

Lesson II. During the next mathematics period, the teacher continued the instruction by going over the solutions to the previous day's assignment. Then two verbal problems were written on the chalkboard (see below), and the class was asked to write mathematical sentences that could be used to solve the problems. The pupils were not asked to compute the answer.

---

[10] Note the incorrect use of the sign of equalities. This is a frequent mistake of children and adults. Howard is stating that $45 + 60 = 276\cancel{c}$.

1. There were 34 radios in a store. At the end of the day, 29 of them were left. How much money did the store receive from the day's sale of radios if each sold for $17.50?

2. Ken's father's car travels an average of 15 miles per gallon of gasoline. At 30¢ a gallon, how much will the gasoline for a 450-mile trip cost?

Unlike the previous problems, these problems involved subtraction and division. They were used to show that parentheses can be used for setting off the various operations.

As an assignment the pupils were asked to write an explanation of how parentheses could be used to solve verbal problems.

Other uses of mathematical sentences

The mathematics program of today makes many uses of mathematical sentences. One of the most popular is the use of frames. In this situation the teacher uses geometric shapes to represent the place holders. A pupil may be challenged to find the solution set of the mathematical sentences.

$\square + \triangle = 8.$

or

$\square$	$\triangle$
0	8
1	7
2	6
3	5
4	4
5	3
6	2
7	1
8	0

In this case the solution set is (0,8), (1,7), (2,6), (3,5), (4,4), (5,3), (6,2), (7,1), (8,0). Some persons will not accept the notion that $4 + 4$ is a possible replacement for $\square + \triangle$. However, this is quite possible. Frames are used in the same manner as X and Y. It is very possible to have an equation $X + Y = 8$ in which the value of X and the value of Y are equal.

Formulas. Another use of the mathematical sentence is in the development of formulas. In the traditional mathematics program the formula for finding the answer to a particular type of problem was given to the pupil for study. Then problems were given in which the formula was used.

With the guided discovery approach a problem situation is presented and analyzed. Then several other problems of this type are solved. After the pupil has a good understanding of this problem type, he is challenged by the teacher to develop a formula for the solution of similar problems. For example, a pupil has worked several problems that involve finding the distance when the speed (rate) of a vehicle and the time traveled are known. He will make the statement: "The distance traveled equals the rate of the car times the time taken for the trip." This is shortened to distance traveled = rate (speed) $\times$ time, and finally $D = R \times T$.

After the pupil has developed a formula, he should be challenged to develop variations of it. For example, What is the formula for the rate? What is the formula for the time? The pupil made use of basic axioms of equations, and beginning with $D = R \times T$, he divided both members by T to find the rate: $D = R \times T; \dfrac{D}{T} = \dfrac{R \times T}{T}; \dfrac{D}{T} = R.$

The guided discovery approach to the development of formula has several advantages. (1) If a pupil has developed a formula on his own, he is much less likely to forget the formula than if he memorizes someone else's formulas. (2) If a pupil does forget the formula, he can once again go through the process necessary for the development of the formula. (3) The pupils develop confidence in formulas that they have discovered themselves and are less frightened by letters that name numbers. At the present time, adults often have difficulty when any symbols except numerals are used. Thus, while almost any adult can easily understand $2 + 3 = 3 + 2$, they are baffled by $a + b = b + a$.

USING ORALLY PRESENTED PROBLEMS

One of the most valuable techniques for the improvement of problem solving is the use of orally presented problems.[11] In addition to the improvement of "in-school" problems, the orally presented problem is much nearer the average "out-of-school" problem than is the pencil and paper problem. Children and adults are often confronted with mathematical problems that are stated orally rather than presented in writing. Such problems are also of value in inducing pupils to listen carefully and to concentrate on the most significant aspects of the problem.

The teacher can introduce the oral procedure by saying "Solving problems without the use of pencil and paper is a good way to improve your problem-solving ability. Today we will have practice in solving problems that I will read orally to you. I will read each problem one time only. Solve the problem without using paper and pencil. As soon as you have an answer, write it on your paper. Listen carefully; remember, I will read each problem only once. The first problem is, 'Mr. Marks paid 90¢ for his movie ticket and 20¢ for his son's ticket. How much did he pay for the two tickets?' "

The teacher paused for about fifteen seconds to allow the pupils to compute their answers. Then the problem was discussed by the class. After the discussion the teacher said, "For the remainder of the exercise I will alternate the problems between rather difficult and somewhat easy ones. Those who wish to try the difficult problems should answer the odd-numbered ones—1, 3, 5, and so on. Those who wish to try the easier problems should answer the even-numbered ones—2, 4, 6, and so on. Some of you may wish to try all of them."

---

[11] M. Frances Flournoy, "The Effectiveness of Instruction in Mental Arithmetic," *Elementary School Journal*, Vol. 55 (November 1954), pp. 148–153.

The teacher then read the problem set slowly. After the children had finished the problems, the teacher read the answers and the pupils discussed the problems.

These additional suggestions may aid the teacher in effectively using orally presented problems.

1. Because orally presented problems proceed at a fixed pace, it is suggested that not over five or ten minutes at one time be spent on this procedure.

2. An effective means of filling in a minute or two before lunch, recess, or the arrival of the music teacher is to use orally presented problems.

3. Problems that involve complicated computation may be handled by suggesting that the pupils only determine the operations to be used and then write A for addition, S for subtraction, M for multiplication, and D for division. Another possibility is that the pupils be instructed to write only the mathematical sentence that is necessary to the solution of the problem.

4. If the teacher wishes to determine the pupils' answer as the problem set progresses, she may use 3-by-5-inch cards on which the various numerals have been written. Pupils hold the correct cards in front of them. For example, if the answer were 35, the pupil would hold a card with the numeral 3 in his right hand and a card with the numeral 5 in his left hand.

5. Orally presented computational or "follow-me" exercises also are helpful in problem solving. They form an important part of orally presented materials. A teacher may say, "See if you can follow me. Start with 5, add 7, subtract 2, square this number, subtract 50, divide by 5. What is the answer?"

6. The tape recorder is a useful device for orally presented problems. Pupils are intrigued by the tape recorder, and they also pay greater attention to it than to a teacher because they realize that the recorder will not repeat the problem.

USE OF DIAGRAMS, GRAPHS, AND DRAWINGS

Diagrams, graphs, and drawings are useful problem-solving aids for pupils of all ability levels. (In the past such an aid was often reserved for only the slow student.) These aids force the pupil to consider the problem situation. He cannot just manipulate numerals without understanding the basic structure of the problem. Another valuable feature of graphic aids is versatility. Drawings may be used by a slow pupil to solve problems that he would otherwise find unsolvable. The advanced student finds drawings of value in the solution of problems that involve complex relationships.

The use of diagrams is particularly helpful for solving problems that involve rates, distances, and measures of quantities. The use of diagrams can and should begin at the early primary level and continue in each succeeding grade. A representative lesson and a teaching procedure for problem solving using drawings and diagrams were presented in chapter 3.

The graphing of problem situations is also often helpful. In fact, it is probably the best procedure for the solution of a problem that involves a solution set of several numbers. A teacher may begin graphing with a problem such as "To win a dart game a team must score at least 5 points. Each player can score from 0 to 5 points a turn. What scores can the team of Jim and Phyllis make to score a victory?" The teacher can then direct the pupils to find the ordered pairs of numbers (the solution set) that would give Jim and Phyllis a victory. She may make the suggestion that graph paper can be used to help in the solution.

In solving the above problem many pupils will either randomly or systematically develop the number pairs that satisfy the sentence $J + P \geq 5$ (Jim's score plus Phyllis's score is equal to or greater than five). Those using a graph will arrive at the following solution:

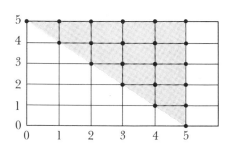

$J = $ Jim's score
$P = $ Phyllis's score
Solution Set:

$J = $ first member of the ordered pair
$P = $ second member of the ordered pair

{ (5,0), (5,1), (5,2), (5,3), (5,4), (5,5), (4,1), (4,2), (4,3), (4,4), (4,5), (3,2), (3,3), (3,4), (3,5), (2,3), (2,4), (2,5), (1,4), (1,5), (0,5)}

OTHER PROBLEM-SOLVING HELPS

Use of restatement or analogies

Asking a student to restate a problem in his own words is helpful in problem comprehension. The teacher may also suggest that the student develop a problem that is of the same structure as the original, but one that uses simpler numbers. In some cases the teacher may wish to present orally a simpler problem of the same type, ask the student to solve that problem, and then compare the simpler problem with the original one. For example, "A ranch 2.67 miles long and 1.82 miles wide contains how many square miles?" can be parallelled with "A ranch 4 miles long and 2 miles wide contains how many square miles?"

Use of problems without numbers

Problems that do not contain numbers can be presented. The pupils are required to explain how the problem would be worked if the numbers had been given. Such problems are very helpful in forcing pupils to analyze the problem situation rather than just to find means of computing with the numbers.

Two formats can be used effectively in presenting problems without numbers. The problem can be presented and the pupil asked to write a short description of the procedures he would use in solving the problem, or several possible solutions can be presented and the pupil can be asked to pick the correct or best procedure for solving the problem. An example of each technique follows.

1. Read the problems carefully. You will find that they do not contain numbers. You can, however, decide the procedure that would be used if a solution were attempted. In the space below each problem write a sentence or two telling how you would solve it.

Ann weighs herself and her cat together. Then she weighs herself. How can she find the weight of her cat?

2. Choose the correct solution for the problems.

You go to the store and buy a comic book, a package of gum, and a notebook. How can you tell if you have enough money?
   a. Multiply the cost of the items and compare it with the amount of money you have.
   b. Add the cost of the items and then divide it by the number of items.
   c. Add the cost of the items and then compare it with the amount of money you have.
   d. Correct answer is not given.

Problems without numbers can also be used to help teach pupils to use abstraction in writing mathematical sentences. For example, in response to problem 1 above the pupil may answer A = Ann's weight; C = the weight of the cat.

$$(A + C) \qquad - A \qquad = C$$
$$\text{Known} \qquad \text{Known} \qquad \text{Unknown}$$

Using pupils' formulation of problems

When pupils formulate, criticize, and refine problems which they themselves have composed, they often gain insight into the make-up of verbal mathematics problems.

The teacher may begin this phase of problem solving by stating, "One of the best means of improving your problem-solving ability is to make up your own problems. Today let's use the article on 'Active Stocks' as the basis for your problems. You may check other sources of information if you wish. Here is an example of a problem I developed. 'How much more would it cost to buy 3 shares of Brunswick stock than 3 shares of Sperry Rand if both shares were purchased at the closing cost?' " The class may discuss the form of the problems and the importance of clear expression. It is usually wise to suggest that students formulate problems that use various number operations. Also, the development of multi-step problems should be emphasized.

Pupils can formulate problems at all levels of the elementary school. First-grade pupils can make up oral problems to present to the class; higher-grade students can post problem sets on the bulletin board. On occasion, two or three students will benefit from working together on the formulation of verbal problems. Also, pupils may be challenged to develop their own variations or "puzzle-type" problems.

Other techniques to improve problem-solving ability

In addition to the procedures previously suggested for developing problem-solving skills, several other techniques can be used to help pupils improve their problem-solving ability. A number are briefly described below.

1. Make use of problems with *too much* or *too little* data. Such problems force the pupils to focus on the important aspects of the problem situation and are probably more typical of everyday problems than those with the exact amount of data. Periodically a teacher can say to pupils, "Today some of your problems may have too much or too little information. If there is too much information, work the problem and then compose a short sentence that contains the information that was not needed. If there is the correct amount of information, just work the problem. If you do not have enough information to work the problem, indicate 'too little data' and then write a short sentence telling what data you need to work the problem."

In addition to specific lessons that use this type of problem, many of the regular problem assignments should contain problems with too much data.

2. *Estimating the answer* without working a problem is also another device to improve the pupils' analysis of problems. This technique is often difficult to use since many conscientious pupils will work the problem first and then obtain an estimate from the completed problem. To avoid this practice, it is suggested that the estimation of answer technique be used in conjunction with orally presented verbal problems. After a pupil becomes familiar with the value of estimating the answer, he will often use it on his own. Approximating a logical answer is particularly useful in problems involving fractions and decimals. To estimate an answer in fractional or decimal situations, the pupil rounds off the fraction or decimal to a whole number and computes mentally. The use of this procedure helps to eliminate the incorrect placement of a decimal point, or in the case of fractions, it helps to eliminate the use of the dividend as the divisor in the division of fraction problems.

3. The use of *How's Your P.Q.* type problems, as suggested in chapter 3, is one of the most valuable problem-solving techniques. A portion of the arithmetic bulletin board can contain these difficult problems (usually at two or three levels of difficulty). Several of these problems can be presented each week and adequate time given for pupils to think through the problem (at least two days). In addition to the improvement of problem solving, the *How's Your P.Q.* problems act as a good motivational device.

4. *Problem Analysis* was once a very popular phase of problem solving. Textbooks contained directions to follow these steps in solving problems: (a) decide what is given; (b) think about what is asked; (c) think about what operation should be used; (d) estimate the answer; (e) solve the problem; and (f) check the answer. Studies such as the one reported by Burch[12] have indicated that formal analysis is not of great value, since pupils do not normally make use of the six-step procedure. Thus, it is probably better to make use of only one or two of the steps at a time. Another possibility is the use of programmed problem-solving materials in which the pupils respond to specific questions concerning a problem.

A different form of problem analysis that shows promise involves asking a series of questions concerning the problem presented. For example,

"During a 'gas war' the price of gasoline dropped from 33¢ a gallon to 21¢ a gallon. If Joe Davenport's car averages 20 miles per gallon, how much does he save on a 120-mile trip when he buys gasoline at the 'gas-war' price rather than at the regular price?"

    a. How much will a customer save per gallon at the gas war price?

    b. What is the minimum number of gallons of gasoline that will be necessary for the trip?

    c. At the gas-war price how much will Joe Davenport spend on gas per mile traveled?

5. Some pupils find that *analyzing a model situation* (studying a problem that is already worked) helps them to improve their problem-solving ability. For example, "Mary's mother baked 3 cakes. She cut one cake into 10 pieces, another into 8 pieces, and the third into 12 pieces. If she gave 14 pieces to some children, how many pieces would she have left?"

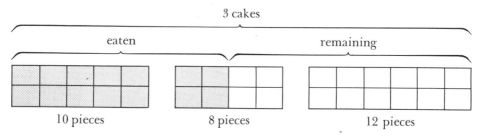

Writing the mathematical sentence: We are to find the total number of pieces and then remove 14 pieces.

$$(10 + 8 + 12) - 14 = N$$
$$30 - 14 = N$$
$$16 = N$$

6. Using problems from a *variety of sources.* Pupils show great interest in problems taken from old textbooks, foreign textbooks, and scientific books. The alert teacher can find old textbooks in secondhand stores and at used-

[12] Robert L. Burch, "Formal Analysis as a Problem-Solving Procedure," *Journal of Education,* Vol. 136 (November 1954), pp. 44–47.

book dealers. At the present time, several publishing companies sell transla-
tions of foreign textbooks. The problems that the teacher finds in these
sources are not superior in quality to those found in the standard textbooks,
but the idea that the problems were used by pupils of the past or are used by
pupils in foreign countries is intriguing to students.

   7. *Use of Intersection of Sets in Operations and Problem-Solving:* Set
language is helpful in dealing with mathematical sentences. The operation
of intersection of sets is also a useful tool in problem solving because there
is no comparable operation that can be performed with numbers. The following problem and its solution using a Venn diagram illustrate a problem
that involves the intersection of two sets. "For their annual party the Girl
Scouts appointed a food committee and an entertainment committee. The
food committee consisted of Betty, Ella, and Eva. The entertainment committee consisted of Edna, Judy, Eva, and Jane. How many girls were on
both committees?"

Union.   Addition is defined in terms of disjoint sets. Problem situations arise
in which the sets that are to be united are not disjoint. In such a case, the
operation must be performed on sets and then the answer changed to the
representative number. An illustrative problem and two solutions follow.
"Mr. Smith was planning to entertain the members of two space and aeronautics committees. The committee on rocketry consisted of Eric G., George
R., Herman K., and Michael E. The committee on rocket fuels consisted
of Wehrner B., Stein T., George R., Michael E., and Robert K. How many
visitors should Mr. Smith tell his wife to expect?"
Set A (rocketry) Eric G., George R., Herman L., Michael E.
Set B (fuels) Wehrner B., Stein T., George R., Michael E., Robert K.

$A \cup B =$

$$\left\{ \begin{array}{l} \text{Eric G., George R.,} \\ \text{Herman L., Michael E.,} \end{array} \right\} \cup \left\{ \begin{array}{l} \text{Wehrner B., Stein T., George R.,} \\ \text{Michael E., Robert K.} \end{array} \right\} =$$

$$\left\{ \begin{array}{l} \text{Eric G., George R., Herman L., Michael E.,} \\ \text{Wehrner B., Stein T., Robert K.} \end{array} \right\}$$

$$N \left\{ \begin{array}{l} \text{Eric G., George R., Herman L., Michael E.,} \\ \text{Wehrner B., Stein T., Robert K.} \end{array} \right\} = 7$$

$$N \{A \cup B\} = 7$$

LOGIC

       Careful analysis of the utterances of political speakers and commercial television announcers often reveals faulty thinking and an incorrect use of logic. As a future voter and consumer, the elementary school pupil will need to make careful analysis of the claims of these and other groups. Some knowledge of logic is also useful in the pupil's work in science and his everyday activities. Traditionally the study of logic has not been included in the elementary school program. This omission of logic has probably been a factor of its comparative recency to mathematics, the abstract nature of symbolic logic, and the rather stable curriculum of the 1940's and 1950's.

       Several representative ideas for the teaching of logic at the elementary school level are presented. The approach to the teaching of logic in the elementary school should: (1) make use of physical world situations for the abstraction of mathematical content; (2) be designed for the average students; and (3) provide for a differentiation of teaching logic by implying varying levels of abstractness.

Foundation experiences

       Early work with both mathematical and scientific *statements* which can be labeled as *true* or *false* provide a groundwork for later study. For example,

> Air is a compound. (True or False)
> Lightning is caused by moisture. (True or False)
> $2 + 3 = 5$ (True)
> $5 - 2 < 2$ (False)

       Some sentences may be ambiguous and not represent a statement. For example, "They like liver," can be considered a statement only if the persons designated as "They" are known and their like or dislike for liver can be ascertained.

       The next step can be to make use of the connective "and" in its mathematical sense. The pupil may decide whether such statements as those that follow are true or false.

                  T   F
Lincoln was the 16th president, *and* he was under 6 feet tall. (False)

     T   T
$4 + 5 = 9$, *and* $5 = 5$ (True)

                     F   T
Patrick Henry was the first president, *and* Patrick Henry lived before 1900. (False)

F   F

Lyndon Johnson was the 32nd president, *and* Lyndon Johnson was an All-American in football. (False)

Note that there is a relationship between the truth values of the original statements and the truth value of the new combinations. If the original statements are both true, so is the combined statement. If, however, either or both are false, so is the combined statement.[13] Discussion and questioning can bring out the reason for the falseness of the statement that contains one part which is true. To further fix this idea, use situations such as the movie at the Capitol Theater is "I Was a 10-Year-Old Werewolf" (true), and the movie at the Capitol begins at 11:00 p.m. (false). In such a case if only the true portion is noted, the pupil will miss the movie (which is probably just as well).

After a large number of "for instances" have been puzzled out by the pupils, a simple truth table can be developed. It may take the form of the short worksheet shown below.

Truth Table

Finish the truth table and figure out an example to illustrate each situation.

	A	B	A and B combined	
(1)	True	True	???	(True)*
(2)	True	False	???	(False)*
(3)	False	True	???	(False)*
(4)	False	False	???	(False)*

Give an example for each type shown on the truth table.

A   B

*(1) Iron is an element, and carbon dioxide is a compound.
*(2) $3 > 2$ and $5 < 3$.
*(3) Gold is a compound and silver is an element.
*(4) Carbon monoxide is an element and oxygen is a compound.

*Not shown on pupil's worksheet.

Once the use of the connective "and" is well developed, the teacher can move to the connective "or." The man in the street employs this connective in two ways. The first is the "either-or" sense called the *exclusive* sense. "Bill, wash the dishes, *or* you can't go to the movies." In such a situation Bill will assume that if he washes the dishes, he can go to the movies. Note that we do not expect both statements to be true. The second use of the connective is

[13] Robert L. Swain, "Logic: For Teacher, For Pupil," *Enrichment Mathematics for the Grades,* Twenty-seventh Yearbook of the National Council of Teachers of Mathematics (Washington, D. C.: The Council, 1963).

the "and/or" sense called the *inclusive* sense. "Bill received an 'A' in spelling the first six weeks, *or* perhaps it was the second six weeks." In this case the statement would normally be accepted if Bill received an "A" either six-week period or both six-week periods.

Since inconsistency or ambiguity hampers mathematical work, only one of the two senses described above can be used. The inclusive (and/or) sense has been chosen by mathematicians. A teacher developed the *or* idea by presenting the following statements with the suggestion that pupils decide (1) whether A is true, (2) whether B is true, and (3) whether A or B is true.

A			B	A or B
A cat is a mammal	or		a dog is a mammal	?
A cat is a mammal	or		a robin is a mammal	?
A robin is a mammal	or		a cat is a mammal	?
A robin is a mammal	or		a pike is a mammal	?

Later a truth table such as that shown below can be developed through individual pupil work.

Truth Table

A	B	A or B
T	T	T
T	F	T
F	T	T
F	F	F

"If, then" statements are often used in mathematics and in many other social contexts. Elementary pupils can improve their mathematical thinking through experience with "if, then" statements. For example,

    T   T
1. If it rains, then the baseball game will be called off. T (If A, then B)

    T   T
2. If Nancy studies, then she will get a good grade on her test. T

          T   F
3. If that substance is oxygen, then it will cause fire to go out. F

The "if" clause may be put either first or second without affecting the meaning of the sentence. For example, "If the liquid is an acid, then it will turn litmus paper red." This can be stated, "Litmus paper will turn red if the liquid is an acid." However, switching the "if" from one statement to another changes the meaning and may result in a new combination called the *converse,* which may be either true or false. For example,

Statement: If the liquid is acid, then the litmus paper will turn red.
Converse: If the litmus paper turns red, then the liquid is an acid.

Statement: If Senator Jones is honest, then he will vote for the law.
Converse: If he votes for the law, then Senator Jones is honest. (This doesn't have to be true.)

Statement: If a geometric shape is a rectangle, then it is a parallelogram.
Converse: If it is a parallelogram, then a geometric shape is a rectangle. (false)

Statement: If my pet is a mammal, then my pet is an animal.
Converse: If my pet is an animal, then my pet is a mammal.

There are many opportunities to develop ideas concerned with logic with elementary school pupils. The teacher should be alert to situations that arise naturally and should also make use of planned situations. Those included above are merely representative.

SUMMARY COMMENTS ON PROBLEM SOLVING

1. No one "best" method of improving problem-solving ability has been developed. Therefore, the teacher should stress several approaches.

2. Some of the programs in elementary school mathematics treat problem solving after a topic has been introduced and developed rather than making use of problems in the introductory phase and again at a later phase of the topic development. This practice is questionable. One of the chief "jobs" of a mathematician is to "take a physical situation or a portion of the real world and represent it by a mathematical model."[14] Use of verbal problems at the introductory stage of a new topic develops skills in this phase of mathematical thinking.

3. The ability to read is an important adjunct to skill in verbal problem solving. The teacher must take care to develop the reading skills required in verbal problem solving.[15]

4. The approach to logic should be problem-centered, and care should be taken not to become involved with symbolic abstractions before pupils have had many opportunities to discuss statements and ideas with which they are familiar.

[14] Robert A. Sebastian, "The New Mathematician," *The Mathematics Student Journal,* Vol. 12, No. 1. (November, 1964), p. 2.
[15] For a helpful treatment of reading in elementary school mathematics see Peter L. Spencer and David H. Russell, "Reading in Arithmetic," *Instruction in Arithmetic,* Twenty-fifth Yearbook of the National Council of Teachers of Mathematics (Washington, D. C.: The Council, 1960), pp. 202–224.

1. Examine an up-to-date elementary school mathematics textbook for grade one or grade two. How many verbal problems are presented? What aids does the book provide for the teacher who wishes to use orally presented verbal problems?
2. Examine the problem-solving program of an up-to-date elementary school mathematics textbook for the intermediate grades. How many specific procedures for solving problems do the authors suggest? How do the authors handle multi-step problems?
3. Several recent mathematics programs rely almost completely on the use of the mathematical sentence as *the* means of improving problem solving. Discuss the advantages and disadvantages of using a single approach.
4. Critics of verbal problem-solving programs have made remarks such as "It hasn't been verified that school arithmetic problems help in life situations," "Why teach verbal problems?" and "If you teach the mathematical ideas, there isn't any need to teach problem solving. Pupils will know how." Analyze the statements. Develop several points for and against each statement.
5. Some teachers say, "Drawings and diagrams are helpful in the problem-solving program of the primary grades but should not be used in the upper grades." Agree or disagree with this statement and list reasons for your position.
6. If you were asked to prepare a number of verbal problems (pick a grade level), what settings would you use for the problems? Explain.
7. Develop a set of suggestions for helping pupils learn to read mathematics problems.
8. Explain how techniques for developing mathematical relationships and problem-solving ability differ. Explain how they are alike.
9. Prepare several reasons for and several reasons against the teaching of logic at the elementary school level.
10. Develop a set of exercises for a one-day lesson in logic which would be appropriate for fifth-grade children.

SUGGESTED REFERENCES

Adler, Irving, *Logic for Beginners* (New York: John Day Company, 1964).
Brownell, William A., "Problem Solving," *The Psychology of Learning,* Forty-

first Yearbook, Part II, National Society for the Study of Education (Chicago: University of Chicago Press, 1942), pp. 415-443.

Corle, Clyde, *Teaching Mathematics in the Elementary School* (New York: Ronald, 1964), pp. 327-356.

Cunningham, John D., "Rigidity in Children's Problem Solving," *School Science and Mathematics,* Vol. LXVI, No. 4 (April 1966), pp. 377-389.

Grossnickle, F. E., and Brueckner, L. J., *Discovering Meanings in Arithmetic* (New York: Holt, Rinehart and Winston, 1963), pp. 301-325.

Hannon, H., "Problem Solving—Programming and Processing," *Arithmetic Teacher,* Vol. 9 (January 1962), pp. 17-19.

Henderson, Kenneth B., and Pingry, Robert E., "Problem-Solving in Mathematics," *The Learning of Mathematics, Its Theory and Practice,* Twenty-first Yearbook of the National Council of Teachers of Mathematics (Washington, D.C.: The Council, 1953), Chap. 8.

Marks, John L., Purdy, C. Richard, and Kinney, Lucien B., *Teaching Elementary School Mathematics for Understanding* (New York: McGraw-Hill, 1965), pp. 393-428.

Monroe, Walter S., "How Pupils Solve Problems in Arithmetic," *Bureau of Educational Research Bulletin No. 44* (Urbana, Illinois: University of Illinois Bulletin, 1928), Vol. 26, No. 23.

Russell, David H., and Spencer, Peter L., "Reading in Arithmetic," *Instruction in Arithmetic,* Twenty-fifth Yearbook of the National Council of Teachers of Mathematics (Washington, D.C.: The Council, 1960), pp. 202-223.

Spitzer, Herbert F., and Flournoy, M. Frances, "Developing Facility in Solving Verbal Problems," *The Arithmetic Teacher,* Vol. 3 (November 1956), pp. 177-182.

Suppes, Patrick, and Hill, Shirley, *First Course in Mathematical Logic* (Waltham, Mass.: Blaisdell Publishing Company, 1964).

USE OF SUGGESTED REFERENCES

1. What are the major points made about problem solving by Brownell (1942)? Do they still have implications for a modern curriculum?

2. Read the analysis of the bacteria problem in Marks, p. 395. Develop this technique for another difficult or enrichment-type problem.

3. Prepare a guide of suggestions for improving reading in mathematics from the suggestions given by Grossnickle, Marks, and the Twenty-fifth Yearbook of the National Council of Teachers of Mathematics.

4. Compare Monroe's (1928) findings and suggestions concerning problem solving with a more recent treatment.

5. Develop a set of problems which makes use of each of the procedures suggested by Spitzer and Flournoy.

6. Study the problem-type that contains a number of sub-questions presented by Corle. Write two or three of these types of problems.

7. Hannon presents several illustrations of structuring physical world situa-

tions in mathematical sentences. Try out Hannon's suggestions with several problems taken from a sixth-grade book.

8. Study the chapter by Henderson and Pingry in the Twenty-first Yearbook of the National Council of Teachers of Mathematics. What psychological orientation do they present?

9. Compare the approach to developing ideas of logic taken by Suppes with that taken by Adler. Are the purposes of the two books different? Which approach would be most appropriate for elementary school pupils? Why?

10. What implications does Cunningham's study of rigidity in problem solving have for the elementary school mathematics teacher?

12

Geometry and the elementary school mathematics program

THE CHANGING ROLE OF GEOMETRY

Traditionally experience with geometry in the elementary school was limited to situations that involved the measurement of distances, areas, and quantities of liquids; the recognition of geometric shapes; and the occasional drawings that used geometric shapes. Recent experimental programs have suggested that a much richer program in geometry be included. A strong emphasis upon geometry has also been integrated into current textbook programs. The current change in geometry instruction can be illustrated by observing the grade placement of topics such as angles and points. The chart below shows the grade level at which each of these topics formerly were introduced and the grade level at which they are now introduced.

	Textbooks Popular in 1962				Textbooks Popular in 1966			
Textbooks	A	B	C	D	E	F	G	H
Grade Introduced Topic: Angles	7	7	7	7	4	3	2	3
Grade Introduced Topic: Points	7	7	–	7	6	4	2	3

The pattern of grade placement of other geometric topics closely follows that displayed above.

To meet successfully the challenge of teaching geometry at the elementary school level, teachers and curriculum workers must find answers to several important questions concerning the teaching of geometry. *What* topics from geometry *should* be taught to elementary-school children? *When* should the topics be taught? *How* should the topics be taught?

The answer to the first question is, for the most part, in the hands of state curriculum development teams, national advisory agencies, and local school curriculum committees. They must experiment, carefully analyze the results of experimental curriculum studies, and note local conditions. In all probability the next few years will bring continued increases in the amount of time devoted to geometry in the elementary schools. Because of wide curricular and textual variations in geometric content, the suggestions that follow will emphasize how a topic in geometry should be taught.

APPROACHING THE TEACHING OF GEOMETRY IN THE ELEMENTARY SCHOOL

The following suggestions are designed to give the reader a perspective on teaching elementary school geometry. After these general suggestions for teaching, representative topics from geometry are presented.

Suggestions

1. Topics in geometry should be introduced through situations that present to the pupils a purpose for the study of the topic. Rather than state "Today we are going to learn to bisect lines," present a situation in which pupils have a reason for bisecting lines.

2. A study of geometry in the elementary school should be based on exploration. Emphasis should be placed on questions such as "What new ideas did you get from today's work?" "What likenesses, differences, and patterns did you see in the geometric figures?" "Why do you think mathematicians consider dots and points as being quite different?" Less emphasis should be placed upon questions such as "Why should you be very careful to sharpen your pencil before working with geometry?" "How many sides does a hexagon have?" and other questions that require a rote response. It should be noted that mathematical abstractions and deductions follow guesses, approximations, investigations, and corrections.

3. Topics in geometry should be taught in short- or medium-length units rather than in isolated, single-day lessons.

4. There should be a *sequential development* of portions of topics in geometry at each grade level. Geometry should be a part of the entire elementary school mathematics curriculum.

5. Imprecise vocabulary should be carefully avoided. However, it is sometimes better to place less emphasis upon the early identification of the name of a geometric idea or concept. Too often in the past pupils had a good memorized mathematical vocabulary and a poor understanding of the mathematical ideas. Vocabulary should follow the development of the geometric idea.

Illustrative topics in elementary school geometry

A thorough development of suggestions for teaching geometry at the elementary school level would require a large volume. Therefore, several illustrative situations are presented to give the reader ideas for approaching various types of geometric topics. Included in the section that follows are suggestions for teaching portions of topics on geometric shapes, geometric construction, measuring angles, topology, projective geometry, and coordinate geometry.

STUDYING GEOMETRIC SHAPES

Spheres, cylinders, and rectangular solids[1]

The most common experiences involving geometry which pupils have deal with three-dimensional rather than two-dimensional shapes. At a very early level situations that further ideas concerning the nature of three-dimensional geometry should be planned. The teacher may use a situation such as "I watched a boy of kindergarten age sort his toys. He put them in boxes according to shape; however, he made a number of errors. I've brought along a number of objects similar to the ones he sorted out. Let's see if we can sort these objects according to shape." On a large table the teacher had placed balls (spheres) of various sizes, several boxes containing games and building blocks (rectangular prisms), and cylindrical building materials, pick-up sticks, tinker toy containers, and Lincoln log containers (cylinders).

The pupils were asked to separate the objects according to shape and to explain the reason why they considered certain objects to be of the same shape.

The teacher then said, "Ray and Phyllis were discussing the geometric shapes in a box of blocks. They couldn't agree as to the best way to describe the three geometric objects that I've brought along. How could you describe them? First, how are they alike?"

(The rectangular solid, the cylinder, and the prism used were constructed of clear plastic.) "Wait, maybe we had better have some way to identify each of the objects. Do you have any suggestions for a letter we could use to identify each object?" Pupils discussed the possibility of using A, B, and C, but decided instead that they would use R because one of the sides of the objects was a rectangle, C because one of the sides was a circle, and T because one of the sides was a triangle. The teacher labeled each object with a china-marking pencil. Again the teacher asked, "How are R, C, and T alike?"

[1] A portion of this section is based on Ruth Hutcheson and George Immerzeel, *Non-Metric Geometry* (Cedar Falls, Iowa: Malcolm Price Laboratory School).

Some of the pupils' suggestions were that all had sides, all were made of plastic, R and T had corners and edges, and R and T had some sides that were rectangular. The discussion continued, and as pupils introduced vocabulary words such as triangle, circle, square, solid, line, and point, these were informally discussed.

The next day pupils discussed ways in which the objects were different. Toward the end of the period each pupil was given a wooden model of each object and asked to develop a summary of the characteristics of the objects. Pupils made use of a table such as the one shown to summarize their findings.

	edges	corners	(angles)	sides
	12	8	24	6
	2	0	0	3
	9	6	18	5

When pupils disagreed on a portion of the table, they were asked to demonstrate the manner in which they had found an answer.

Similar methods can be used to introduce other geometric shapes. The emphasis should center on the identification of characteristics of geometric shapes. Correct geometric vocabulary can be developed, but extreme care should be taken that the study of geometry is not just the naming of the shape itself.

Circles, rectangles, and triangles

A teacher brought several pictures of rectangular, circular, and triangular forms to class and discussed with the students the shape that would frame each picture. Pupils identified the shapes of these objects from home experiences. The teacher then brought out a rectangular picture frame and asked, "What do we say the shape of this picture frame is?" When it was identified as rectangular in shape, the teacher continued by saying, "Yes, this picture frame is a model of a rectangle. How can you tell an object that is the shape of a rectangle?" Pupils identified that opposite sides were the same length and that the rectangle had "square corners."

The next questions posed by the teacher were designed to identify the difference between a rectangle and a rectangular region. She asked, "How is the frame different from the picture?" Pupils suggested that they were the same shape but that the picture frame had nothing inside. The teacher commented, "We can describe the picture frame and the picture by saying that the picture frame is a model of a rectangle and that the picture is a model of a rectangular region. What do you think I mean by a rectangular region? Can you give me examples of representations of rectangles and rectangular regions? Look about the room." Pupils identified the following as models of rectangles: the window frame, other picture frames, and the door molding. They identified windows, doors, and pieces of tablet paper as models of rectangular regions.

Similar discussions of triangles and triangular regions and circles and circular regions can then be developed. In addition to circular and triangular picture frames, models can be made from pipe cleaners, wire, and heavy paper. Darning hoops and bicycle tires make good models for a circle; metal musical triangles can be effectively used as models for a triangle.

When the teacher feels that pupils have gained some insight into the difference between a geometric shape and its region, the teacher can make effective use of worksheets in which pupils are asked (1) to identify triangles, circles, and rectangles, (2) to be ready to describe their characteristics, and (3) to outline the model of the geometric shape and to color the region. A bulletin board using various geometric shapes is also useful.

Source: Still Photo Services U. D. I. S., Pennsylvania State University.

Primary-grade pupils should have many opportunities to identify and discuss many geometric shapes.

Other geometric shapes

As pupils make mathematical progress a wide variety of geometric shapes should be identified. In addition, there should be an increased emphasis upon classifying these shapes. The set of developmental questions concerning quadrilaterals that follows is representative of this type of classifying.

Teacher	Pupil
You have been working with a number of geometric shapes that contain four sides. Name all that you can.	Squares, rectangles, parallelograms, quadrilaterals, trapezoids
Which of these shapes is the most general? That is, which of these has all of the other shapes as subsets?	Quadrilateral
Try to use the Venn diagram to show the relationship. (The following diagram can then be developed.)	

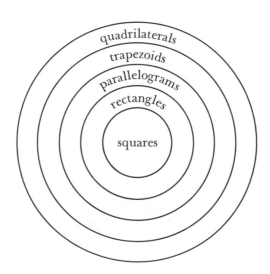

CAN YOU PLACE THE SHAPE?

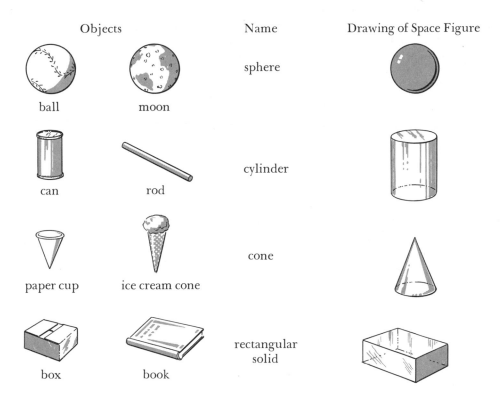

Objects		Name	Drawing of Space Figure
ball	moon	sphere	
can	rod	cylinder	
paper cup	ice cream cone	cone	
box	book	rectangular solid	

Points, curves, lines, planes, and space

Geometry is based on several important constructs, which we will not attempt to define here, but only to describe. A *point* is thought of as being so small that it has no size. It is an exact location. A *curve* may be thought of as a set of points represented by a pencil drawing made without lifting the pencil off the sheet of paper. *Lines* are a set of points of a particular type. *Line* means "straight line." A geometric line extends without limit. When a line has a measurable length, it is called a *line segment*. *Planes* are also a particular set of points. A geometric plane is a flat surface which extends without end. *Space* is considered to be an unlimited number of points; points in space can be thought of as being described by their position. Pupils' understanding of these geometric concepts should be gradually developed throughout the elementary school. Several approaches to developing an understanding of these ideas are presented below.

Points. The idea of a point can be developed through a need to make an exact location. Several possibilities are beginning with statements such as

"On a recent trip I saw the point at which three states meet. Who owns the exact location at which these states meet? Can it have dimension? Would this exact location (that we can't see) be a dot or a point? What is the difference?" "I've drawn a circle cut into fourths. Notice that each of the fourths is a different color. What is the color of the point at the exact center of the circle? Does it have dimension?" "What do we mean by a point at which a space capsule reenters the Earth's atmosphere?"

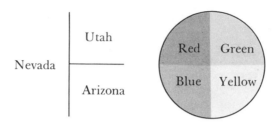

"A friend of mine said, 'I know a very good spot for fishing. I'll take you right to the point where we should fish.' What did he mean?"

Curves.　The topic of curves was developed through the following situation. "I've reproduced a Cub Scout map of a trip to the woods. What would we call the dotted line?" Pupils responded that it would be the trail or the path that Mark took. Then the teacher said, "Right, we could call this Mark's path. Also, we can identify the mathematical idea given by this path as a curve."

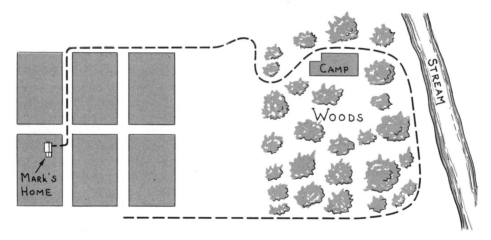

Pupils then suggested that all of the path was not curved; some of it was made up of straight lines.[2] The teacher asked, "Is a straight line a curve? Is a curve a line?" This type of questioning caused some confusion, which provided a need to check reference sources concerning the mathematical meaning of curve. From the sources the pupils learned that all lines and line segments

[2] In this discussion only curves that lie in the same plane are considered.

are curves. They also found that a curve is made up of an infinite set of points.

The teacher then asked for other representations of curves and inquired if the path around the lake shown below was a representation of a curve. Again the class found it necessary to check references to find the answer. They found that the path around the lake was a representation of a closed curve. They also found that geometric shapes such as circles and rectangles are special types of closed curves.

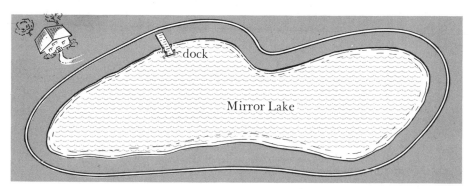

Lines.   Discussion of the idea of lines might be developed by beginning with a statement such as "We talked about a point at which several states meet. What would we call the border between two adjoining states? Which state would own this line? Does a line have dimension? Can I really draw a line on the board? How long should it be? If a line has two end points, it is called a line segment. (See diagram.) Is the border between the two states a line or a line segment? How could we represent a line to show that it goes on without end?" (See diagram.)

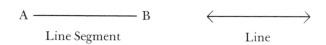

"Nancy and Jane share a room. They draw a representation of a line down the middle of the room to divide it. How wide should this strip be if each girl is to have maximum space?"

Planes.   The topic of planes was introduced by placing a plastic rectangular solid and a plastic rectangular prism on a table and labeling the end surfaces.

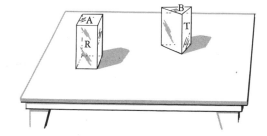

The teacher began the discussion by saying, "Ken said that surface A and surface B were just alike; Nancy didn't think they were. See if you can resolve their argument by thinking about the two surfaces. First, how is surface A like surface B?" Pupils suggested that both were flat, and both were the same distance above the table top. Pupils were then asked to give possible names for smooth surfaces such as A and B. Many suggestions were given; however, the teacher capitalized on the term "plain," which they had been discussing in geography, to develop the term "plane."

Next pupils were asked, "Are A and B in the same plane?" Many pupils were not sure. Through questions such as "Will a jet fly above plane A?" "What if surface A and B went on forever? What could you say about them?" pupils developed the concept of a plane as a flat surface that extended in every direction "forever."

The lesson continued with a discussion of only the plane determined by A. The teacher asked, "Will the peak of Nittany Mountain be above plane A?" (Yes.) "If you were in Pittsburgh, could you find a point on plane A?" (Maybe; it would be there but it would be hard to identify.)

Further discussion can lead pupils to visualize two planes that intersect and to identify the points of intersection of the two planes as a line. Then questions about the difference between the ideas concerning planes which the pupils have been discussing and physical world examples that are like planes can be discussed. For example, doors, windows, and sections of a wall are like planes; however, they are three dimensional and don't go "on and on."

Ray.   The concept of a ray can be developed by questions such as "How would the representation of a rocket sent from earth directly out into space appear on the chalkboard?" "What would the representation of the beam of a flashlight look like?" "Would a lighthouse beacon be a representation of a line? Of a line segment? How is it different from either a line or a line segment?" "What do we call the beam of light from a lighthouse or a flashlight?" Pupils then combine their understanding of representing lines and representing line segments to represent rays—•————▶. Also, they associate an infinite set of points with the ray and know that a ray has one end point.

Further discussion can be used to develop these generalizations about the properties of lines and planes: (1) exactly one line joins any two points in space, (2) if two different points of a plane lie on a line, that line lies in the plane, (3) three points that are not on the same line are in *only* one plane, (4) if two different planes intersect, their intersection is a line, (5) when two different lines intersect, their intersection is a point.

A diagram such as that shown below can help pupils to understand and remember the difference between physical world objects and mathematical ideas.

WHAT'S THE DIFFERENCE?

Physical Object	Mathematical Idea	Drawing

point   P •

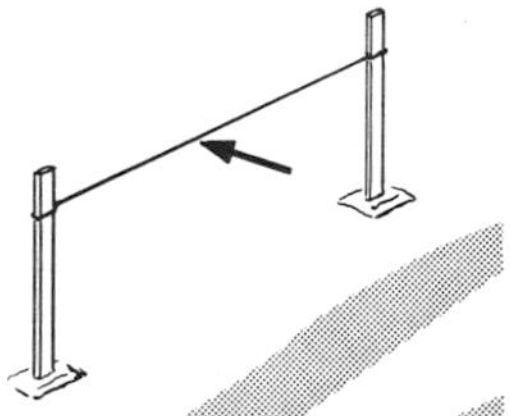

line segment   A •————————• B

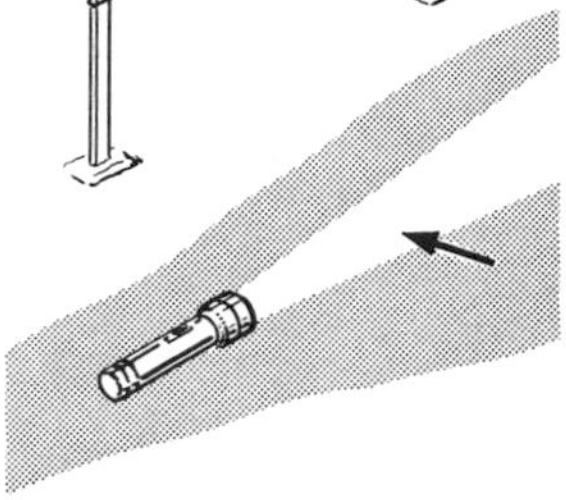

ray   A •————————➤

plane

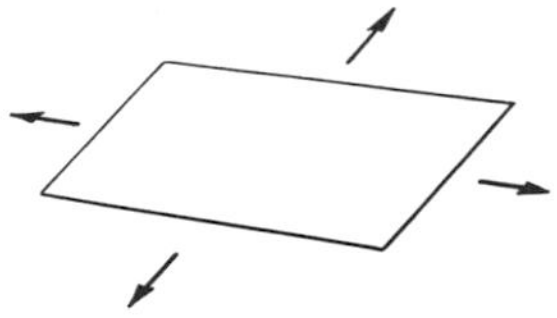

Congruence. One of the basic ideas of geometry is the congruence of geometric figures. Two figures may be thought of as being *congruent* if the model of one figure will fit exactly on the model of the other.

The study of congruence was introduced with the following question. "Modern companies often employ people whose job involves checking for the quality of the product. This is often called quality control. See if you can identify the major quality control check for each of the products I mention."

A square which you use in shop work
  (angles must be the same).

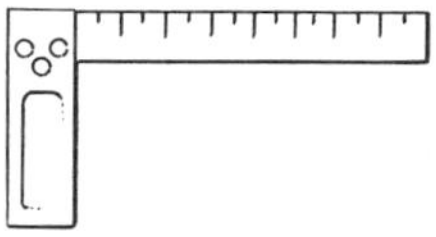

Checkers (circles of the same dimension).

Rulers (must be the same length).

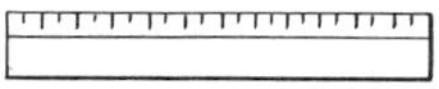

Pupils were then given an opportunity on a worksheet to identify geometric forms which were of the same size and shape. The teacher asked, "Do any of you know what geometric forms that fit exactly over one and another are called? _____ No? _____ Turn to your textbooks and find the term that is used." Pupils identified the vocabulary word congruent and checked their description of congruence with that given in the book.

WHICH FIGURES ARE CONGRUENT?

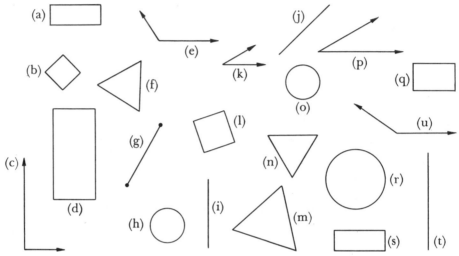

Which figures are congruent:	Line segments?	i	and	j
	Rectangles?	a	and	s
	Angles?	k	and	p
	Circles?	h	and	o
	Triangles?	f	and	h

Later, problem situations were given which required pupils to construct congruent geometric shapes.

GEOMETRIC CONSTRUCTION

Use of compass and straight edge

A variety of situations can be provided in which a compass and a straight edge are used for solving problems or developing materials. The vignette that follows develops teaching strategies for using a compass and bisecting an angle. Several other possible geometric constructions are then listed.

The following situations were used by a teacher to introduce the use of the compass. "A group of students at Longfellow School needed 45 circles that measured 8 inches across to decorate the stage for a school play. How could they make these circles?"

Class members made suggestions such as "They could get one and use it as a pattern." "They could use an eight-inch pie pan as a pattern." "Make use of a compass to draw them." The various proposals were discussed. The class decided: (1) if a good pattern of the right size were available, it could be used; (2) an eight-inch pie or cake pan was eight inches on the inside and thus could not be used for the circle; and (3) in general, the compass would probably be the best bet.

The teacher provided each member of the class with a compass, paper, a piece of cardboard to prevent the compass point from marking the desk, and a set of instructions for using a compass. She suggested, "Other students have found these directions for the use of a compass to be handy. See if you can think of other suggestions. Now see if you can draw a circle that is eight inches across. Experiment to find a means of getting a circle as close to eight inches across as possible. Incidentally, we call the distance across a circle that goes through the center of the circle a diameter."

The following suggestions were reproduced on the paper:

1. Place the steel point of the compass on the point which you wish to be the center of the circle.

2. Hold the compass at the top with one hand.

3. Let the compass swing around on the steel point so that the pencil draws a complete circle in one sweep.

Bisecting an angle

The bisection of an angle was introduced with this problem: "Ken had a triangular (equilateral) piece of plywood which he needed to cut into two congruent regions. The only instruments he had that might help him were a compass and a straight piece of wood. He reasoned that if he could cut angle (a) into two equal angles, then he could extend the line and thus cut the board into two congruent regions. How could he accomplish this?" The teacher then gave each pupil a dittoed representation of the triangle.

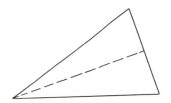

The teacher asked for suggestions concerning the partitioning of the angle into two congruent angles. Pupils suggested that there might be some way to do it with an instrument to measure angles. The teacher agreed but suggested that a more accurate result could be obtained by using a compass and a straight edge. She stated that the method was discovered by the Greeks over two thousand years ago and was normally called bisecting an angle. Pupils were instructed to use their compasses and straight edges to experiment with approaches to bisecting an angle. The teacher provided each pupil with a duplicated sheet of angles of varying sizes.

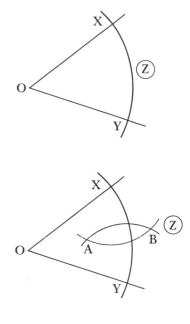

Pupils experimented for a short time. None seemed to have a very good lead. The teacher noticed that several pupils had placed the metal tip of the compass on the vertex of the angle and drawn an arc that cut both sides of the angle. The teacher went to the board and said, "I notice that several persons have started out in this manner. It is a good start. The rest of the class can use this as a start and see what you can do from here." After a minute or two the teacher asked, "Do any of you have ideas on how to proceed?" John suggested that if a point Z could be found midway between points X and Y, then a line segment joining O and Z should bisect the angle. Kathryn placed the metal tip of the compass at point X and tried to draw an arc half-way between X and Y. Then (keeping the same radius) she drew another arc placing the compass point at Y.

The teacher noted the meeting points of the two arcs and asked, "What would happen if we joined points O, A, and B?" Several pupils used the straight edge to draw a line through these points; they noted that this line appeared to bisect the angle.

Several other angles were treated in the same manner. Pupils checked their mathematics books to determine whether or not their method was correct. They noted that the bisection of an angle could be accomplished by using two arcs rather than four. (See diagram below.) Then the class returned to the original problem and found the midpoint of the triangle.

rather than

The development above can be extended to finding the midpoint of a line segment, to drawing a right angle without using a set square or a protractor, and to copying angles. Elementary school pupils may also use the compass and the straight edge to perform the following tasks:

1. Draw line segments equivalent (congruent) to a given line segment. This can be developed by asking pupils to make an exact copy of a chart, graphs, etc.

2. Draw equivalent geometric shapes: circle, squares, rectangles, triangles, etc. Art projects, copying, and bulletin board displays can be used as introductory procedures.

3. Inscribe geometric shapes within a circle. Developing displays and ornaments can introduce this topic.

4. Construct parallel lines. This can be introduced as a check of pupils' ability to use a ruler to draw parallel lines for borders on art work.

5. Construct *similar* geometric shapes: rectangles, triangles, and other polygons. This topic can be developed through situations in which the teacher asks pupils to make a model of a geometric figure that is larger or smaller than the original figure.

TOPOLOGY

The majority of topics in geometry taught in the elementary school are concerned with the properties of rigid geometric figures. The study of topology (sometimes referred to as rubber sheet geometry) can be useful in broadening the mathematical thinking of elementary school pupils. Topology is not concerned with measurement or exact shape. For example, in topology, a circle and a triangle are treated as equivalent figures.

Pupils can examine the properties of various geometric shapes drawn on rubber sheets and solids made of rubber or foam. The rubber may be twisted, kneaded, and pulled, but should not be torn. Several geometric shapes cut from rubber foam may be used to begin the topic. One teacher began by saying, "I've placed a number of geometric solids made from rubber on this table. Note that they can be changed in shape by pulling and pushing on them. What properties of the shape will change? What properties will not be changed by twisting and pulling?"

Pupils found that the volumes and the surface areas of the cubes were changed. They also suggested that neither the number of faces nor the number of edges changed. The teacher then asked if the number of corners (vertices) changed. A check by the class members revealed that the number of vertices remained the same.

Then the teacher stated, "We can discover some generalizations concerning the faces, vertices, and edges of these shapes. Make a table of the number of faces, vertices, and edges for these shapes, and then see if you can discover a pattern."

		faces	vertices	edges
(a)		4	4	6
(b)		6	8	12
(c)		5	6	9
(d)		9	9	16

By studying the pattern pupils were able to discover the formula faces + vertices = edges + 2, or $F + V = E + 2$. The teacher said, "We certainly haven't proved this relationship. Some of you will want to check the several reference books I have on the table to find out if this relationship has been proved mathematically." A check of reference material will provide the information that this formula is called Euler's formula and has been proved true for all polyhedra.

Networks

Many doodling-type puzzles for adults and children involve the concept of networks. Networks are diagrams consisting of a number of lines, called arcs, and a number of points that are joined by the arcs. The points are named *vertices* and can be either odd or even depending upon the number of arcs joined by the vertex.

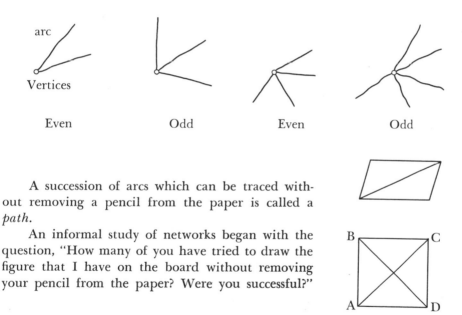

A succession of arcs which can be traced without removing a pencil from the paper is called a *path*.

An informal study of networks began with the question, "How many of you have tried to draw the figure that I have on the board without removing your pencil from the paper? Were you successful?"

The majority of pupils had tried the drawing in the past and had been unsuccessful. A number of pupils mentioned that they still attempted to accomplish the feat. The teacher then said, "What do we call A, B, C, and D? —— Vertices —— right. How many lines—arcs—meet at each of these vertices? —— Three —— right. Let's see if we can make some discoveries concerning the possibility of 'traveling' various drawings without removing the pencil from the paper. Look at the duplicated sheet I'm giving to you. We'll answer the first few questions together. Finish the remainder, and see if you can develop any generalizations."

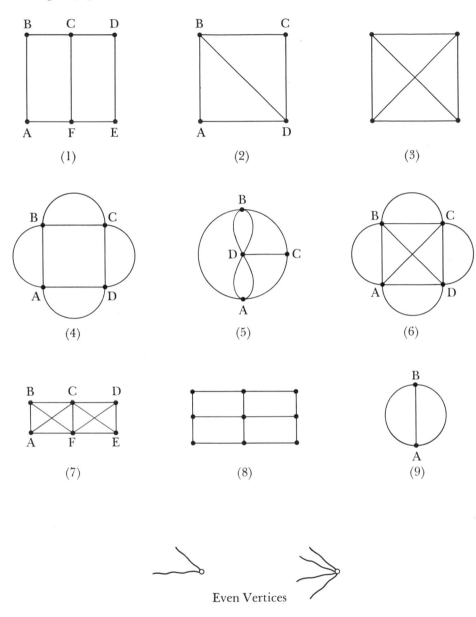

Even Vertices

Odd Vertices

Network	Number of even vertices	Number of odd vertices	Can it be traced without removing pencil from paper?
1	4	2	yes
2	2	2	yes
3	0	4	no
4	4	0	yes
5	2	2	yes
6	0	4	no
7	2	6	no
8	4	5	no
9	0	2	?

It may be necessary to work with a much greater number of patterns before pupils are able to develop any generalizations. If pupils are not able to come up with possible patterns for solutions, the teacher may state several of the generalizations (some correctly and some incorrectly) and then ask pupils to verify her statements. Such statements might include:

1. The number of odd vertices in a network is always even if it is to be traveled without removing pencil from paper. (true)

2. A network containing no even vertices cannot be traveled without removing pencil from paper. (false, see (9) above)

3. Any network with all even vertices can be traveled in one journey. (true)

4. A network containing two odd vertices can be traveled in one journey. (true)

5. Networks containing {4, 6, 8, . . . , 2n} cannot be traveled in one journey. (true)

Introductory work with networks can lead into the old standard network problem—the Koenigsberg Bridge problem. The problem is as follows: In the 1700's the city of Koenigsberg, Germany, was situated on an island at the meeting point of two rivers. The community and the island were connected by means of seven bridges. (See figure below.) Citizens of Koenigsberg tried to take a walk about the city and the surrounding area by crossing each of the seven bridges once and only once. Is this possible?

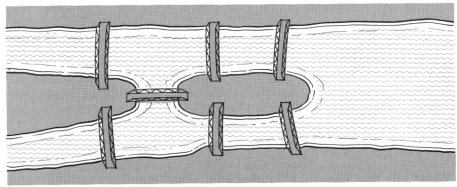

Pupils' previous experience with networks should allow them to give a reason for the inability of the residents of Koenigsberg to complete their journey without recrossing at least one bridge.

There are other excursions into the world of topology which may be taken. Pupils can study equivalent surfaces. For example, a cube can be stretched to form a door knob without tearing the surface of the cube, and a doughnut-shaped object may be stretched to form a teacup.

Another kind of surface that can be investigated can be formed by cutting a long thin sheet of paper and giving the paper one twist before pasting the ends together.

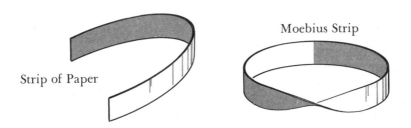

Strip of Paper

Moebius Strip

This strip is a one-sided surface called a Moebius strip. It is named for its discoverer, A. F. Moebius, a German mathematician of the nineteenth century. This idea used in the Moebius strip is commonly used in factories where long belts are attached to two wheels. The twist in the belt allows for even wear.

An interesting experiment may be conducted by cutting on a line along the center of the strip. Instead of two circular loops, a single loop results, with two twists instead of one. Experiment and continue by cutting the strip again. What happens?

PROJECTIVE GEOMETRY

Another form of geometry with which pupils should be briefly acquainted is known as projective geometry. Projective geometry is the study of geometrical properties that remain the same when a figure is projected from one plane to another. One of the more common physical world situations involving projective geometry is that found in projecting a map from a sphere to a plane.

Discussions of map-making in social studies classes in the upper inter-mediate grades can be used to identify geometric properties that remain

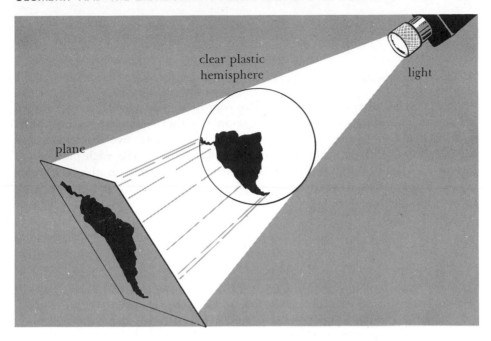

invariant under projective geometry. Guided discussion can develop the notions that lines project into lines, points into points, and intersections do not change under projection. Pupils can also be led to note that under projection (1) a circle may become an ellipse, (2) the measure of angles changes, (3) straight-line segments remain straight-line segments, and (4) straight-line segments change in length. Through a study of projective geometry pupils may become aware of the difficulty of interpreting a three-dimensional surface such as the earth on a two-dimensional surface such as a map.

COORDINATE GEOMETRY

The use of coordinate geometry as a problem-solving technique was identified in chapter 11. In addition to the basic algebraic function of coordinate geometry, it can be used in developing ideas concerning maps, charts, and graphs.

Early work can begin with problem situations involving the locations of points on a map of a community and in the trial-and-error search for routes from one location to another. As the pupil progresses in his use of community maps, a road map can be used to further his understanding of coordinates. He may locate the community that is at A - 7 on the road map and give the coordinate location of major cities in the state.

One of the best devices for developing the coordinate plane is to use the childrens' game of Battleship. One variation of this game is described below.

Battleship (two players)

Each player is given a sheet of coordinate paper (such as that shown below) and a number of ships. (For example, a short game might be played with each player having four battleships, three cruisers, five destroyers, and six P.T. boats.) Without allowing the other player to observe, each player then locates each of his ships at the intersection of two lines on the coordinate plane. The location of each set of ships, e.g., battleships or P.T. boats, must form a straight line.

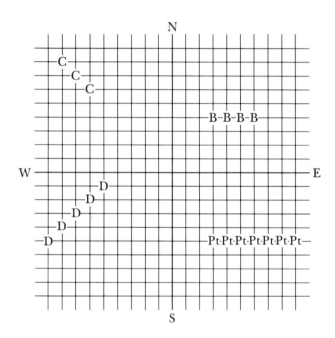

The object of the game is to "sink" the other person's ships. This is accomplished by calling out a location on the coordinate plane. Player one begins play by indicating three locations such as 5 East, 3 North; 2 West, 4 South; and 6 West, 5 North. The other player then informs him whether he has sunk any of his ships. (A ship is sunk by having its location called out by the opposing player.) The players continue alternating turns until all ships of one player are destroyed.

Once the game is developed, the teacher may add several variations designed to acquaint the players with the coordinate plane. Variations might include:

1. Instead of calling 4 East, 3 North introduce negatives into the system and the X and the Y to designate horizontal and vertical lines.

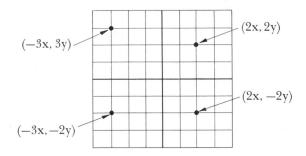

2. When they are familiar with the X, Y and the use of negatives, pupils can be led to use notation such as (3,4) and (−4,2) to designate the points on the plane. The first member of the order pair of numbers is the location on the X coordinate; the second, the location of the Y coordinate.

Longitude and latitude

Games such as Battleship are helpful in creating a readiness for longitude and latitude. Longitude and latitude can effectively be introduced in grades five and six and handled in either the mathematics or the social studies class. Probably the best pattern is to teach the topic in social studies with a mathematical point of view. This suggestion is made because the social studies provide many good "use" situations for introducing longitude and latitude. A discussion can center around the voyages of the early explorers and their need to locate points on maps and globes. The short teaching sequence that follows provides an illustration of a possible introductory sequence.

The teacher began by pointing to a map he had drawn on the chalkboard. He said, "You've been reading about Prince Henry, the navigator. How could he explain to someone the location of the two islands I've marked A and B?" Various suggestions were offered, but the most common one suggested was to draw horizontal and vertical lines on the map. The teacher then asked how they should be located, directing pupils to a geography reference. From this reference work pupils located zero degrees north and south at the Equator and zero degrees east and west as a line passing through England. Pupils then identified locations in terms such as 4 East and 3 North. Later in the year the terms "longitude" and "latitude" were introduced.

Guided discussion and discovery exercises should then be used to develop these facts about longitude and latitude:

1. There are 360 degrees of longitude and 360 degrees of latitude. This corresponds to the measure of circles.

2. All points located on the same line of latitude are the same distance from the Equator (are on the same X coordinate line).

3. All latitude lines are parallel to each other and are known as *parallels*.

4. The Equator is designated as zero degrees latitude. Latitude is mea-

sured in terms of degrees north and south of the Equator (from 0 to 90 degrees north and from 0 to 90 degrees south).

5. Longitude lines are Y coordinate lines. They converge at both Poles and bisect the lines of latitude. They are measured from a zero point that passes through Greenwich, England.

6. Each circle of longitude partitions the globe into hemispheres. Each meridian of longitude is a semicircle extending from the North Pole to the South Pole.

7. The zero point of longitude, located at Greenwich, England, was an arbitrary, man-made choice. The zero point of latitude, located at the Equator, was located astronomically.

8. Degrees of latitude are equal in length (about seventy miles). Degrees of longitude decrease in length from the Equator to the Poles (from about seventy miles in length at the Equator to zero at the Poles).

The topic of longitude and latitude demands a great deal of complex thinking on the part of the pupil. Therefore, it should not be taught in a single unit, but should slowly be developed over a period of one or two years.

The possibilities for using geometry in the elementary school are almost endless. The ideas discussed in this chapter are representative of the many topics in geometry that can be effectively used with elementary school pupils.

STUDY SUGGESTIONS

1. Select a topic in nonmetric geometry that is not discussed in this chapter. Develop a plan for teaching the topic by starting with a problem situation.
2. Some current mathematics programs begin nonmetric geometry in kindergarten. Others delay nonmetric geometry until grade three. Discuss the justifications for these two treatments of nonmetric geometry. Which do you favor? Why?
3. Compare a current textbook at the grade level which you teach or would like to teach and another textbook that was copyrighted before 1960. How do they compare in respect to the emphasis given to geometry?
4. Explain how the emphasis given to elementary school geometry materials is different from that of high school geometry.
5. Develop a method of comparing the use of "set language" in arithmetic and in geometry. How does the use of set language help relate the two portions of mathematics?
6. Discuss this question: What phase of geometry should be introduced first?

SUGGESTED REFERENCES

To improve content background in geometry see the bibliographies of content books and reference books at the end of this volume.

Bentley, W. H. E., and Potts, E. W. M., *Geometry, Part One: Discovery by Drawing and Measurement* (Boston: Ginn, 1958).

Corle, Clyde G., *Teaching Mathematics in the Elementary School* (New York: Ronald, 1964), Chap. 12.

Elementary School Science Project, *Astronomy: Charting the Universe* (Urbana: University of Illinois, 1963).

Flavell, John H., *The Developmental Psychology of Jean Piaget* (Princeton, New Jersey: Van Nostrand, 1963).

Grossnickle, F. E., and Brueckner, L. J., *Discovering Meaning in Elementary School Mathematics* (New York: Holt, Rinehart and Winston, 1963), Chap. 15.

Johnson, Donovan A., *Paper Folding for the Mathematics Class* (Washington, D. C.: National Council of Teachers of Mathematics, 1957).

Johnson, Donovan A., and Glenn, William H., *Topology, The Rubber Sheet Geometry* (St. Louis: Webster Publishing Company, 1960).

Piaget, J., Inhilder, B., and Szeminska, A., *The Child's Conception of Geometry* (New York: Basic Books, Inc., 1960).

Robinson, Edith G., "The Role of Geometry in Elementary School Mathematics," *The Arithmetic Teacher,* Vol. 13, No. 1 (January 1966), pp. 3–10.

School Mathematics Study Group, *Intuitive Geometry,* Studies in Mathematics, Volume VII (Leland Stanford Junior University, 1961).

Skypek, D. H., "Geometric Concepts in Grades 4–6," *The Arithmetic Teacher,* Vol. 12, No. 6 (October 1965), pp. 443–499.

USE OF SUGGESTED REFERENCES

1. Use Bentley and Potts as a resource to develop a lesson on geometric construction.

2. Corle states several purposes for studying geometry at the elementary school level. Develop a list of reasons for the study of geometry and compare them with Corle.

3. Study the uses of geometry made in the University of Illinois Elementary-School Science Project. A number of good physical world situations are provided for the study of geometry at the intermediate grade level.

4. Study the findings of Piaget (either in Piaget or Flavell) concerning the young child's development of geometric ideas. What implications do these findings have for the sequence in which we teach topics in geometry?

5. Compare the topics listed by Grossnickle and Brueckner (pp. 337–338) with the context of a current elementary school mathematics series.

6. From Johnson's pamphlet on paper folding select several paper-folding sequences and develop a lesson for elementary school pupils.

7. Study the booklet on topology by Johnson and Glen. What material in it would be appropriate for a normal elementary school sixth grade? For a superior sixth grade?

8. The small volume by S.M.S.G. should be a help to the elementary teacher for the improvement of his knowledge of geometry.

9. Robinson gives several excellent suggestions concerned with teaching geometry. Study your current elementary school mathematics textbook series. Does it use ideas such as those suggested by Robinson?

10. Study the suggestions for teaching topological relations suggested by Skypek. How could you use these ideas in the intermediate grades?

13

Measurement

Two types of measurement can be readily discerned. One involves the use of *discrete* variables such as the cost of postage stamps, the size of families, and census enumerations. Discrete data are usually expressed as integers and are characterized by gaps on a number line. The second type involves the use of *continuous* variables such as heights, weights, time, temperature, and blood pressure. Continuous variables may be viewed as being represented on an uninterrupted scale. The material in this chapter emphasizes continuous measurement.

Since antiquity, man has been interested in measuring. Many phases of mathematics have developed because of this interest in measuring, and any educated citizen today makes use of some type of measurement in every kind of endeavor. Today's space scientist refers to measures such as light years, parsecs, and Angstrom units. Textbooks of the early 1800's contained terms such as Perch, Ell-Flemish, and hogshead. Thus, while the units have sometimes changed, the need for measurement continues to exist.[1]

Today's advertising requires the consumer to be discerning in his use of measurement. For example, a teacher asked, "Bill had to decide which of two types of soda pop to buy, a half quart for 35¢ or a pint for 34¢. If he likes both types of soda pop equally well, which would be the best buy?" The majority of her class felt that the half quart for 35¢ would be the "best buy." This problem of packaging and measurement is also a problem for adults.[2] Sometimes the housewife finds that the unit cost of the "Giant" size box of soap is higher than that of the "Regular" size.

In his attempt to measure such things as time, volume, area, temperature, energy, etc., man has arrived at the following generalizations, which should be considered when developing possible learning experiences for children.

---

[1] The scope of this book does not allow for an historical treatment of measurement. A knowledge of the history of measurement is of great value to the elementary school teacher, for it can provide possible approaches to teaching measurement. For historical material see the references marked with an asterisk (*) listed in the bibliography at the end of this chapter.

[2] See "Deceptive Packaging . . . Our Readers Write," *Consumer Reports*, XXV (September 1960), pp. 488–492.

1. Measurements of continuous data, no matter how precise they may be, are approximations. Most measures can be refined enough to be precise for practical purposes, but the general statement, *"Every time you measure, you're wrong,"* merits consideration. Even though a scientific instrument is measured to the nearest millionth of an inch, there is still some error. Thus, statements such as "He's exactly 5 feet 4 inches tall," should be avoided.

2. Some things, such as the length of a room, can be measured directly. Other things, such as the distance to a star, must be measured indirectly.

3. The units used for measuring have developed over a period of time and possess much historical interest. At one time, each community, or at least each country, had its own units of measure based on familiar facts such as the length of the parts of the body of a king or the distance between two well-known communities. Over a period of time, and with a great deal of effort, units of measure have become standardized to a certain extent in many countries.

4. Each type of measure normally has units of varying value. Just as the number system is based upon ones, tens, hundreds, etc., a system of measures may possess proportional units.

5. The combination of several measures possess only the degree of accuracy that is possessed by the least precise measure. For example, if one distance is measured to the nearest mile, one to the nearest yard, and one to the nearest foot, and the distances are added, the sum will be only accurate to the nearest mile.

6. Measurements are relative. For example, a 4,000-foot mountain might be classified as "very high" by a pupil in Florida, while a pupil in Switzerland might classify the mountain as "very low."

7. Measurements are used to describe or as a substitute for an actual "thing" being measured.

MEASURING SPACE

Linear measure

The concepts necessary for the study of linear measure go hand in hand with the basic geometric concepts of points and line segments. The early study of linear measurement can be introduced well through the need to compare the length of two objects that cannot be compared directly. One teacher introduced the topic by stating, "I'm thinking about moving this bookcase (touches bookcase) to the rear of the room to fit between the radiator and the end of the room. Another teacher told me that she didn't think there would be enough room for the bookcase there. How can I find out?"

Various suggestions were presented by the class members. The pupils rejected the idea that the bookcase be moved to the rear of the room to see, since this would involve a good deal of physical work. Several suggested that rulers be used to measure the widths of the bookcase and of the space. Others suggested that they could find how many lengths of a piece of paper each unit was. The teacher focused on the nonstandard unit of measure, and the pupils checked by using a piece of paper. The space was over a paper length larger than the bookcase, so the problem was easily resolved.

Then the teacher asked, "What would we have done if there had been much less than a paper length of difference in the two units?" Again the pupils suggested the use of a ruler. The teacher asked, "Could I find out if there wasn't a ruler or a yardstick in the room?" The suggestion was given that a small length could be marked off on a piece of paper and then other pieces of paper marked off in these units. The teacher suggested that the pupils actually try to make a ruler of their own in this manner.

When pupils had finished making their own rulers, several pupils were asked to measure the space by the windows and the width of the bookcase. Because each one had selected his own length for units, the measurement varied, but each found that there would be enough space for a bookcase.

After the pupils had made several other measurements using the home-made ruler, the teacher presented a situation in which a standard unit of measure was needed, and a study of the units used on the standard ruler began.

After the basic concepts of linear measure had been intuitively developed, the teacher began to develop the vocabulary that is essential to an accurate understanding of the discussion. The pupils recognized that representation of line segments was being measured.

During the elementary school years the concept of linear measure can be refined. Pupils should learn to work with parts of an inch and (later) feet, yards, meters, and centimeters. A helpful historical study of the development of standard units of measure can be developed during the intermediate grades and ancient measures such as spans, hand, cubit, digits, reed, and fathoms can be studied.

During the teaching of linear measurement in the elementary school the following concepts can be developed:

1. A line segment is used to measure line segments. (A line segment can be considered to be a set of points consisting of two different points A and B and all of the points between A and B on that line.)

2. The measure of a line segment is the number of accepted "units" and portions of units. Normally, inches, feet, yards, and miles, or centimeters, meters, decimeters, and kilometers are used.

3. The choice of the units used for measure is arbitrary. Any unit length could be used if enough people agreed upon the unit.

4. The selection of standard units is of great help in commercial dealings.

Perimeter.   Many everyday situations arise in which children and adults find the perimeter of a polygon (a simple closed curve which is a union of line segments.) The perimeter can be considered to be a special name for the length of a polygon.

One teacher introduced this concept by saying, "Look at the duplicated
sheet of paper I've given to you; it contains a drawing of a design that Jill
wishes to outline with gold thread. How
many inches of gold thread will she
need to outline the design? How can
you find out?"

The pupils decided to use rulers to measure the distance around the
polygon. They quickly established the length to be six inches.

Several other problems concerned with finding the perimeters of triangles,
rectangles, and other types of polygons were then worked. The problems involved topics such as fencing a garden and covering the edge of a bulletin
board with plastic. Then the teacher asked the pupils to describe the nature
of the various problems. All agreed that they were finding the length of a
polygon, or the sum of the sides of a polygon. The teacher asked, "Do any of
you know the term we use for the measure of a polygon or the boundary
around a closed figure made up of line segments?" One pupil thought that
the term was either perimeter or area. The teacher suggested that the pupils
turn to their textbooks and reference books to check to see which term was
correct and to check the definition. The pupils also generalized that the perimeter of a polygon could be found by finding the sum of the measure of the
line segments. The term "perimeter" was introduced only after the pupils
were well acquainted with the concept of perimeter. Later in the study of
perimeter the pupils can discover shortcuts for computing the perimeter of
regular polygons.

Several other curves were also measured using string and a ruler. The
pupils discussed the differing lengths they had found. They decided that they
were due to the inaccuracies that occur when string is used.

Area

The idea of finding a measure of a region (the number of congruent
copies of a unit region) can be introduced in terms of rectangular regions at
the end of the primary grades. Then the concept of area can be refined in the
following grades through problems concerned with finding of the areas of
triangular, quadrilateral, circular, and irregular regions.

Finding the area of a rectangular region.   The topic was introduced with
this problem: "I've brought in a new bulletin board for our use. How can we
find the number of sheets of construction paper that will be needed to cover
the region?" The class discussed possible means of determining the number of
sheets of construction paper. The students agreed that the best solution would

be to lay the bulletin board on the floor and actually to cover it with sheets of construction paper. This was done, and the pupils found that 48 sheets of construction paper were required, although the fit was not exact.

Follow-up questions guided the pupils to identify the measure of the rectangular region as 48 units. (A unit represented one 12-inch by 18-inch sheet of construction paper.) The pupils also generalized that to measure a region, a unit which itself is a region is needed.

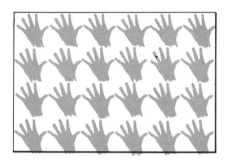

The discussion was followed by problems involving the measuring of regions. The pupils were asked to find the measure of the surface of their desks. Several suggestions were used in measuring those regions. First, the pupils found the number of "hands" that the desk top contained.

Because of the varying sizes of the pupils' hands, the class decided that while a measure could be taken with a hand, it would be better to have a measure that would not vary. This idea lead to a discussion of a possible standard measure of regions. The suggestions most often made was that such a standard region would best be described in terms of inches or feet. The pupils were then given a 6-inch by 4-inch sheet of paper and asked to experiment with measuring that region. Several pupils suggested that the paper be marked off into squares 1-inch by 1-inch. When the paper was marked into 1-inch by 1-inch regions, the pupils found that the measure was 24 of that unit. These 1-inch by 1-inch units were identified as being 1 square inch.

Next the teacher asked if any of the pupils knew the name that is usually given to the measure of a region. Several had heard the term "area" and suggested that term. The class was referred to textbooks to check the correctness of the term.

The lessons that followed involved using squared paper and finding the area of various rectangular regions marked off on the paper. Familiarity with the array pattern (studied earlier) allowed the pupils to discover quickly that the number of units could be quickly determined by multiplying the number of the length by the number of the width. Mathematical sentences for finding the area were written.

At a later stage of development the pupils should abstract the general formula for the area of a rectangle: area = length × width; $A = LW$.

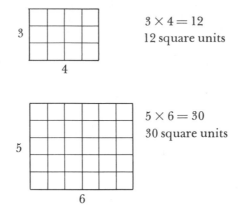

$3 \times 4 = 12$
12 square units

$5 \times 6 = 30$
30 square units

Areas of other polygons. Once pupils have developed the basic idea of finding the measure of a region by determining the number of square inches that will cover the region, they can discover methods of determining the areas of other polygons. A representative problem that can be used in introduction and possible discovery follows.

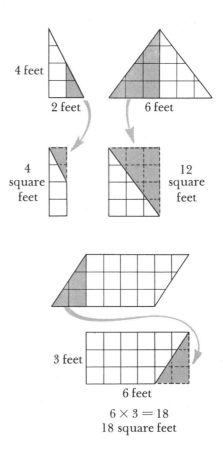

Triangular region. Jim read on the label of a half-pint of paint that it would cover an area of 25 square feet. Would this cover the surface shown at the right?

What is the area of each triangular region? Pupils cut the triangular regions to form rectangular regions. Later they generalize the formula $A = \frac{1}{2}ba$ (Area = $\frac{1}{2}$ base × altitude).

Parallelogram. Again the region is cut to form a rectangular region. Later the pupils generalize the formula $A = ba$ (Area = base × altitude).

4 feet

2 feet

6 feet

4 square feet

12 square feet

3 feet

6 feet

$6 \times 3 = 18$
18 square feet

The areas of other regions formed by line segments may be found by similar processes. Actually, the procedures mentioned above are rather imprecise. Both the dimensions must be measured in the same linear unit, and the area must be measured in the associated unit area.

Measuring the areas of regions provides a good use situation for metric measure. The centimeter is a handy size for designating the dimensions of small polygons. The measure of the region can be expressed as square centimeters.

A study of area in the elementary grades should help pupils to understand concepts such as those listed below.[3]

1. The union of a simple closed curve and its interior produces a *plane region*.

2. A standard plane region is used to measure plane regions. The standard plane region for the metric system is the *square meter*. The standard plane region for the English system is the *square foot*.

3. A plane region is measured in terms of the number of unit regions and portions of unit regions that will fit into the plane region. These unit regions must not overlap.

4. The precision of the measurement of the plane region depends upon the size of the unit that is used for the measurement. The smaller the unit, the greater the precision of measurement.

5. The area of a plane region is designated by the number of unit regions and is named by this number followed by the designation of the unit region. For example, 5 square centimeters, 9 square yards, etc.

6. The surface (area) of a solid region may be obtained by finding the area of the plane regions that is needed to cover the surface of the solid.

7. It is possible to develop efficient formulas for obtaining the measure of a region.

Perimeter and area. Relationships can be studied by studying the specific relationship between perimeter and area. Exercises such as those suggested here for rectangles can be developed for other polygons. The following questions can provide the basis for a bulletin board that emphasizes pupil-doing:

1. What is the area of a rectangular region 3 inches by 6 inches? What is the perimeter of a rectangle 3 inches by 6 inches?

[3] School Mathematics Study Group, *Mathematics for the Elementary School, Grade Five,* Part II (New Haven: Yale University Press, 1963), p. 759.

2. What is the area of a rectangular region 2 inches by 9 inches? What is the perimeter of a rectangle 2 inches by 9 inches?

3. What is the largest perimeter you can develop for a region having an area of 24 square inches? (Use only whole inches for dimensions.) What is the smallest perimeter you can develop from a region having an area of 24 square inches? (Use only whole inches for dimensions.)

Volume

The development of the concepts involved in the measurement of volume requires the addition of another type of region, the *space region*. Just as a plane region was described as the union of a simple closed curve and its interior, the space region can be described as the union of a simple closed surface and its interior.

The topic of volume can be begun with a problem such as "The Science Club of Kennedy School enclosed specimens of evergreen needles in 1-inch by 1-inch by 1-inch pieces of clear plastic. They wished to package these specimens in boxes that had interior measurements of 2 inches by 3 inches by 4 inches. How many specimens will the box hold?" This problem provides an opportunity for the pupil to develop a drawing of the box or, if blocks with a volume of 1 cubic inch are available, to actually build a 2-inch by 3-inch by 4-inch space region.

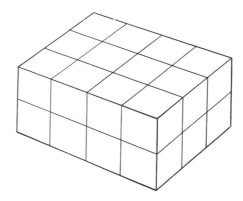

When pupils have identified that the box will hold 24 pieces of plastic, the teacher can use a question such as "What should we call the measure of a cube that is 1 inch by 1 inch by 1 inch?" A student who relates his thinking to the earlier study of area will suggest that this cube could be called 1 cubic inch in measure. A check of reference sources will bear him out on his contention. This measure is then identified as a measure of **volume**.

After several similar problems have been solved, the teacher can use a discussion to ascertain if any pupils have discovered a means of finding the volume of a rectangular solid. The pupils can be guided to discover that the length times the width will determine the number of cubes in the first row and that multiplying this product by the height will produce the volume. The volume can then be identified in terms of the cubic units used for measuring.

Further problem solving, experimentation, discussion, and consultation of references should be used to develop the following concepts, which relate volume to the previous measures studied.[4]

1. A set of points in space is called a *space figure*.

2. A simple closed surface divides space into two parts. There is an interior and an exterior set.

3. The union of a simple closed surface and its interior produces a *space region*.

4. The volume is the measure of a space region and is determined by the number of cubic units.

5. Several space regions are used as standard units. A cube whose edge is 1 inch is one standard and is called a *cubic inch*. A cube whose edge is 1 centimeter is called a *cubic centimeter*. Cubic yards and cubic meters also are used as standard measures.

6. The interior of a cubic foot contains 1,728 cubic inches. The interior of a cubic meter is 1,000,000 cubic centimeters. The interior of a cubic yard contains 27 cubic feet.

MEASURING ANGLES

The measuring of angles can be introduced by a situation requiring the drawing of a circle graph. One class was attempting to draw a circle graph which compared the time that was spent on various subjects. They represented the portions of time in tenths: Science $\frac{2}{10}$; Mathematics $\frac{2}{10}$; Language Arts $\frac{2}{10}$; Social Studies $\frac{2}{10}$; Others $\frac{2}{10}$.

The teacher used a large compass to draw a circle on the board, marked the midpoint of the circular regions, and then asked, "How can we mark off this circular region to represent the correct proportions for the various subjects?" Various suggestions were given by the pupils. They knew that the circle could easily be separated into two equivalent regions by drawing a line segment through the midpoint. The problem then became one of finding $\frac{2}{10}$ and $\frac{3}{10}$ of this region to mark off mathematics and language arts. One pupil suggested that they might try to develop a "unit angle" which could be laid "around" the center of the circular region "ten times." (See drawing.) This

[4] School Mathematics Study Group, *Mathematics for the Elementary School, Grade Six* (New Haven: Yale University Press, 1963), Vol. II, pp. 666–667.

was attempted, and after a struggle, a reasonable approximation of the circle graph was completed.

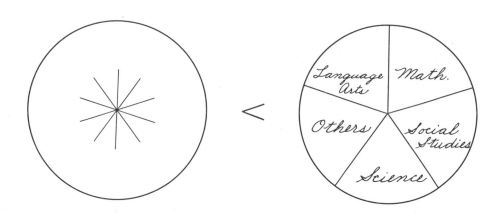

Then the teacher said, "How could we partition a circular region into a measure other than tenths?" A class member suggested that it would be necessary to develop some standard unit of measuring angles, just as inches or centimeters were used to measure line segments. Many of the pupils then referred to the fact that older brothers or sisters used protractors to perform this task. The teacher took this lead to provide each pupil with a protractor. Pupils noted that the protractor was marked in degrees and that the semicircle of the protractor contained 180 units. Discussion brought out the idea that the angle measure of an entire circle would be 360 units.

The teacher suggested that pupils experiment with the protractors and attempt to draw angles of various sizes. She asked, "How many units would we have in a right angle?"

The children experimented with the protractor for about five minutes. Many seemed to be making good progress. Occasionally the teacher stopped to ask an individual pupil a question such as "What do you do to make sure that you have the vertex of the angle in the spot that you want?" Then the teacher said, "Let's stop for a few minutes and compare notes on what you've found out. Does any one know the name given to the units on the protractor?"

Several pupils raised their hands and one said that he thought the unit was called a degree. Discussion continued during the days that followed and was used to bring out the following ideas:

1. The degree is a standard unit for measuring angles.

2. We can now define the terms "acute," "right," and "obtuse" angle in terms of degrees.

3. To measure an angle the center of the protractor should be placed at the *vertex* of the angle. The number of degrees in an angle is indicated by

the spot where the other side of the angle crosses the scale. The degrees should be counted beginning at zero on the base line of the angle.

4. The two scales on the protractor are simply for convenience.

Pupils were then given a variety of experiences measuring and reproducing angles of various sizes in various positions on the paper. During the months that followed, pupils measured angles when making mobiles, holiday ornaments, animal feeders, and posters, and in doing other art, science, or social studies projects.

MEASURING TIME

Clocks

Measuring time is one of the more difficult skills for many elementary school pupils. It has been suggested (with tongue in cheek) that the majority of first graders could learn to tell time to the nearest minute if they each received a working watch at the beginning of the school year. There is some justification to this claim, for many pupils who receive watches as holiday gifts return from their winter vacation with a greatly increased ability to tell time.

Teaching children to tell time is unlike many of the other mathematical tasks, for it is usually done informally. Reference to time and the development of pupils' ability to tell time should be emphasized every day.

The clock can be thought to possess two number lines, the hour number line 1 to 12 and the minute number line 1 to 60. The small hand is used to designate the hour number line, and the large hand is used to designate the minute number line.

 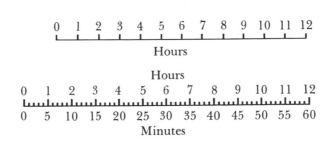

The following suggestions should prove helpful in teaching time:

1. Use a variety of materials and procedures for telling time.

2. As often as possible, use actual clocks for telling time.

3. "Count" activities to develop time concepts. For example, "Let's see how long it takes us to get ready for recess."

4. The usual developmental sequence for telling time begins with identifying the time that particular events occur, such as the time school is out. Then a study of one-half hours and then of one-quarter hours is initiated. It is debatable whether the next step is to study time by 5-minute or 1-minute periods.

5. Remember that the passage of time is relative. Ten minutes is quite a long time for a person who is waiting anxiously for an overdue airplane. Ten minutes is a short time for persons who are engaged in a game of cards. (It can also be a very long time for the nonplaying onlooker.)

The calendar

Concepts involving calendar use are usually developed through daily discussion of the current date, the day of the week, the number of days until a significant event, etc. These discussions usually occur during the opening exercises in kindergarten and in the primary grades. The two main things that the teacher at these grade levels needs to remember is (1) to stress ideas concerning the calendar, and (2) to vary the questions asked.

In the majority of elementary schools, once the basic idea of the calendar has been developed, little additional attention is given to the study of this topic. This is unfortunate because many misconceptions about and questions concerning the calendar arise in adulthood. Some of the questions are the following:

1. If this is 1966, why is this the 20th century rather than the 19th century?

2. I sometimes hear that there wasn't a "zero year." Is this true?

3. How can I find out on which day of the week an event in the past occurred?

4. One often hears arguments concerning the adoption of a "world calendar." What are the advantages and disadvantages of such a scheme? How would the world calendar work?

5. When will the 21st century begin?

Finding and discussing answers to the above questions can be both interesting and challenging to intermediate-grade pupils. A very brief lead into each of the above questions is provided below.

Why is this the twentieth century?   Such a question often arises without teacher direction. In such a case the teacher can suggest, "Let's develop a number line of centuries.

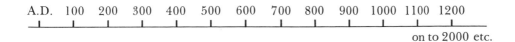

on to 2000 etc.

What name should we give to the century that includes the year A.D. 50?" After an often heated discussion it is usually agreed that this would be the first century. Then, by following the number line development, pupils realize that this is indeed the 20th century, not the 19th.

Was there a "zero" year?[5] The answer to this question is arbitrary, but pupils should be guided to see that the development of the time line from B.C. to A.D. does not fit the normal number line from positive to negative. A correct and an incorrect representation of the late B.C.'s and the beginning A.D.'s are shown below.

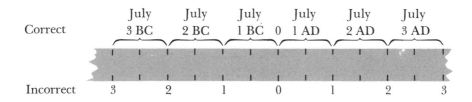

Analogies can be drawn between this idea and the first century idea presented earlier, the idea that there is no zero house on a block, or the idea that there is no zero page in a book.

How can the day of any week be identified? Developing the techniques for finding the day of the week on which an historical event occurred can be an enrichment project for intermediate-grade pupils. The rule for finding the day of the week for any day since A.D. 1 was developed by the German mathematician Carl F. Gauss (1777–1855). The development is as follows:

[5] Herbert F. Spitzer, *The Teaching of Arithmetic,* 3rd ed. (Boston: Houghton Mifflin, 1961), pp. 238–240.

December 7, 1941
(Pearl Harbor Attack)
Not a leap year.

Jan 31
Feb 28
Mar 31
Apr 30
May 31
Jun 30
Jul 31
Aug 31
Sep 30
Oct 31
Nov 30
Dec 7
$D =$ 341

(1)
$$\frac{485}{4\overline{)1940}}\ (X)$$

(2)
$$\frac{19}{100\overline{)1940}}\ (Y)$$
$$\frac{1900}{40}$$

(3)
$$\frac{4}{400\overline{)1940}}\ (Z)$$
$$\frac{1600}{}$$

(4)   1940 = N
$$\frac{\begin{array}{r}341 = D\\485 = X\\4 = Z\end{array}}{}$$

2770
$$\frac{-\ 19}{2751}\ (A)$$

(5)
$$\frac{393\ R = 0}{7\overline{)2751}}$$
$$\frac{21}{65}$$
$$\frac{63}{21}$$
$$\frac{21}{0}$$

$N =$ the number of the year minus 1. For 1885 $N = 1884$. $D =$ the number of the date of the year. Thus, February 10 = 41. (Whether or not the year was a leap year must be determined so one knows whether to add 28 or 29 for February. This may be determined thus: Every century year that is divisible by 400 is a leap year. For example, 1600 was a leap year; 1900 was not; 2000 will be. The four-year sequences of leap years can be determined using this information. To be a leap year, the number of the year must be even and divisible by four.)

Rule:

    (1) Divide N by 4, and call the quotient X.

    (2) Divide N by 100, and call the quotient Y.

    (3) Divide N by 400 and call the quotient Z.

    (4) Add N, D, X, and Z. Subtract Y. Call the result A.

    (5) Divide A by 7 and call the remainder R. $R =$ the day of the week of the given date. 0 = Sunday, 2 = Tuesday, etc.

Answer = Sunday

What is the world calendar?   The world calendar has been proposed several times in the United Nations and has the support of many nations. A discussion of the advantages and disadvantages of the proposed world calendar should emphasize the ideas that measurement involves arbitrary decisions by men and that attempts to change the basic unit of measure or the order of measurement is difficult. The world calendar is reproduced below.[6]

The Proposed World Calendar

FIRST QUARTER

	JANUARY								FEBRUARY								MARCH				
S	M	T	W	T	F	S	S	M	T	W	T	F	S	S	M	T	W	T	F	S
1	2	3	4	5	6	7				1	2	3	4						1	2
8	9	10	11	12	13	14	5	6	7	8	9	10	11	3	4	5	6	7	8	9
15	16	17	18	19	20	21	12	13	14	15	16	17	18	10	11	12	13	14	15	16
22	23	24	25	26	27	28	19	20	21	22	23	24	25	17	18	19	20	21	22	23
29	30	31					26	27	28	29	30			24	25	26	27	28	29	30

SECOND QUARTER

	APRIL								MAY								JUNE				
S	M	T	W	T	F	S	S	M	T	W	T	F	S	S	M	T	W	T	F	S
1	2	3	4	5	6	7				1	2	3	4						1	2
8	9	10	11	12	13	14	5	6	7	8	9	10	11	3	4	5	6	7	8	9
15	16	17	18	19	20	21	12	13	14	15	16	17	18	10	11	12	13	14	15	16
22	23	24	25	26	27	28	19	20	21	22	23	24	25	17	18	19	20	21	22	23
29	30	31					26	27	28	29	30			24	25	26	27	28	29	30

THIRD QUARTER

	JULY								AUGUST								SEPTEMBER				
S	M	T	W	T	F	S	S	M	T	W	T	F	S	S	M	T	W	T	F	S
1	2	3	4	5	6	7				1	2	3	4						1	2
8	9	10	11	12	13	14	5	6	7	8	9	10	11	3	4	5	6	7	8	9
15	16	17	18	19	20	21	12	13	14	15	16	17	18	10	11	12	13	14	15	16
22	23	24	25	26	27	28	19	20	21	22	23	24	25	17	18	19	20	21	22	23
29	30	31					26	27	28	29	30			24	25	26	27	28	29	30

FOURTH QUARTER

	OCTOBER								NOVEMBER								DECEMBER				
S	M	T	W	T	F	S	S	M	T	W	T	F	S	S	M	T	W	T	F	S
1	2	3	4	5	6	7				1	2	3	4						1	2
8	9	10	11	12	13	14	5	6	7	8	9	10	11	3	4	5	6	7	8	9
15	16	17	18	19	20	21	12	13	14	15	16	17	18	10	11	12	13	14	15	16
22	23	24	25	26	27	28	19	20	21	22	23	24	25	17	18	19	20	21	22	23
29	30	31					26	27	28	29	30			24	25	26	27	28	29	30

Worldsday (a World Holiday) W or December 31 (365th day) follows December 30 every year. The Leap Year Day (another World Holiday) W or June 31 follows June 30 in Leap Years.

[6] For further information on the world calendar and calendar reform see E. Achelis, *Of Time and the Calendar* (New York: Hermitage House, 1955); and David E. Smith, *History of Mathematics* (New York: Dover, 1958) Vol. II, pp. 650–670.

When will the twenty-first century begin?　Because of the difference in the time line and the number line, the 21st century will not begin until January 1, 2001. A time line-number line comparison can be used to develop this idea.

MEASURING TEMPERATURE

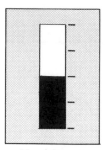

Hard Board

As in the case of teaching time, the best teaching method for the measurement of temperature is through daily use. Every classroom should be provided with an indoor-outdoor thermometer, and this should be used to check the temperature at the time school begins and then again just before noon. These checks allow for comparisons of temperatures and changes in temperature. A "ribbon thermometer" can be used to record the temperature.

Elastic Ribbon
$\frac{1}{2}$ white and $\frac{1}{2}$ black

The teacher will find that, in addition to daily checks of temperature, asking pupils to approximate the temperatures of various objects and then to compare the temperatures with thermometer readings helps the pupils develop a "temperature sense." One way in which this can be handled is to ask pupils to (1) estimate the temperature of a pan of water by testing it with a finger, (2) check the temperature with a thermometer, (3) add ice to or heat the water, (4) reestimate the temperature, and (5) retest the temperature with the thermometer.

In addition to providing a means of measuring temperature, the thermometer provides one of the best "use" settings for introducing and working with signed numbers.

THE METRIC SYSTEM

The ancient systems of measures were not uniform from country to country, nor were they planned in a fashion that allowed for simple conversion from one unit to the next larger or smaller unit.

The beginning of the metric system

Probably the leading country in the field of measurement reform was France. Beginning in A.D. 650 and continuing under Charlemagne there were attempts to make the standards of measure somewhat uniform. In 1670 Gabriel Mouton proposed a system of measurement using a scale of ten and taking as its base length a 1-foot arc on a great circle of the earth. In 1789 the French Academy of Sciences appointed a committee to work out a plan of decimal measure. Several earlier English proposals had been that the linear unit be the length of a pendulum beating half-seconds. This suggestion was considered by the French but dropped in favor of an arc of one ten-millionth of a quarter of a meridian. A slight error in measurement caused this proposal to be dropped, but a standard meter of similar length was adopted and all civilized countries received copies. The following official names and definitions were given to the various basic units of measure:

Meter—The measure of length equal to the ten-millionth part of a terrestial meridian contained between the North Pole and the Equator; *Liter*—The measure of capacity for both liquids and dry materials whose extent will be that of a cube with edges equal to one-tenth of a meter; *Gram*—The absolute weight of a volume of pure water equal to a cube with edges equal to one-hundredth part of a meter and at the temperature of melting ice. In addition, basic units for the area of land (Are) and fire wood (Stere) were also defined.

In 1795 the Latin prefixes by which the decimal multiples of the meter, the liter, and the gram are now known were designated.

Basic Metric Units

Meter (length)
Liter (liquid)
Gram (dry weight)

Myria	Kilo	Hecto	Deca		Deci	Centi	Milli
10^4	10^3	10^2	10^1	10^0	10^{-1}	10^{-2}	10^{-3}
10,000	1,000	100	10	1's	$\frac{1}{10}$	$\frac{1}{100}$	$\frac{1}{1000}$

The metric units can be related to English measure using the following approximations:

meter   39.37 inches
liter   0.908 dry quart or
               1.0567 liquid quarts
gram   15.432 grains
kilogram   2.2046
inch   2.54 centimeters
ounce   28.35 grams
dry quart   1.101 liters
liquid quart   0.9464 liter

The government of the French Revolution also decreed a new series of units of time. (See table below.) These units were never accepted by the population, and about twelve years later they were discarded.

100 seconds = 1 minute
100 minutes = 1 hour
10 hours = 1 day
10 days = 1 week or decade
3 weeks (30 days) = 1 month
12 months plus 5 or 6 carnival days = 1 year

Many articles have been written about the merit or lack of merit of using the metric system as the one system of measurement in the United States. At the present time the United States operates under a dual system; either English or metric measure is legal. In fact, the units of English measure are defined in terms of metric units.

Because the metric system is widely used, it should receive adequate attention in the curriculum of elementary school mathematics. Problem situations involving chemistry, Olympic track and field records, and trade with Latin America are some of the many "use" situations suitable for introducing units of the metric system. In the past one deterrent to the effective teaching of the metric system has been the tendency to devote the major portion of the study to transforming from the English system to the metric system or vice versa. This is a rather artificial situation. If the metric system is used in a chemistry laboratory, there is no need to convert an answer to the English system. Also, the stress on conversion from one system to the other detracts from the actual ease in the use of metric measure. To avoid this difficulty several suggestions are provided.

1. Rather than present exercises in which the pupil is to convert from metric to English or vice versa, use charts that present both measures (in much the same manner in which signs are written in two languages in cities such as Montreal, Canada).

2. Provide many opportunities for the pupils to work on an entire topic

in which they will use only metric measures (without any conversion to English measures).

3. Encourage discussion and debates concerning the merits of the two systems. Library research usually reveals the following: (a) The metric system is in general superior to the English system. (b) The English system has the advantage of possessing units of a "handy" size. There are no basic metric equivalents for feet, pounds, gallons. (c) Industry and trade have decimalized many English measures to a great extent. Many factories deal with inches, tenths of an inch, hundredths of an inch, etc.

4. The teacher should become very familiar with the literature on the metric system.[7]

COMPUTATION INVOLVING MEASUREMENT

Measuring situations are some of the most common applications of number. There is, however, much controversy concerning the use of number and measurement. Many mathematicians will not accept inches, feet, or gallons as being a part of the number.[8] They would ask for a statement such as "The length of the desk in inches is 34." The scientist, on the other hand, multiplies 3 feet $\times$ 4 pounds and arrives at 12 foot-pounds.

Swain states:[9]

The matter of writing units into equations is controversial. Engineers and physical scientists do not hesitate to write units in whenever this seems desirable. Mathematicians studiously avoid putting units in, though insisting upon full descriptions, with units specified, of all physical quantities that are symbolized in the work. A reason for this "purism" is that the theories underlying mathematical operations are framed in terms of numerical variables, and would be unduly and unnecessarily complicated in terms of measurement variables . . . the college mathematics professor usually requires his students to test the units as an aspect of the problem apart from the numerical or algebraic manipulation.

This controversy will probably continue for years to come.

Because in the teaching of elementary school mathematics it is desirable to present many "use" situations and to be mathematically correct, the writer suggests that teachers adopt the following approach. At the intermediate-

[7] The teacher might look at B. R. Buckingham, *Elementary Arithmetic: Its Meaning and Practice* (Boston: Ginn, 1953), pp. 717–735; National Council of Teachers of Mathematics, *The Metric System of Weights and Measures*, Twentieth Yearbook (Washington, D. C.: The Council, 1948); and Guy Wilson, and others, *Teaching the New Arithmetic*, 2nd ed. (New York: McGraw-Hill, 1951), pp. 293–302.
[8] Francis J. Mueller, *Arithmetic: Its Structure and Concepts*, 2nd ed. (New York: Prentice-Hall, 1964), p. 314.
[9] Robert L. Swain, *Understanding Arithmetic* (New York: Holt, Rinehart and Winston, 1957), pp. 202–203. Copyright © by Robert L. Swain, 1957. Revised 1965, by Nichols and Swain.

grade level discuss the problem and agree to assign a meaning to the measurement units as long as it is consistent; that is, choose a meaning that proves useful.

Addition and subtraction situations involving several units of measure can be labeled in the following manner:

yards	feet	inches		meters	decimeters	centimeters
3	2	9		3	6	7
+ 6	2	11		4	5	9
9	4	20		7	11	16
10	2	8		8	2	6

gallons	quarts	pints		deckograms	hectograms	grams
4 ~~5~~	4 ~~0~~ ~~1~~	2 ~~0~~		3	4	3
− 4	2	1		− 2	9	3
					5	2

Multiplication and division can be written:

tons	pounds	ounces		liters	deciliters	centiliters
5	30	8		(5	①6	8) ÷ 4
		× 2		1	4	2
10	60	16				
10	61	0				

It is apparent that the English system of measure has a consistent base. Thus, renaming is done in terms of the relationship between a measurement unit and the next unit that is greater or less in value. In addition and multiplication the computation may be performed and then the sum or product converted to the simplest form. When subtraction or division are performed, renaming is necessary as a part of computation. When pupils become sophisticated with regard to the multiplication and division of measurement units and also know something about numeration systems with bases other than 10, the analogy between those computations can be developed.

TABLES OF MEASURES

Textbooks of the 1800's required pupils to memorize very detailed tables of various weights and measures. Today, the value of this procedure is questionable because many units are seldom used. A visit to the grocery store will suffice to point out the diminishing number of common measures. In the past, meat was weighed in pounds and ounces; today's supermarkets weigh meat in pounds and tenths of a pound. Formerly, potatoes were measured in pecks; today they are measured in pounds. Thus, while it is still necessary to know many common weights and measures and the pupil should know several good sources of locating this information, some of the less common units should not be memorized. Some of the sources that should be used often in the classroom and with which the student should be familiar are the dictionary, the encyclopedia, and the world almanac.

USING MEASURING INSTRUMENTS

Normally the best method of acquiring an understanding of a measuring instrument and the units it measures is actually to use the instrument. The elementary school classroom should be well equipped with devices for making measurements. Pupils (not the teacher alone) should make many measurements during the course of a year. The list of measuring devices below should be readily available for classroom use.

Temperature:	Indoor-outdoor thermometer, candy thermometer, thermostat.
Weight:	Chemical-balance scales, bathroom scales, spring scales, grocer's scales.
Length:	Ruler, yardstick, meter stick, micrometer, calipers, tape measures (steel and cloth).
Time:	Calendar, clock, stopwatch, sundial, hourglass, metronome, water clock, candle clock.
Capacity:	Half-pints, pints, quarts, half-gallons, gallons, measuring spoons (variety of sizes), teaspoon, tablespoon, rainfall gauge.

SCALE DRAWINGS

The topic of scale drawings is useful in map work in the social studies and in representative scale drawings in science. This topic also provides a good "use" setting for the concepts developed in the study of ratio and proportion. It is quite possible for pupils to work with scale drawings without grasping the basic idea. The following beginning presentation is designed to call attention to the basic reason for scale drawings (that we use a smaller unit to stand for a larger unit) and to lead pupils to think of possible scales.

To introduce this topic a teacher told of a boy who had an L-shaped table. His uncle, who worked in South America, said that he would bring the boy a jaguar skin rug to cover all of the table. The teacher said, "I've drawn the table top on the chalkboard. How could the boy let his uncle know the exact size and shape rug to buy?"

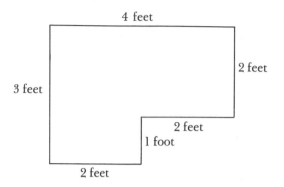

A discussion followed. The pupils first thought of cutting out a piece of butcher paper the size of the rug. This idea was discarded because of the necessity of sending the copy to South America. Then it was suggested that a picture of the table top which was the right "size" be developed. Further discussion elicited the suggestion that the class use 1 inch to represent 1 foot of the table. Then each of the class members developed a scale drawing of the table top.

After the idea of 1 to 1 (1 inch to 1 foot) had been developed, the use of scale drawings was expanded to situations requiring 1 to many ratios. During that period, scale drawings of pupils' rooms, suggested bulletin boards, and a map of the area of the community near the school were drawn.

REFERENCE MEASURE

Pupils often develop a knowledge of standard measure without really understanding actual measurement situations. Thus, the third-grade pupil who knows there are 5,280 feet in a mile and knows the approximate distance of a mile may say to his father after 3 hours of car travel on a 400-mile trip, "Are we almost there? Will we get to Grandpa's in the next few minutes?" Another pupil may know that a ton is 2,000 pounds and still say, "A huge ship that I read about carried a cargo of 18 tons." (Actually the ship carried a cargo of over 18,000 tons). Probably the best way to give pupils a greater "measurement sense" is to develop common reference measure; that is, to develop common objects, distances, etc., which will give the pupils a starting point in making comparisons and estimating measures.

It is desirable to develop a list of common reference measures for each grade of the elementary school. It should be expected that these will vary from school to school in terms of distances. Many of the common reference measures for weights and temperature can be used for any school. The abbreviated list is representative of the types of reference measures that can be developed for kindergarten.[10]

1 pound	A pound of margarine or butter.
5 minutes	The time it takes to get ready for lunch.
1 minute	The time it takes to count each pupil in the room twice (if there are about 30 pupils).
1 hour	TV program.
$\frac{1}{2}$ hour	TV program.
acre	State in terms of the school grounds or the area of a building lot near by.
100 yards	Football field.
$\frac{1}{4}$ mile	Distance around the track.
10 feet	Height of the classroom ceiling.
8 feet	Height of most ceilings at home.
3 feet	Distance of the rail of the chalkboard from the floor.
1 mile	Distance to _____. (Pupil should both ride and walk this distance.)
50 miles	Distance to Altoona, Pennsylvania, from State College, Pennsylvania.
100 miles	Just beyond Harrisburg, Pennsylvania, starting from State College, Pennsylvania.
— feet	Height of the school building.
—	Persons in our town. (Round to the nearest 100 or 1,000 as is appropriate.)
80,000	Persons in the city of Harrisburg, Pennsylvania.
2,000,000	Persons in the city of Philadelphia, Pennsylvania.
45,000	Area of Pennsylvania, or native state, in square miles.
30 inches	Height of teacher's desk, a door knob, several tables.
A square mile	Find out.

In addition to using reference measures in the classroom, the teacher should often challenge pupils to estimate the measure. Studies by Corle[11] reveal that both children and adults are very inaccurate in their estimates of linear distances, weights, temperature, and volume. In addition, children often exhibit a complete lack of knowledge of any but the most common measuring instruments. Corle's studies emphasize the idea that children should make measurements and think about measures.

[10] Also see Herbert F. Spitzer, *The Teaching of Arithmetic*, 3rd ed. (Boston: Houghton Mifflin, 1961), pp. 235–236.
[11] Clyde G. Corle, *Teaching Mathematics in the Elementary School* (New York: Ronald Press, 1964), pp. 247–250.

A FINAL NOTE

Measurement is one of the most important social uses of geometry and arithmetic. Instruction in measurement provides an alert teacher with opportunities to make use of historical materials that help pupils see mathematics as a constantly growing and changing subject. Extreme care should be taken by the teacher to make the study of measurement stimulating and worthwhile. Too often in the past the main emphasis has been upon the memorization of tables of weights and measures.

STUDY SUGGESTIONS

1. Plan a series of lessons in which you develop a standard system of linear measure which differs from either the English or the metric.
2. Discuss the issues involved in changing from one system of measure to another. Should a teacher advocate that we change to the world calendar or to the metric system? What issues are involved?
3. Should measures be labeled for computation? For example, 4 pounds $\times$ 6 feet = 24 foot-pounds. Explain how this use of number and measure in science fits into the mathematics program.
4. Describe how you would use a guided discovery approach to develop the formula $V = lwh$. Start with a verbal problem and concrete materials.
5. What part do you think devices such as centimeter rods, inch cubes, etc. have to play in the teaching of measurement? Discuss.
6. Describe a method for developing an understanding of π.

SUGGESTED REFERENCES

Books marked with an asterisk (*) contain treatments of the history of measurement.

Achelis, Elizabeth, *Of Time and the Calendar* (New York: Hermitage House, 1955).
Banks, J. Houston, *Learning and Teaching Arithmetic*, 2nd ed. (Boston: Allyn and Bacon, 1964), pp. 365–403.
*Buckingham, B. R., *Elementary Arithmetic: Its Meaning and Practice* (Boston: Ginn, 1947), pp. 456–735.
Corle, Clyde G., *Teaching Mathematics in the Elementary School* (New York: Ronald Press, 1964), pp. 247–265.
*Epstein, Beryl, and Epstein, Sam, *The First Book of Measurement* (New York: Franklin Watts, 1960).
*Larson, Harold D., *Arithmetic for Colleges* (New York: Macmillan, 1950), pp. 149–222.

National Council of Teachers of Mathematics, *The Metric System of Weights and Measures* (New York: Teachers' College, Columbia University, 1948).

Sanford, Vera, *A Short History of Mathematics* (Boston: Houghton Mifflin, 1930), pp. 351–378.

Smart, James R., and Marks, John L., "Mathematics of Measurement," *The Arithmetic Teacher,* Vol. 13, No. 4 (April 1966), pp. 283–287.

*Smith, David E., "Arithmetic" and "Mathematics," *Cyclopedia of Education,* Paul Monroe, ed. (New York: Macmillan, 1918), Vol. I, pp. 203–207; and Vol. II, pp. 159–160.

——, History of Mathematics (New York: Dover, 1953), pp. 634–675.

*Wheat, Harry G., *How To Teach Arithmetic* (New York: Harper & Row, 1951), pp. 365–394.

USE OF SUGGESTED REFERENCES

1. Read Achelis' suggestions on calendar reform. Make a list that favors the world calendar and a list that favors remaining with our present calendar.

2. Study the suggestions for computation with measurement numbers made by Banks. Develop a sixth-grade lesson based upon multiplication of numbers involving measurement.

3. Use material on the history of measurement from Buckingham, Sanford, Smith, and Wheat to develop a series of introductory and reintroductory lessons based upon the history of measures.

4. Corle reports on errors in measuring and in using the instruments of measure. Use some of his questions with elementary school age children and compare your results.

5. Check the chapters in the yearbook on the metric system. Make up an outline for grade-by-grade development of the metric system from grade four through grade six.

6. How do Smart and Marks suggest the teacher use mathematical models in teaching measurement?

14

Probability
and statistics

Probability has its historical origin in the study of games of chance. Some problems concerning the probability of occurrence in games were solved by the mathematicians Pascal and Fermat, who worked on probability problems during the middle 1600's. Pascal and Fermat are often considered to be the first expounders of probability theory. As early as 1662, probability theory was applied to mortality tables in London. Today, insurance companies, opinion samplers, and statisticians in most professions make wide use of probability statements.

The topics of probability and statistics are just now entering the elementary school mathematics program. With today's overcrowded curriculum one might well ask whether these topics should be introduced into the elementary school. The writer would give a qualified "yes" to that question. If properly taught, the topics are valuable for several reasons.

1. Increasingly, news items, magazine articles, and advertising refer to probability or statistical statements. For example, two recent ads stated: "The probablity is that one of every three persons listening to me will have a stalled car at least once this winter" and "Statistics show that Brand Q is an effective aid to preventing cavities." All citizens should have a good grasp of the meaning, the strengths, and the limitations of probablity statements.

2. These topics lend themselves to experimentation and generalizations. Pupils have a good opportunity to search for patterns.

3. The topics provide novel and interesting approaches to standard elementary school mathematical topics such as ratio and measurement.

4. The topics can provide interesting methods for use in the practice of essential mathematical topics.[1]

Probability theory can be a highly abstract mathematical topic, and statistical ideas go far beyond the scope of the elementary school curriculum.

---

[1] See also David A. Page, "Probability," *The Growth of Mathematical Ideas Grades K–12*, Twenty-fourth Yearbook of the National Council of Teachers of Mathematics (Washington, D. C.: The Council, 1959), p. 230.

Thus the study of these two topics should be of an exploratory nature. The emphasis should be on gaining insight, experimenting, and solving simple problems involving the topics. Emphasis should not be placed on a formal look at probability and statistics.

PROBABILITY

Introducing Probability

Probability can be introduced to elementary school pupils with a problem situation similar to the following. A teacher stated, "Today we're going to be drawing a name out of the hat to see who will be the leader of the lunch line. How many do we have here today? —— Thirty-three. Each person's name will appear once. What is the probability of Hank's getting to be first in line?"

The pupils responded that they felt that he had 1 chance out of 33, or $\frac{1}{33}$ The class members admitted that they were somewhat hazy as to the meaning of the question, "What is the probability of?" To clarify this concept to a certain extent but to avoid treating the definition formally, the teacher asked several questions. Often a debate as to the answer followed. The questions were the following:

1. You said that the probability of Hank's getting to go first was $\frac{1}{33}$. Does this mean that were I to draw a name from the hat 33 times (we put the name back in after every draw), Hank would be sure to win at least once? —— No.

2. Would he probably win at least once? —— Yes.

3. Were we to draw 66 names (replacing the name after each draw), would Hank win 2 times? —— Not necessarily. He might, but he might not.

4. Were we to draw 660 names out of the hat, would Hank ever have to win? —— No, but he probably would.

5. From 1, 3, 5, 7, 9, 11, 15 picking a number at random, what is the probability of choosing a number less than 8? Of 5 or more? —— $\frac{4}{7}$; $\frac{5}{7}$.

From this discussion the class may move to a topic such as coin tossing or opinion sampling. Introductory remarks and possible questions and answers are given in the material that follows.

The teacher said, "We can get a better idea of probability if we try to answer a few more questions and then do some experiments.

1. One of you registers 6 times for a drawing on a bicycle. There are 2,567 tickets in the drawing. What is the probability that you will win? Answer: $\frac{6}{2567}$.

2. There are 16 girls and 17 boys in our class. What would be the probability of drawing a girl's name from a hat containing the names of all class members? Answer: $\frac{16}{33}$.

3. Bill knew that the answer to a social studies question was either Washington or Lincoln. He decided to pick one of the names at random. He said, "The odds are 50 to 50 that I will be right." What was the probability that he would be right? Answer: $\frac{1}{2}$. Discussion should bring out the idea that the odds of success are

$$\frac{\text{chances of success}}{\text{chances of failure}}$$

while the probability of success is

$$\frac{\text{chances of success}}{\text{chances of failure} + \text{chances of success}}$$

After other similar questions, the teacher concluded the lesson. The next day each pupil was given a penny and asked what was the probability of heads in a large number of tosses of 1 coin? The pupils responded that the probability would be $\frac{1}{2}$. Then the teacher used questions to emphasize that while the probability of heads occurring was $\frac{1}{2}$, heads would not necessarily come up $\frac{1}{2}$ of the time. The pupils then tallied the number of heads and tails in 100 flips of the penny. They noted that the typical results were 48 H, 52 T; 49 H, 51 T; 50 H, 50 T; 51 H, 49 T; 52 H, 48 T; etc. However, occasionally a child found results of 40 H, 60 T, or the like. A discussion on the possible results of 1,000 tosses followed. Several pupils performed 1,000 tosses after school and found that their results closely approximated a 500 to 500 split.

Pascal's triangle

The probability of the number 1 even occurring in a given number of events, each with a probability of $\frac{1}{2}$, can be developed using Pascal's triangle. The teacher began by saying, "Last year I had two students who became interested in the possibilities of throwing a given number with dice. They went home and started talking about the probability of other events occurring. They started by tossing pennies. What is the probability of heads when pennies are tossed? —— $\frac{1}{2}$ —— right. These boys then began to wonder what the probability of various combinations would be if they tossed a large number of pennies. Let's see what they found. If we toss 1 coin, what are the possible outcomes? —— 1 head or 1 tail —— right.

1 1	1 1
	1 2 1
	1 3 3 1
	1 4 6 4 1

"What possibilities do we have if we toss 2 coins? _____ H, H; H, T; T, H; T, T. Thus, we have 1 possibility of 2 tails; 2 possibilities of a head and a tail and 1 possibility of 2 tails. How about 3 coins?" Pupils continued to diagram all of the possibilities. They found that 3 coins yielded 1 HHH; 3 HHT; 3 TTH; 1 TTT. Four coins yielded 1 HHHH; 4 HHHT; 6 HHTT; 4 TTTH; 1 TTTT.

When the triangle had been completed through 4 coins, the teacher asked the pupils to see if they could discover a pattern that would allow them to determine the possibilities with 5 coins. After some thought, the pupils proposed the pattern illustrated below.

1 coin					1	1		
2 coins				1	2	1		
3 coins			1	3	3	1		
4 coins		1	4	6	4	1		
5 coins	1	5	10	10	5	1		
6 coins	1	6	15	20	15	6	1	

Note: All of the adjoining numbers are added to fill the "gap" between them in the row below.

The pupils were then given a sheet of exercises based upon "arguments" the boys had had. For example, if 7 pennies are tossed, Bill thought that there should be 40 possible ways to throw 3 heads and 4 tails. Was he right? If not, how many possible ways are there to throw 3 heads and 4 tails with 7 coins?

The probability of two events

A teacher introduced the probability of two independent events occurring with situations involving the game of Monopoly. He said, "Let's suppose that you were playing a game of Monopoly and owned Park Place and Boardwalk, and that you collected about the same for a house on each property (actually you collect more for one on Boardwalk). Now look at the diagram. If you had an opponent 2 spaces from Park Place and 4 spaces from Boardwalk and you could only afford to put a house on one of those properties before the opponent throws the dice, on which property would you put the house?"

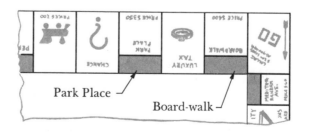

Park Place

Board-walk

Several pupils responded that they thought there was a better chance of landing on Boardwalk than on Park Place. The teacher questioned them concerning their reasons and after a little thought one pupil suggested, "I have more ways of throwing a 4 with two dice than I do of throwing a 2. There is only 1 way I can throw a 2: 1 and 1. There are 3 ways I can throw a 4: 1 and 3, 3 and 1, 2 and 2." The teacher gave the pupil a red die and a white die and he explained his statement. Then the teacher asked, "What is the probability of throwing a 4?" The pupils were not sure and debated about it. Many thought that the probability would be 3 in 12 since there are 6 faces on each die. Several pupils suggested that they list all of the possibilities of throwing two dice. The pupils were given a few minutes to write all of the possible throws when using two dice. Because of previous experience with array patterns when studying multiplication, the most popular systematic approach to the listing of all the possibilities was that illustrated below.

White Dice

	1	2	3	4	5	6
1	1,1	1,2	(1,3)	1,4	1,5	1,6
2	2,1	(2,2)	2,3	2,4	2,5	2,6
3	(3,1)	3,2	3,3	3,4	3,5	3,6
4	4,1	4,2	4,3	4,4	4,5	4,6
5	5,1	5,2	5,3	5,4	5,5	5,6
6	6,1	6,2	6,3	6,4	6,5	6,6

Red Dice (label at left of table)

Possible ways of throwing a 4 are circled.

Using the table, the pupils decided that the probability of throwing a 4 was $\frac{3}{36}$ or $\frac{1}{12}$ and that the probability of throwing a 2 was $\frac{1}{36}$. Next the teacher asked, "If you were to make a guess as to the space on which a player who was beginning the game of Monopoly at GO would land, what would be your best guess?"

The pupils suggested 5, 6, 7, 9, and 11. They were asked by the teacher how they could check to see if they were right or wrong. Referral to the chart confirmed the fact that the probability for throwing a 7 was higher than for any of the other totals (6 in 36). Thus, it was a good "guess" that a person would land on CHANCE (seven spaces from GO) his first turn.

The idea that the pairs of numbers are ordered, that is (1, 6) and (6, 1) are not the same, can also be developed, as can the terminology "order pairs of numbers."

The teacher may then lead into a discussion of some fundamental facts of probability. Several generalizations, along with possible "lead-ins," are given below.

1. The probability of occurrence of one or another event that is "mutually exclusive" is found by adding the individual probabilities. What is the probability of getting "one thing" or the "other?" The teacher could again use the Monopoly situations and ask, "What is the probability of landing on Boardwalk or Park Place?" The probability for Boardwalk was $\frac{3}{36}$; the probability for Park Place was $\frac{1}{36}$. The probability of one or the other is $\frac{4}{36}$. Note: the probability of either one event or another event that are not mutually exclusive is found by adding the two probabilities and subtracting the overlap, since the overlap is "added twice." (See Venn diagram.)

$A_2:B_2$

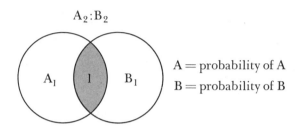

A = probability of A

B = probability of B

Probability of A or B = probability of A_1 + probability of B_1
$\qquad$ − probability of either A_2 or B_2.

Thus, $\qquad\qquad P[A \cup B] = [P(A) + P(B)] - [P(A \cap B)]$

2. The probability of an event occurring must be greater than or equal to 0 and less than or equal to 1. A teacher might ask, "What is the probability that we will throw a pair of dice and get a sum greater than 4 or less than 5?" Study of that situation reveals that the occurrence is a certainty. A toss of a pair of dice would always be $N < 5$ or $N > 4$. Thus, the probability would be $\frac{36}{36}$ or 1. Situations can also be used in which there is no possibility of an event occurring, and thus the probability would be 0.

3. The probability of one event occurring and another event that is independent of the first occurring is found by taking the product of the two probabilities. "What is the probability of drawing a spade from a deck of cards? ($\frac{1}{4}$, since $\frac{13}{52}$ of the cards are spades.) What is the probability of drawing an ace?" ($\frac{1}{13}$, since there are 4 aces in a 52-card deck.)

The next step is to consider drawing not only a spade, but the ace of spades. The pupils at first will wish to add the two probability statements, $\frac{1}{4}$ for a spade plus $\frac{1}{13}$ for an ace $= \frac{17}{52}$. However, closer inspection and a little thinking reveals that if the question is asked, "What is the probability of drawing the ace of spades," the answer would be $\frac{1}{52}$ since there is only 1 ace of spades in a 52-card deck. Reexamination of the two probability statements shows that the probability of getting an ace of spades is $\frac{1}{4} \times \frac{1}{13} = \frac{1}{52}$.

Other situations such as the probability of getting 1 six with one die and another six with another die is $\frac{1}{6} \times \frac{1}{6} = \frac{1}{36}$ aid in developing the idea that the probability of two independent events occurring is the probability of (A) times the probability of (B).

Sampling

The day following the coin tossing the teacher brought in a fish-bowl filled with blue and red marbles. She presented this situation. "At election time groups often want to predict the result of the election. Let's assume that the blue marbles represent persons for one candidate and the red marbles represent persons for the other candidate. How could we get an idea of the election outcome without counting all of the marbles?"

Class members suggested that a sample of the marbles could be taken to make a determination. Discussion then centered on an appropriate method of taking a sample of the marbles. This discussion emphasized the term *random sample*.[2]

A paddle constructed of two pieces of plywood was used to dip into the bowl to select a sample from the population. In drawing 5 samples from the bowl, the following results were obtained. (Each sample was returned before drawing the next.)

$\frac{1}{2}$-inch plywood

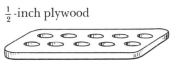

hole drilled slightly larger than the diameter of the marble.

$\frac{1}{4}$-inch plywood

finished paddle

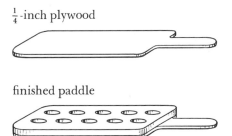

Red	Blue
8	2
7	3
6	4
6	4
7	3
34	16

The pupils estimated that the candidate represented by the red marbles would probably win by something like a 2-to-1 margin. (There were actually 800 red marbles and 400 blue marbles in the fish bowl.)

At this point the teacher directed questions to the class concerning the basis of obtaining a good sample. The sampling of persons in political and other surveys was emphasized, and the need for a *representative sample*[3] was stressed. Some of the generalizations reached were the following:

[2] A *random sample* is drawn in such a way that every possible sample of the given size has an equal chance of being selected.
[3] A *representative sample* matches the population from which the sample is drawn. For example, it would be poor sampling procedure to take an entire national survey from persons living only in small towns.

1. Each individual (or object, etc.) should have some known probability of being selected. For example, $\frac{1}{23,000}$ in a sample of voters in a community. The choice of one is not dependent upon another.

2. The sample should be taken by some automatic or prescribed means. It should avoid bias toward or against any portion of the population.

3. There should be some kind of randomness in the selection.

Number of events

This topic can be introduced with a problem such as "Three pupils are running for school offices. The pupil receiving the most votes will be chairman of the entertainment committee. The person receiving the second highest number of votes will be the vice-chairman. If Mary, Nan, and Jack are running for office, in how many possible ways can the offices be filled?" Diagrams such as those below can be used by pupils to solve the problem. Some pupils will suggest that the answer can be found by multiplying 3×2. (Multiply the number of choices for chairman by the number for vice-chairman after the chairman has been selected.

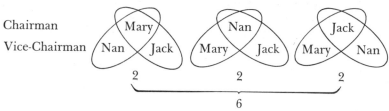

Chairman	Vice-Chairman
Mary	Nan
Mary	Jack
Nan	Mary
Nan	Jack
Jack	Mary
Jack	Nan

A further extension of this idea of more than two events can begin with a problem such as "Ken has 3 shirts, 4 pairs of trousers, and 2 pair of shoes. How many different 'outfits' can he make from these sets of clothing?" Again a diagram is helpful. The pupils will note that the same result will come from multiplying $3 \times 4 \times 2 = 24$.

Enrichment and extension to a basis for permutations can be developed by questions such as "How many ways can 3 letters of the alphabet be arranged?"

Example,   A B C   A C B
             B A C   B C A
             C A B   B C A $(3 \times 2 \times 1) = 6$

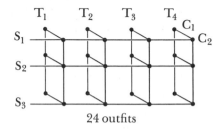

24 outfits

S = Shirts (S$_1$, S$_2$, S$_3$)
T = Trousers (T$_1$, T$_2$, T$_3$, T$_4$)
C = Shoes (C$_1$, C$_2$)

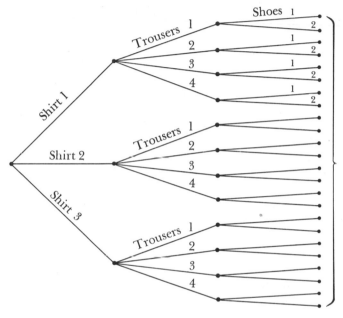

Total of
24 possible
outfits

"Car tires are often rotated. In how many different ways can the four tires be installed? Use this set to represent the tires. {1, 2, 3, 4}"

1234	1324	1432	1324	1243	1423
2134	2341	2413	2143	2314	2431
3124	3241	3142	3214	3421	3412
4123	4132	4231	4213	4321	4312

$(4 \times 3 \times 2 \times 1) = 24$

"How many ways can five numerals be arranged?"

$$1, 2, 3, 4, 5 \quad (5 \times 4 \times 3 \times 2 \times 1) = 120$$

STATISTICS

Developing critical analysis

Present-day reporting of statistics is often sketchy, and in some cases the devices used to obtain the statistics are questionable. Analysis of newspaper reports, advertising, and magazine articles can be helpful in developing a sense of "proceed with caution" among elementary school pupils. When a report states that 3 out of 4 doctors interviewed favored a certain medicinal product, pupils should think, "I wonder how many doctors they asked and how they decided which doctors to ask." It might be possible that they only surveyed the staff of doctors working for the company. Also, did they survey medical doctors or Ph.D.'s? Quite likely an historian is not a good authority on the quality of medicinal products.

Analysis of statistical reports is a fascinating project for elementary school pupils. They enjoy looking at reports and raising questions. This is good; however, the teacher should take care that pupils do not become so overly critical that they can no longer obtain any information that they consider at all accurate. A good start for looking at statistical misinformation is a paperback book by Darrell Huff.[4] The teacher can find a number of examples of common statistical errors. Some of the common errors that can be detected by elementary school pupils include:[5]

1. A shift in definitions. For example, at one point the writers may use the *mean* as the average. At another point they may use the *median* as the average.

2. Inappropriate comparisons. For example, a small manufacturer may report: "We have the fastest growing sales record in the industry." This might be based on the fact that in one year they sold 250 machines and that during the next year they sold 500 machines. In the meantime, a large producer of the machine may have increased his sales from 250,000 to 450,000. The first company has increased sales by a greater percentage than the second company, but its claim does not mean much.

3. Inaccurate measurement. In any statistical treatment an inaccurate measurement may cause enough difference to effect the results greatly.

4. An inappropriate method of selecting a sample. (See section on sampling.)

5. Technical errors.

6. Misleading charts. (See section on charts and graphs.)

Charts and graphs

The reading and construction of charts and graphs often occur as a part of instruction in science and in the social studies. The development of charts and graphs in these areas has the advantage of providing "use" situations for the charts and graphs made by the pupils. Also, the charts and graphs contained in social studies and science textbooks clarify concepts in those areas.

[4] Darrell Huff, *How to Lie with Statistics* (New York: Norton, 1954).
[5] Richard S. Pieters, and John J. Kinsella, "Statistics," *Growth of Mathematical Ideas K–12,* Twenty-fourth Yearbook of the National Council of Teachers of Mathematics (Washington, D. C.: The Council, 1959), p. 277.

When a need for interpreting and constructing graphs occurs in one of the content fields, it is suggested that time be taken in mathematics class to clarify concepts concerning graphs and to stress the mathematical concepts involved. The development of charts and graphs that follows illustrates procedures that could be adapted to social studies and science content.

Teaching charts and graphs.   The opportunity to develop a graph can arise from the need to make a comparison of the various products of foreign countries, of gravity on the various planets, of surveys of class interests, of distances of planets from the sun, or of populations of cities and states. Since there are many use situations for developing charts and graphs, the material presented will be limited to suggestions for teaching and comments concerning the necessary accuracy of charts and graphs.

Varying types of graphs should be developed, and the relationships among them should be understood. The teacher can begin with some data that needs to be organized into a form that can be readily interpreted. One such instance occurs when pupils vote on their preferences of types of free-reading books. When the teacher had the ballots, she asked, "How can we show the comparison among the various choices?" It was first suggested that a tally system such as that shown below be used.

Book Categories	Votes
Adventure	13
Animals	5
Biography	8
Geography	4
History	8
Science	10
Sports	11

Then the teacher asked, "Can we display the results of this survey in a manner that will be more colorful to visitors during library week?" It was suggested that some type of graph might be helpful. The teacher then suggested that the pupils check references and make rough drafts of the various types of graphs that could be used "to tell the results." The pupils were then to pick the best type from the rough drafts and develop an accurate graph.

On the following day the rough drafts shown below were presented for class consideration.

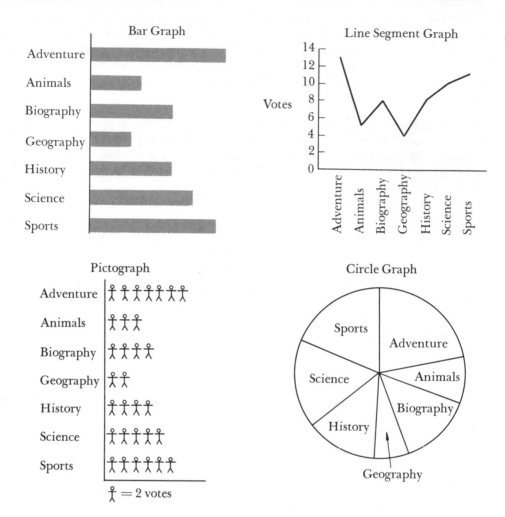

Class members discussed their preferences. They liked the appearance of the pictograph and the overall effect of the circle graph. They felt that the bar graph would present the data most accurately. They also noted that the line segment graph was not appropriate because the only usable information was the location of the points. The lines between the points were meaningless.

After a variety of experiences with graphs, class discussion, and a check of reference books, the following generalizations concerning graphs were developed:

1. While pictographs are the simplest type to read, they give only an approximation of the data. Care must be taken to insure that pictographs actually are representative. One picture can represent 10,000 cars and two pictures of the same size can accurately represent twice as many cars. However, the use of a picture of one car to represent 10,000 cars and of another

drawing that is twice as high as the first one to represent 20,000 cars is misleading because the area of the second drawing is about four times that of the first.

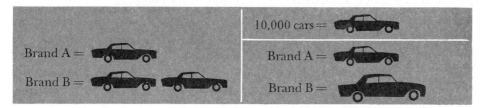

Sales: Brand A = 10,000; Brand B = 20,000

2. The bar graph, while not quite as easy to read as the pictograph, is easier to construct accurately. The bars in a graph normally should be of a constant width. Thus, the area of the bar is proportional to its frequency. Bar graphs can be misleading if units are compressed or extended and if zero is not the starting point. (See below.) Proportional bar graphs are often called *histograms*.

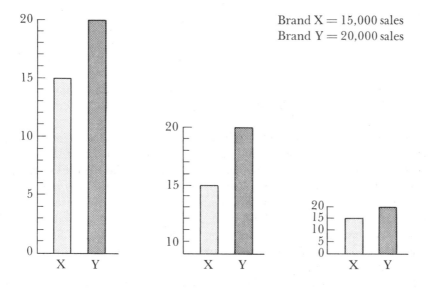

Brand X = 15,000 sales
Brand Y = 20,000 sales

3. Line segment graphs should be used only when there is a continued trend from one point to the next one. For example, the yearly per capita income in a country in 1950 was $2,000 and in 1960 was $2,500. If there had been a general trend of increase each year between 1950 and 1960, the line

segment connecting the points for 1950 and 1960 would be helpful. If however, the income had been $1,800 in 1955, the line segment connecting 1950 and 1960 would be misleading. As in the case with bar graphs, line segment graphs may be misleading if the scale is mixed or if the starting point is not zero. Line segment graphs are often called *frequency polygons*.

4. A circle graph is particularly helpful if percents totaling 100 are being graphed or when the graph is concerned with parts of a whole. A knowledge of angle measurement and decimal division is necessary for the construction of circle graphs.

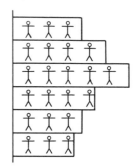

5. On occasion it is desirable to use a combination of the formats described above in constructing a graph. The general impression is conveyed by the pictograph. An accurate assessment can be made by the bar graph.

Measures of central tendencies

Finding a representative number is important in any type of statistical work and is often important in everyday life. Pupils are interested in batting averages and test averages. Adults are interested in salary, bowling, and work-load averages. Almost any evening paper uses the term "average" several times.

The term may be misleading since there are several ways of looking at "average." Probably the most common average is the result of a "leveling-off" process. This is normally done by finding the sum of the measures and dividing by the number of measures. This average is called the *arithmetic mean*. A second type of average commonly used is the middle measure of a distribution, called the *median*. In addition to these measures of central tendencies, the measure that occurs most often, or *mode,* is also used. There are also geometric and harmonic means that are not necessary to an understanding of simple statistical concepts.

The grading of papers and lessons in social studies or science can provide a real "use" setting for introducing the *mean*. One teacher asked the following question: "You read in your social studies book today that the average yearly rainfall for Central Texas is about 25 inches and that the average yearly rainfall for the coast of Oregon is about 70 inches. What do they mean by 'average?' "

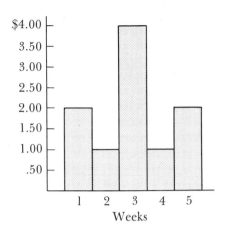

After a discussion in which pupils emphasized that "average" probably meant typical or usual, the teacher said, "Let's take another look at 'average'. Look at the graph of the weekly earnings Nancy made from baby sitting. What would be the amount of her average weekly earnings?"

Most pupils used a leveling-off process such as that diagrammed at the right.

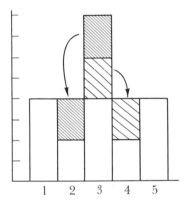

Then the teacher asked, "Can we find a quick method of finding the average?" Discussion and the teacher's questions brought out the idea that the average could be found by totaling the wages and dividing that total by the number of weeks. The teacher stated, "This type of average is called the arithmetic mean. See if you can find the average or mean for the following problems. Express your answer in fractional form if the division is not even."

1. Bob's test scores were 88, 76, 92, 86, and 90. What was his mean score?

2. During his vacation, Jim's daily catches of fish were 5, 7, 2, and 9. What was the average number of fish he caught per day?

3. Jane was to make paper flowers for a school play. On Monday she made 15, on Tuesday, 12, on Wednesday 18, and on Thursday 24. What was the average number of paper flowers she made per day?

When the problems had been solved, the teacher again referred the class to the question concerning the scores on the recent spelling quiz. She asked, "Is there any other way that you can get an idea of a typical score for the spelling test, particularly if you wish to do so in a shorter time." She wrote thirty-two scores on the board. Two methods were used. Some pupils counted half-way from the top score to the bottom score (the median). Others took the score which occurred most often (the mode). In this particular case, it was agreed that the median was a better representation than the mode.

Spelling Scores

Number correct	Number of scores	
25	///	
24	////////	
23	////	
22	////	
21	////	Mean $= 21\frac{19}{34}$
20	/////	Median $= 22$
19	///	Mode $= 24$
18	//	
17	/	
16	/	

Then several exercises were given in which the correct choice of the mean, the median, or the mode was emphasized.

1. What would you consider the most typical or average salary for paper boys?

2. Is it possible to have more than one mode? Give an example.

3. Is it easier to find the median of 33 scores or 34 scores?

4. What measure would be best for telling the average height of houses in a community? Of dining room tables?

5. Could any of the three averages be as large as the largest measure? As small as the smallest measure?

6. If you were to predict the type of weather that Miami, Florida, will have tomorrow, would you use the mean, the median, or the mode?

During the work on measures of central tendencies the following general-izations should be developed and emphasized:

1. An incorrect selection of the measure of average used can often distort facts. For example, "The mean yearly family income of a small community in Vermont[6] is $20,000." There is one very wealthy person in the community who earns several thousand dollars a day on investments. The median yearly family income of this community is $6,000. The modal yearly family income is $5,000. If the mean income were used in reporting, the type of community could be completely misgauged.

2. The mean provides some features which the median and the mode do not. The mean of a number of means can be taken by the add and divide method and be accurate. The mode of a group of modes or the median of a group of medians is not necessarily the actual mode or median of the entire group.

3. The mean is affected by extreme measures on either side of the scale, as the average income in the Vermont community points out.

4. An example in which the mode would be the most logical measure of central tendency would be a case in which a group of persons were deciding on the time for holding a meeting. If six different times were proposed, taking the mean or median of these times would not be helpful, for it could be possible that very few of the persons would be available at these times. More persons could be at the meeting at the modal time than at the mean or median time. In this case the mode is by far the most useful measure.

Meeting times suggested	Number of persons available
5:00 P.M.	//
6:00 P.M.	//
7:00 P.M.	///
8:00 P.M.	////
9:00 P.M.	//////
10:00 P.M.	////

Mean = 8:00 P.M.   Median = 8:00 P.M.   Mode = 9:00 P.M.

Also the mode would be most useful in determining the average size dress that a store should stock. If a store were to decide to stock heavily the mean or median size, it would be possible that very few persons were actually that size.

---

[6] Incomes rounded to the nearest $1,000 per year.

Source: Still Photo Services U. D. I. S., Pennsylvania State University

Game situations provide opportunities for children to explore probability.

Analysis

Once pupils have mastered the basic ideas of sampling, graphing, averages, etc., a variety of statistical projects may be undertaken. A survey of the TV interests of an elementary school was one such project. The following steps were used in the survey.

1. The class agreed upon the nature of the problem. "What are the television viewing interests of the pupils in our school?"

2. The class discussed the selection of a "representative sample" of the school. (It was agreed that surveying every student would be too time consuming. Also, the pupils wanted to test sampling techniques.) A sample was selected.

3. An appropriate method of gathering data was decided upon.

4. The data were gathered.

5. Interpretations were made from the data.

In activities such as those described above extreme care should be taken to make the pupils aware of the difficulties that arise in statistical work and the inaccuracies that may occur. For example, in one fifth grade the pupils thought they could report the reading interests of fifth graders in general (throughout the United States) from a sample taken in one community of 1,200 persons. Such errors in thinking should be corrected. In fact, it is sometimes wise to let pupils jump to false conclusions and then by discussion have them discover the fallacies in their thinking.

Many worthwhile learning experiences can be developed by exploring the ideas of probability and statistics. The teacher should be alert to situations in the sciences and social studies which can be interpreted more effectively with probability statements and simple statistics.

1. Make use of the chart of flower color shown below to develop a lesson plan that emphasizes the probability of red, pink, or white flowers.

    R = gene for red
    W = gene for white
    RW or WR = a pink flower

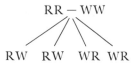

2. Develop a list of three topics that pupils could explore from the standpoint of gathering and analyzing data and drawing some tentative conclusions.
3. Develop arguments for both points of view in a discussion on whether or not probability and statistics should be taught in the elementary school?
4. Work out three examples of appropriate use of each of the three measures of central tendencies—mode, median, and mean.

Cohen, L. W., "Upper-Elementary-School Children Use Statistics," *The Arithmetic Teacher*, Vol. 9, No. 4 (April 1962), pp. 212–214.

Grass, Benjamin A., "Statistics Made Simple," *The Arithmetic Teacher*, Vol. 12, No. 3 (March 1965), pp. 196–198.

Huff, Darrell, *How to Lie with Statistics* (New York: Norton, 1954).

Page, David A., "Probability," *The Growth of Mathematical Ideas Grades K–12*, Twenty-fourth Yearbook of the National Council of Teachers of Mathematics (Washington, D. C.: The Council, 1959), pp. 229–271.

Pieters, Richard S., and Kinsella, John J., "Statistics," *The Growth of Mathematical Ideas Grades K–12*, Twenty-fourth Yearbook of the National Council of Teachers of Mathematics (Washington, D. C.: The Council, 1959), pp. 272–326.

School Mathematics Study Group, *Mathematics for the Elementary School, Grade Six, Part II* (New Haven: Yale University Press, 1963), pp. 737–826.

Smith, R. R., "Probability in the Elementary School," *Enrichment Mathematics for the Grades*, Twenty-seventh Yearbook of the National Council of Teachers of Mathematics (Washington, D. C.: The Council, 1963), pp. 127–133.

Wilkinson, Jack D., and Nelson, Owen, "Probability and Statistics—Trial Teaching in Sixth Grade," *The Arithmetic Teacher*, Vol. 13, No. 2 (February 1966), pp. 100–106.

USE OF SUGGESTED REFERENCES

1. Check the article by Cohen for suggested elementary school projects that use statistics.

2. How could the presentation by Grass be developed into teaching units on statistics?

3. Study *How to Lie with Statistics* for illustrative materials for class discussion of errors in reporting statistical materials.

4. Why does Page suggest that ideas involving probability be developed in the elementary school mathematics program?

5. Study the chapter by Pieters and Kinsella for possible statistical topics for the elementary school mathematics program.

6. What activities does Smith suggest for experimenting with probability in the elementary school?

7. Study the S.M.S.G. material on organizing data. Develop those ideas to encompass a guided discovery approach to teaching the topic

8. Wilkinson and Nelson give several suggestions for teaching probability and statistics. How could these suggestions be incorporated into the mathematics program at the grade level of interest to you?

15

Evaluation of learning in elementary school mathematics

Measuring and evaluating pupil achievement in any area of the curriculum is difficult. Mathematics is no exception. However, there is a tendency to believe that the measurement of educational goals is easier in mathematics than in areas such as science or the social studies. This belief is fostered because of the ease with which the teacher can obtain an objective measure of certain computational skills that form a portion of the mathematics curriculum. Measurement of the other goals of the mathematics program requires a great deal of thought.

The suggestions that follow focus on emerging developments in the measurement of mathematical maturity, as well as on the traditional aspects of elementary school mathematics.

SUBJECTIVE AND INFORMAL PROCEDURES

Pupil observation

The phase of a mathematics lesson that is called "study time" is perhaps the single most important means of evaluating pupils' mathematical behavior. The teacher can use this time to move quietly about the room observing the pupils at work, making notes, questioning the children, and making suggestions. The teacher may also very effectively use *class discussion* time to gain insight into the pupils' thinking processes.

It is suggested that the following observations be made and that the teacher ask herself the related questions.

Note the attack used by the pupils. Is progress consistent? Is Bill always a slow worker? Does he seem to like some phases of mathematics better than others? Is Jean poor at computation, or does she become careless when she gets bored with practice materials?

Limit the observation to some specific aspect of pupil performance. How competent are pupils in solving a problem in more than one way? What errors are most common in multiplying numbers when one or both of them contain an internal zero?

Check the depth of pupil thought. Is the pupil interested in going beyond the lesson? Does Mary consistently try a "just-for-fun" exercise? How often do class members check their work when they are not asked to do so? How many sources does Nancy check when she is preparing her report on the history of decimals?

Observe the emotional climate. How relaxed is the pupil while he is working? Does Bob seem to be under pressure when he is doing a geometric construction? Does Alice begin her nervous mannerism of twisting her hair during most mathematics assignments?

Check study habits. How good or bad are the study habits of the pupils? Does Ken seem to be more interested in the actions of others than in his work? Bill seems to be looking out of the window most of the time. Is he daydreaming, or is he thinking? (He may be doing either.)

Note skill development. How effective is the numeral writing of the pupils? Will a suggestion now and then help Jerry to write the numeral 2 so that it does not look like a 3?

Observe pupil independence. Do students really need your help when they raise their hands? Did Chris really know how to work the division exercise she asked about? Was her question a need for reinforcement and praise? How can I give her the needed praise and still develop her independence? How dependent upon the textbook and teacher suggestions are the pupils? Does Joe always look back to the book to check on the method used by the authors to solve an exercise? How many pupils use the teacher's techniques in solving a problem or an exercise?

Because many of the individual observations that a teacher makes are quickly forgotten, it is suggested that written anecdotal records be kept. The stock 3-by-5-inch cards or a small note pad are easy to use. As the teacher notes an action of significance, it can be recorded briefly on a card or the pad and dropped into the pupil's arithmetic folder later. (See page 405.)

Source: Still Photo Services U. D. I. S., Pennsylvania State University.

Observation of individual pupils at work can provide the teacher with insights into pupil achievement.

It is often suggested that daily records of this type be kept on each pupil. Daily records may be unrealistic, but if significant pupil actions are recorded periodically—at least ten times a year—they will provide the teacher with perceptions which she may have overlooked. Also such records are helpful in preparing for parent and pupil conferences. A sample record follows.

CHARLES YEAGER — GRADE 3

1966

September 30   Seems able to move from a problem situation to the mathematical idea. Is very interested in puzzle-type problems.

October 10   Makes careless errors in addition and subtraction exercises. Seems to know the addition combinations.

October 15   Charles understands the renaming principle when subtracting multi-digit situations.

October 20   Showed originality in developing several solutions to mul-
                    tiplication situations. Presented his ideas clearly to the
                    class.

Interviewing pupils

A study in greater depth may be made using the interview technique.[1] The teacher may begin by presenting some previously taught material
to an individual child and asking for an answer and an explanation. As the
interview progresses new material that makes use of the same basic ideas as
the previously taught material may be interjected. The following sequence
could be used to study a pupil's thinking on division combinations.

Teacher	Pupil
What is $12 \div 3$?	Four
How did you get the answer?	I just knew the answer. I guess that I could have subtracted 3 from 12 until I got to zero.
What is $18 \div 6$?	I'm not sure. Do you want me to figure it out?
Yes, think out loud as you work the exercise.	I want to find out how many 6's equal 18. I know that two 6's equal 12. Twelve plus 6 equals 18. Three 6's equal 18.

Every effort should be made to ease the pressure on the pupil. In fact, it
might be better to use only material that the teacher feels the pupil will
know when conducting a first interview.

Arithmetic folders

Manila folders containing samples of the daily work, anecdotal
records, and copies of their arithmetic themes are important devices for continuous evaluation of students.

Pupils should periodically be asked to give short answers to questions
that require pencil and paper computation. Questions of the following variety
can be used effectively.

[1] J. Fred Weaver, "Big Dividends from Little Interviews," *The Arithmetic Teacher*, Vol. 2
(April 1955), pp. 40–47.

1. Give an example of a problem situation that describes a use of the median, of the mean.

2. Show in at least three ways that the answer to this division situation is correct.

$$\begin{array}{r} 7 \\ 6)\overline{42} \end{array}$$

3. Tell why the quotient is larger than the divisor in the division situation that follows.

$$5 \div \tfrac{1}{4} = \square$$

The folders serve as a means of systematizing informal evaluative techniques and are convenient depositories for most types of information. Also, the folders provide a fine source of information for parent conferences and can be of great aid to the teachers of the pupils during each succeeding year.

Oral evaluation and the tape recorder

The tape recorder is a unique device for evaluating pupils' mathematical abilities. At least three procedures can be used effectively with tapes.

The teacher and the pupil can discuss some aspect of mathematics, with the student using the recorder. The teacher would make comments and ask questions, as follows: Describe the procedures you would follow to solve this problem. Tell me why you carry the 1 in addition. Look at this division exercise, which has been worked incorrectly. Can you tell me where the pupil went wrong in his thinking? Here is a phase of mathematics that you haven't studied. What would be the first thing that you would do to attempt a solution?

At the end of the day or in the evening the teacher can play back the tape and take notes. The answers of the pupil are useful in gaining insight into the thinking pattern followed by the pupil. Because many significant bits of pupil thinking may have been overlooked in the original discussion, the tape recorder provides a means for a more careful analysis of the situation. This analysis requires a good deal of teacher time, but it is often well worth the time because of the opportunity it affords the teacher to "think through" a discussion with an individual pupil.

Several pupils can work together at the tape recorder and discuss some mathematical concept. Questions such as the following can be discussed: What is the *best* method to add $\tfrac{2}{3}$ and $\tfrac{4}{5}$ without using paper and pencil? In what ways can you estimate the quotient of $345 \div 23$? How can $\tfrac{1}{3}$ be expressed as a decimal? Why?

An individual child may use the tape recorder to analyze his own thinking. For example, a pupil may orally explain a problem and then play it back on the tape recorder to see how clearly he has stated his reasoning. Great effort should be made to help the pupil relax when he is using the tape recorder.

EVALUATING WITH TESTS

Characteristics of good tests

Any test, whether constructed by an individual teacher or by a team of specialists for a commercial publisher, should meet several criteria, including acceptable validity, reliability, and good format.

Validity.   If a test is valid, it will effectively measure the skills, understanding, or knowledge that it was intended to test. Often a mathematics test that purports to measure understanding measures only computational ability. It may be a good test of computational ability, but if it misses its assigned task of measuring understanding, the test would not be valid.

In checking the validity of a test, the teacher should ask questions such as the following: How well does this test represent the significant behaviors that I want measured? Are all of the items relevant to these behaviors? Is the test a balanced sample of the behaviors I want to assess?

In general, the best method that a teacher has of ascertaining these answers is to take the test. If it is a standardized test and does not seem to measure the objectives of the mathematical curriculum, its use would be of questionable value. In the case of the teacher-made test, it is probably wise to write the test, let it remain in a desk drawer for a time, and then take the test. This later reading of the test allows the writer to see clearly items that need rewording. It is also helpful for the teacher to have a colleague look at the test and make suggestions.

Reliability.   An important factor in the value of a test is the *consistency* of the measurement of a particular achievement. This consistency is usually called reliability. To be considered reliable a test must consistantly and repeatedly measure the same achievement. Fortunately, the nature of mathematics helps make mathematics tests reasonably reliable. The reliability of a carefully constructed teacher-made mathematics test need not be of extreme concern to the teacher.

Good format. The choice of a good format is an important aspect of test selection or construction. A test with good format should meet the following criteria:

1. It can be easily understood by the pupils. The format helps the pupil to understand the basic goals of the test.

2. There are few possibilities of wrong answers because of poor directions.

3. The test can be scored easily.

4. The format does not add distance to the test.

5. Test questions can be interpreted accurately.

TEACHER-MADE TESTS

Construction of tests

Teacher-made tests are important for an evaluation of pupil achievement of the curricular goals of the particular school he attends. Well-constructed, teacher-made tests also provide a means of motivating and directing student learning. The continual evolution of the elementary school mathematics program forces the teacher to rely heavily on her tests as a means of evaluating the changing program.

When a teacher sits down to develop a test, she must answer several questions. Among the more important are (1) What are the topics or concepts for which I must provide a representative sample of test items? (2) How many questions shall I include in the test? (3) What emphasis shall I give to various types of learning? (4) What type of test items shall I use? Suggestions for answering these questions follow.

To answer the first three questions the teacher must (1) decide the specific purposes of a unit in elementary school mathematics, (2) outline the section, and (3) develop a blueprint for constructing the test.

The teacher may begin by listing the specific learnings of a mathematics unit. Then she can decide upon a sample of these learnings on which to develop test items and the number of items for each topic. An illustrative listing appears on the next page.

What type of items shall I use? The suggestions on informal evaluation have focused on essay-type evaluation. Therefore, this discussion will focus upon objective test items. There are several types of objective items that can be used; true-false items, completion items, multiple-choice items, and matching items are all possibilities. Probably the two most useful types for mathematics tests are completion items and multiple-choice items. The suggestions that follow are primarily concerned with writing good multiple-choice items. However, each of these suggestions could be used in writing a completion-type item. In addition, suggestions are given for measuring specific skills.

Grade 6—Topics from Number Theory

Skills To Measure

items

Topics	Vocabulary	Knowledge	Explanation	Application	Calculation	Total for Topic
Factors: 　prime factors 　one as a unit	2	3	1	2	1	9
Composite Numbers 　multiples 　factoring 　Factor trees	2	4	2	2	1	11
Greatest Common Factor	1	1	1	2	1	6
Least Common Factor	1	1	1	2	1	6
Total Per Item Test	6	9	5	8	4	*(32)

*Total items in test.

General suggestions.

Express an item as clearly as possible. Lack of clarity may cause the superior student to make an incorrect response. For example, the following problem might cause an analytical student to make an incorrect response.

One hundred fifty-two pounds of potatoes are to be put into ten pound bags. How many bags of potatoes will there be? (An asterisk indicates the correct answer.)

　　*(1) $15\frac{1}{5}$
　　(2) $30\frac{2}{5}$
　　(3) 152
　　(4) Not given

It is possible that a student would answer "not given," thinking that in truth only fifteen bags could be filled and therefore the answer should be (4) not given.

Choose precise vocabulary in developing items. Because precision in mathematical vocabulary is stressed in today's mathematics program, the teacher should avoid terms that might recall several responses.

What is the exact length of the line shown below?

Two elements of confusion might arise from such a statement. First, the student may realize that it is impossible to measure anything "exactly," and second, he may realize that the "line" is actually a "line segment." A better wording for the item would be, What is the length of the line segment shown below? Measure to the nearest $\frac{1}{16}$ of an inch.

Avoid complex or awkward word arrangements. It is often advisable to break a complex sentence into two or more separate sentences. The question should be as direct as possible. The following item is an example of awkward wording.

Kim cut a length of cloth tape that was 45 inches long into pieces from which to make headbands that measured 15 inches long. How many headbands did she get?

This item could be revised to read as follows: Kim made headbands from some cloth tape. She cut a 45-inch piece of material into 15-inch headbands. How many headbands could she make from the material?

Include all of the qualifications that are necessary to provide a reasonable basis for responding. The test-item writer may not state explicitly the information or qualifications that he automatically takes for granted. This omission may cause difficulty, especially with above average students. The following problem illustrates such an omission.

Several jet planes flew over the playground during recess time. Janet counted 5 planes; Bill counted 3 planes; and Nancy counted 2 planes. How many planes in all flew over the playground?

> (1) 5
> (2) 8
> (3) 10
> (4) Not given

In this case the student cannot be sure of the number of planes that flew over the playground. It is quite possible that some of the planes that Bill saw were the same planes that Janet saw. The writer of the item wanted the pupil to assume that each child saw different planes. However, it is not specified.

Eliminate irrelevant clues to the correct response. Often the grammar used in an item leads the student to the correct answer, or a portion of the item uses the language pattern of the correct response. The grammar of the following item demonstrates such a pattern.

The following check of a multiplication computation is an _____ check. (An asterisk indicates the correct answer.)

$$
\begin{array}{rl}
35 & \\
\times\,24 & \\
\hline
140 & \\
70 & \\
\hline
840 &
\end{array}
\qquad
\text{Check:}
\qquad
\begin{array}{r}
35 \\
\times\,6 \\
\hline
210 \\
\times\,4 \\
\hline
840
\end{array}
$$

(1) commutative

*(2) associative

(3) distributive

(4) none

The use of "an" leads to the correct answer of "associative." The question could have been stated, "Which property is used for the check of multiplication shown below?"

Eliminate irrelevant sources of difficulty. Frequently, reasoning problems are answered incorrectly because pupils who have reasoned correctly have not computed the answer correctly. A number of students who knew how to compute the average missed the following test item because of computational inaccuracy.

Bill received marks of 87, 69, 49, 98, and 79 on his weekly spelling tests. What is the average (mean) for the marks recorded above?

If the major purpose of the item is to test ability to make use of the idea of the arithmetic mean, an item that uses a simpler computational pattern would be of greater validity. It is also possible to ask the student to describe how he would find the mean. For example, Bill received marks of 8, 9, 7, 6, and 10 on his weekly ten-item math tests. What is the average (mean) for the weekly tests?

Avoid the type of question that allows a rote response and rewards the rote learner. Many vocabulary items can fall into this category. An item such as the following may be answered by a student who has memorized a term but has little or no understanding of its mathematical significance.

Which of the following illustrates the commutative property of addition? (An asterisk indicates the correct answer.)

*(1) $a + b = b + a$

(2) $(a + b) + c = a + (b + c)$

(3) $a \times b = b \times a$

(4) $a \times (b + c) = (a \times b) + (a \times c)$

If knowledge of the name property is required, it is suggested that an illustrative numerical example be used rather than the often memorized response shown above.

Which of the following illustrates the commutative property of addition? (An asterisk indicates the correct answer.)

*(1) $\frac{2}{3} + \frac{3}{4} = \frac{3}{4} + \frac{2}{3}$

(2) $(\frac{2}{3} + \frac{3}{4}) + \frac{5}{8} = \frac{2}{3} + (\frac{3}{4} + \frac{5}{8})$

(3) $\frac{2}{3} \times \frac{3}{4} = \frac{3}{4} \times \frac{2}{3}$

(4) $\frac{2}{3} \times (\frac{3}{4} + \frac{5}{8}) = (\frac{2}{3} \times \frac{3}{4}) + (\frac{2}{3} \times \frac{5}{8})$

Adopt the level of difficulty of a test item to the group and the purpose for which it is to be used. A test designed for sampling the student's mastery of a basic computational process would have items at a difficulty level different from a test of ability to solve multi-step verbal problems. As a general rule, a test should not be of a difficulty level based on the 90–100 = A, 80–90 = B, 70–80 = C, and so on, but should allow a range wide enough to determine pupil differences and difficulties. Thus, for a four-response multiple-choice test of mathematical understandings containing 50 items, a reasonable difficulty level would allow the average student to obtain a score of about 38, or about half of the items plus chance score. An item is considered to be of appropriate difficulty if about one-half of the class members answer it correctly. A test of a difficulty level which allows the average student to respond correctly to only one-fourth of the items would be almost meaningless.

There are some occasions in which a valid test may be much less difficult than the suggestion above indicates. This would be the test for mastery in which the teacher reasonably expects the average student to respond correctly to the majority of items. For example, a much higher average pupil score would be expected on a test of ability to compute using addition.

Measuring educational goals

Testing computational skill. The ability to compute is the skill most frequently measured. The most obvious method is to assign the students a number of computational exercises and then check the results. This procedure will suffice if an overview of the students' computational background is desired. If, however, specific computational skills are to be measured, it is necessary to have a check on the portions of an exercise in which an error is made. For example, a teacher wished to determine whether or not her pupils knew how to compute a multiplication situation in which an internal zero appeared in the multiplier. She presented several questions of the following type:

1. What error in thinking has been made on the following multiplication?

$$
\begin{array}{r}
5,357 \\
\times\,406 \\
\hline
32142 \\
21428 \\
\hline
246,422
\end{array}
$$

2. Which of the following is the best estimate for $205 \times 695 = \square$

    (a) 1,400

    (b) 14,000

    (c) 140,000

Testing understanding and concept development. Authorities on the teaching of elementary school mathematics are in agreement that reasoning, understanding, and concept development should be heavily emphasized. Measurement of these achievements is at best difficult, but pioneer work in their measurement reveals a lack of knowledge of this nature among elementary school pupils.[2]

Measurement of understanding is fraught with difficulty. At times an item that measures the understanding of one pupil may measure a memorized response of another. Realizing this difficulty, the writer will attempt to present several items, such as the following, which are aimed at measuring understanding.

1. In the number 444, the 4 on the left represents a number of how many times the 4 on the right? (place value understanding) (An asterisk indicates the correct answer.)

    (a) The same value (1)

    (b) 10

  *(c) 100

    (d) 400

2. When a whole number is divided by a whole number larger than one, how does the answer compare with the whole number that has been divided? (understanding of division process) (An asterisk indicates the correct answer.)

    (a) It is the same.

    (b) It is larger.

  *(c) It is smaller.

    (d) It may be either larger or smaller.

3. What do we mean by the "area" of a rectangle? (understanding of a term) (An asterisk indicates the correct answer.)

    (a) It's the product of the length times width. We are multiplying a linear measure by a linear measure.

    (b) It's the distance around something.

[2] Vincent J. Glennon, "Testing Meanings in Arithmetic," *Arithmetic 1949* (Chicago: University of Chicago Press, 1949); David Rappaport, "Understanding Meanings in Arithmetic," *Arithmetic Teacher,* Vol. 5, No. 2 (March 1958), pp. 96—99; and *Measurement of Understanding,* The Forty-fifth Yearbook of the National Society for the Study of Education (Chicago: University of Chicago Press, 1946), Chap. 7.

*(c) It's finding how many of a given measure can cover a surface.
(d) It's the product of feet × feet, inches × inches, etc.

Short essays are often very helpful in measuring understanding:

1. Why are you able to invert the divisor and multiply to solve a division of rational numbers exercise?

2. When we multiply two whole numbers we get another whole number as an answer. Is this true of dividing two whole numbers? Why?

3. What happens to a rational number represented by a fraction when the numeral representing the denominator is increased?

Testing problem-solving ability. Research studies reveal that a number of factors operate to produce a good problem solver. For the teacher who wishes to do more than determine the pupils' ability to solve typical textbook problems, it is suggested that a variety of types of items be used.

1. The tape recorder or an oral presentation of a verbal problem can be helpful in reducing the emphasis that may be placed on reading ability. A combination approach in which the teacher or tape recorder gives the problem and the student has a duplicate copy of the problem on his test sheet allows for interpretation from either the spoken or the written word. Because the majority of "actual life" problem situations occur in oral settings, this technique comes closer to measuring the major objectives of the problem-solving program than does the straight written problem.

2. Items in which the pupil is required to suggest the mathematical sentence that would solve the problem allow the teacher to determine to what extent computational ability is a factor in a pupil's problem-solving ability. Occasionally an item that requires a selection of the correct mathematical sentence can be used. Such items can usually be written using the following format:

John has a quarter. He wants to buy an airplane model that costs 59¢. How much more money does he need? (An asterisk indicates the correct answer.)

*(a) $25¢ + \square = 59¢$
(b) $59¢ - 24¢ = \square$
(c) $25¢ + 59¢ = \square$
(d) Not given.

3. The use of problems in which the student is to identify the operations necessary for problem solution is helpful. Students can be instructed to write a letter (A for addition, S for subtraction, M for multiplication, and D for division) to represent the process that they would use if they were to solve the

problem. For problems in which more than one step is necessary the pupils write the letters that indicate all the processes that should be used. Care should be taken in correcting items of this type, for it is possible to vary the operations in solving a problem. For example, the following problem can be solved in three ways.

During a "gas war" the price of gasoline dropped from 33¢ a gallon to 21¢ a gallon. If Joe Ravenport's car averages 20 miles per gallon, how much should he save on a 120-mile trip when he buys gasoline at the "gas war" price?

The three ways in which the problem can be solved are by (a) subtracting, dividing, and then multiplying, (b) dividing, subtracting, and then multiplying, or (c) dividing, multiplying, multiplying, and then subtracting.

4. Effective use can be made of problems without numbers in determining ability to do problem reasoning. Examples of a primary-grade item and of an intermediate-grade item of this type follow.

The following problems do not contain numbers. Decide how you would solve each problem if it did contain numbers. Then decide which of the answers is correct.

You know the number of pages in a book that you plan to read and the number of days that you plan to spend reading the book. How can you find the average number of pages you should read each day if you are to finish the book on time. (An asterisk indicates the correct answer.)

    (a) Multiply the number of pages in the book by the number of days you plan to spend reading the book.
    *(b) Divide the number of pages in the book by the number of days you plan to spend reading the book.
    (c) Divide the number of days you have to read the book by the number of pages in the book.
    (d) None of the methods will work.

You spend a certain fraction of your savings; how can you find the amount of money left in your savings? (An asterisk indicates the correct answer.)

    (a) Subtract the fraction from your total savings.
    *(b) Multiply the amount of your savings by the fraction spent and then subtract this amount from your total savings.
    (c) Divide the amount of your savings by the fraction spent and subtract this amount from your total savings.
    (d) None of the methods will work.

5. Presenting a problem and asking the pupil to solve the problem in several ways is helpful in determining a pupil's originality and flexibility of thought.

6. A pupil's ability to visualize a problem situation may be measured by asking the pupil to produce a drawing or a diagram that will help to solve the problem. An item of the type that follows may also be used.

Decide which drawing or diagram can be used to help solve the problems. Mark the correct answer.

Jill had 6 baby chicks. She bought 7 more chicks that were 4 days old. Assuming that all of the chicks lived, how many chicks did she then have? (An asterisk indicates the correct answer.)

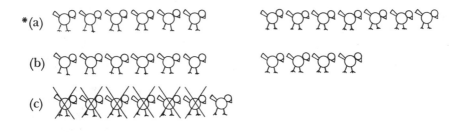

(d) All of the methods are correct.

(e) None of the methods is correct.

7. The ability to note the presence of unnecessary data and the absence of essential data is important in problem solving. At the primary-grade level items of the following types have been used effectively.

Harry has some toast. There are 2 slices in the toaster and Jean has 1 slice of toast. How many slices are there in all? (An asterisk indicates the correct answer.)

      (a) 3
      (b) 4
      (c) 5
    *(d) Not enough information is given to solve the problem.

In each of the following problems some information that is not needed to solve the problem may be included or some information needed for the solution of the problem may be omitted. Decide which of the responses is the best statement concerning the amount of information given in the problem. Mark that space in front of the appropriate answer.

Jim's marble collection consisted of 7 green marbles, 5 orange marbles, and 4 clear, colorless marbles. How many colored marbles did he have? (An asterisk indicates the correct answer.)

> *(a) "4 clear, colorless marbles" is unnecessary information.
> (b) "7 green marbles" is unnecessary information.
> (c) All of the information is needed.
> (d) There is not enough information to solve the problem.

Jill's birthday was on the tenth; this was three days before her brother Tom's birthday. Jill looked at the calendar on the fourth. How many days would she count off until her birthday? (An asterisk indicates the correct answer.)

> *(a) "This was three days before her brother Tom's birthday" is unnecessary information.
> (b) "Jill's birthday was on the tenth," is unnecessary information.
> (c) All of the information is needed.
> (d) There is not enough information to solve the problem.

Measuring performance.   Measurement of the ability to apply mathematics in performance situations should occupy an important place in the program of evaluation. The pupil can demonstrate his ability to use mathematical concepts by performing physical acts. Questions such as those that follow lend themselves to physical demonstrations.

1. What is the weight of this piece of metal? (use of scale)
2. How long is your desk? (use of ruler)
3. What time is it? (use of clock)
4. What is the circumference of this basketball? (use of tape measure)
5. Draw a parallelogram, ABCD, in which $\angle$ A is 35°. (use of protractor)
6. Draw an angle of 80° and bisect that angle. (use of protractor and compass).

Mathematics as a curricular area lends itself to application questions. Correction of such questions can be difficult, and care should be taken to allow for reasonable deviations from a set answer. For example, in correcting question number (6) the teacher could accept an angle from 79° to 81° to allow for slight differences in equipment.

Inventory tests and readiness.   The administration of a mathematical inventory test that surveys the previous year's work is a helpful aid in determining the mathematical level of individual pupils and of the class as a whole. Such a test will also be an aid in assessing the readiness of the pupils for more advanced work. This test should include a sampling of the important understandings and skills. Normally this may be a rather short test (about 30 minutes), a portion of which is given orally by the teacher. The test is usually filed in the student's arithmetic folder. It can be referred to by the teacher at a later date and also used in parent–teacher conferences.

An abbreviated inventory test for grade three appears below. The directions were read by the teacher. "For our mathematics work today, I am going to read some questions and ask you to answer these. I will also ask you to work some exercises. Do only what the exercise suggests." The pupils were also given a sheet containing the questions.

1. Write the numeral for the number that comes after 86.

2. How would you *best* measure the distance from our town to the state capital?

        (a) In feet
        (b) In miles
        (c) In inches
        (d) In yards

3. Which of these would be about a foot high?

        (a) Your reading workbook (standing)
        (b) Your desk
        (c) A cake of soap
        (d) The door to the classroom

4. Draw a square. Shade one-fourth of the square.

5. Write the numeral that stands for 8 tens and 5 ones.

6. Write the name of a person who is in the fourth row from the windows.

7. What number is represented by the place-value frame I have drawn on the board?

hundreds	tens	ones
II	IIII	IIIII

8. Look at the clock. What time is it? (The teacher notes the time on her copy of the test.)

9. Today is Tuesday, September 12. What will be the date next Monday?

10. Alice and Sue picked some flowers. Alice picked 7 flowers and Sue picked 6 more flowers. What was the total number of flowers picked by the two girls?

11. Jill bought a bag of 25 apples that were on sale. When she looked them over at home she found that 4 of the apples were spoiled and could not be used. How many of the apples were usable?

12. Larry's mother is having card club. If 4 persons can play at each table, how many will be able to play at 3 tables?

13. Chris plans to make 12 party favors. She has completed 5. How many more does she need to make?

14. Ken is giving away 10 baseball cards. He gives 2 cards apiece to friends. To how many friends will he give cards?

Diagnostic or analytical tests.   The purpose of analytical tests is to determine pupil deficiencies so that an instruction program may be inaugurated to correct a given difficulty. Usually such a test is used as a follow-up to a standardized achievement test. The achievement test helps the teacher determine the general standing of the pupil, but it does not give enough information to pinpoint weaknesses. In such cases, the teacher may use portions of a standardized "diagnostic" test or may develop a set of items, each of which measures a particular mathematical aspect that could be a possible cause of difficulty. In general, there is little reason to use a standardized test if items that measure the required skills are available. The norms that are so important to the standardized achievement survey battery are not necessary when the teacher is trying to determine "What is wrong?" rather than "How does the pupil compare with others?"

The role of the teacher in developing an analytical test is that of breaking the larger mathematical concepts down into smaller segments to determine specific areas in which the student needs aid. A fourth-grade teacher who noted that some pupils were having difficulty in multiplication followed this procedure:

1. A general survey quiz from the textbook was given to determine general progress in multiplication.

2. The teacher developed a series of multiplication exercises (about three items measuring each skill) such as the following:

(a) A sampling of basic multiplication combinations

(b) Single digit multipliers and multi-digit multiplicands without renaming

$$\begin{array}{ccc} 23 & 31 & 12 \\ \times\,3 & \times\,5 & \times\,4 \\ \hline \end{array}$$

(c) Single digit multiplier and multi-digit multiplicands with renaming

$$\begin{array}{cc} 28 & 44 \\ \times\,6 & \times\,7 \\ \hline \end{array}$$

(d) Multiplication of even tens

$$\begin{array}{cc} 30 & 50 \\ \times 7 & \times 9 \\ \hline \end{array}$$

(e) Multi-digit numerals with renaming

$$\begin{array}{cccc} 23 & 65 & 348 & 456 \\ \times 45 & \times 72 & \times 56 & \times 734 \\ \hline \end{array}$$

(f) Multi-digit numerals with internal zero in multiplier

$$\begin{array}{cc} 594 & 745 \\ \times 206 & \times 608 \\ \hline \end{array}$$

(g) Multi-digit numerals with internal zero in multiplicand

$$\begin{array}{cc} 408 & 902 \\ \times 342 & \times 371 \\ \hline \end{array}$$

(h) Multi-digit numerals with internal zero in multiplier and multiplicand

$$\begin{array}{cc} 605 & 702 \\ \times 409 & \times 508 \\ \hline \end{array}$$

3. The test was administered to the pupils who scored below a reasonable cut-off point on the survey. The teacher introduced the test by saying, "You apparently missed some ideas in multiplication which kept you from making a good score on the test yesterday. I have an analytical test that may help us find out what our multiplication difficulties are. If you would like to try this test, you may pick one up on my desk and take it during our work period.

4. The analytical test was scored, and individual errors were noted. A note such as the following was written at the bottom of each analytic test: Ken, notice that your difficulty in multiplication seems to be centered on using zeros in multiplication. Page — of the supplementary book on the arithmetic table should help you understand this mistake. Try to work several exercises in this book and then bring them to the desk and we'll go over them.

If a number of pupils were experiencing the same difficulty, the teacher formed a small group for instruction in the skill that was misunderstood.

5. The pupils worked on remedial materials designed to correct their errors.

Attitude and preference tests.   It is axiomatic that the attitude of a student toward a subject is an important factor in achievement. Attitudes toward arithmetic are probably developed from early childhood through adult life. However, findings suggest that grades three through six are the most crucial.[3]

[3] Wilbur H. Dutton, "Measuring Attitudes Toward Arithmetic," *The Elementary School Journal*, 55:24–31; September, 1954.

Thus, the elementary school teacher has the responsibility of determining student attitudes toward arithmetic and, when necessary, of improving attitudes.

There are two common means of determining the feelings that students have for mathematics. An attitude inventory such as the Dutton scale (see below)[4] may be used in combination with a sheet on which the pupils are asked to rank in order of preference the subjects which they are studying. This combination approach has certain advantages over the use of only one measure.

1. It is possible for some pupils to like all subjects. Thus, arithmetic may be well liked but appear rather low on the preference ranking. The Dutton scale will pick up this apparent discrepancy.

2. A pupil may rate arithmetic very high on the Dutton scale but may have other subjects which he or she ranks higher on the preference scale. The two used together give greater insight into the pupil's feelings.

3. There is a tendency to rate a subject well on an attitude scale in order to please the teacher. There is little reason to respond insincerely to a performance ranking.

REACTION TO ELEMENTARY SCHOOL MATHEMATICS

Check (x) only the statements which express your feeling toward arithmetic.

_____1. I feel arithmetic is an important part of the school curriculum.

_____2. Arithmetic is something you have to do even though it is not enjoyable.

_____3. Working with numbers is fun.

_____4. I have never liked arithmetic.

_____5. Arithmetic thrills me, and I like it better than any other subject.

_____6. I get no satisfaction from studying arithmetic.

_____7. I like arithmetic because the procedures are logical.

_____8. I am afraid of doing word problems.

_____9. I like working all types of arithmetic problems.

_____10. I detest arithmetic and avoid using it at all times.

_____11. I have a growing appreciation of arithmetic through understanding its values, applications, and processes.

_____12. I am completely indifferent to arithmetic.

_____13. I have always liked arithmetic because it has presented me with a challenge.

_____14. I like arithmetic, but I like other subjects just as well.

_____15. The completion and proof of accuracy in arithmetic gave me satisfaction and feelings of accomplishment.

[4] Adapted from an attitude scale appearing in Wilbur H. Dutton, and L. J. Adams, *Arithmetic for Teachers* (Englewood Cliffs, New Jersey: Prentice-Hall, 1961), pp. 361–362.

Before scoring your attitude scale, place an "x" on the line below to indicate where you think your general feeling toward arithmetic might be.

11	10	9	8	7	6	5	4	3	2	1

Favor Strongly   Neutral   Strongly Against

Scoring Procedure. Place the scale value of the items you check on the test in the left margin of the page. Total all items checked and divide by the total number of items you checked. This will give you an average score on the test. Compare this average with the estimated placement shown on the line indicating your general feeling toward arithmetic.

Item	Scale value	Item	Scale value
1	7.2	9	9.6
2	3.3	10	1.0
3	8.7	11	8.2
4	1.5	12	5.2
5	10.5	13	9.5
6	2.6	14	5.6
7	7.9	15	9.0
8	2.0		

STANDARDIZED TESTS

There is an ever-increasing use of standardized tests in the majority of areas of the elementary school curriculum. With this increased use have come many popular articles critical of standardized objective tests. When the evidence for and against the standardized tests is carefully weighed, the findings reveal that the standardized test is helpful if PROPERLY USED. The major difficulty lies in the misuse rather than in the use of such tests. The section that follows will describe some of the features of standardized tests in elementary school mathematics and will make suggestions for their use and interpretation.

Standardized tests in mathematics for the elementary school normally fall into two categories, achievement tests and diagnostic and readiness tests.

Achievement

The standardized achievement test differs from the teacher-made test in at least four ways.[5]

1. The objectives and content of standardized tests tend to be based upon those that are common to many school systems, while those of teacher-made tests are specific to a given classroom setting.

[5] Robert L. Thorndike and Elizabeth Hagen, *Measurement and Evaluation in Psychology and Education,* 2nd ed. (New York: Wiley, 1961), p. 289.

2. The standardized test surveys a large portion of knowledge, while the teacher-made test usually is related to a limited topic.

3. Standardized tests are usually developed by a team of curriculum workers, test editors, and reviewers. The teacher typically works alone.

4. The standardized tests provide norms that are based upon the performance of a large sample of elementary school pupils from representative schools throughout the nation. The teacher-made test usually depends solely upon the performance of from twenty to forty pupils.

The standardized test in elementary school mathematics may serve many purposes. Some of the more common are

1. To provide the teacher with a general picture of achievement in mathematics for individual pupils and for the class as a whole. The teacher can observe from standardized test results the "spread" in achievement in her class. The test also may give some direction to grouping procedures and the need for special materials.

2. To provide a comparison of her pupils scores with those made by students in the standardization group. The teacher may see if the class seems on the whole to be above average or below average relative to the pupils on whom the test was standardized.

3. To study pupil growth over a period of months or years. Standardized tests given at regular intervals help the teacher to study pupil growth. Some pupils of above average ability can be expected to make well over a year's growth each year. Other pupils will not make a year's growth per year. The teacher can analyze the pattern of growth indicated by the test to ascertain whether or not the pupil is progressing at a faster or slower pace than he previously has.

4. To help determine curricular weaknesses. Careful study of the results of a standardized test in mathematics often helps the teacher to see areas of the mathematics curriculum that have been neglected. For example, the results of standardized tests have caused some teachers and school districts to give greater emphasis to basic mathematical concepts and to problem solving.

Diagnostic and readiness tests

These have already been discussed under the section on teacher-made tests. Therefore, only a list of the current standardized tests in these catagories is included at the end of the chapter.

Selection of standardized tests

Perhaps the best method of measuring the validity of standardized tests for a given school is to have teachers take the test themselves, comparing the items with the purposes of the local mathematics curriculum. Once tests that measure behaviors important to the curriculum have been identified, several other checks should be made. Some questions which should be asked are

1. Is there good evidence that the test has been well analyzed statistically?

Are the norms appropriate? Can raw scores be readily converted to derived scores?

2. Can the information obtained be easily and correctly interpreted?

3. Is the manual adequate? Does it give good suggestions for application of test results?

4. Can the test be scored by the agency or with a reasonable amount of clerical time?

5. Are there alternate forms so that scores can be compared from year to year? How comparable are these forms?

Interpretation of standardized test data

The results of standardized tests in elementary school mathematics are usually reported in terms of grade equivalents, percentile ranks, or standard scores.

Grade equivalent. A given raw score is interpreted in terms of the average person in the group taking the test for standardization purposes at a grade level. For example, a grade equivalent of 6.0 would mean that an individual's raw score was the same as that of the average *beginning* sixth grader in the standardization group. A score of 6.5 would mean that the score was the same as the average *middle-of-the-year* sixth grader in the standardization group. Thus, 6.5 can be read sixth grade, fifth month.

Growth is not always the same from grade level to grade level, so an increase in correct answers may produce varying improvement in grade equivalents from grade to grade. A grade equivalent score of 6.5 does not mean that the student is doing or can do middle-of-the-year sixth-grade work. It simply means that the student obtained the same score on the test as the average middle-of-the-year sixth-grade student. Examine the scores made by a beginning sixth grader (6.0) on a current achievement battery (1964 copyright).

Tom's Scores

Subject	Grade equivalent
Reading	
Word meaning	9.0
Paragraph meaning	10.4
Spelling	10.2
Language	10.5
Arithmetic	
Computation	8.6
Concepts	8.5
Science	10.7
Social Studies	10.7

How would you compare his achievement in arithmetic with that in reading or language? Could you guess Tom's grades in each subject?

Percentile rank.   In determining the percentile rank, a student is usually compared with students of a like grade level in the standardization group. Thus, a beginning-of-the-year sixth grader who obtained a percentile rank of 75 would have scored higher than about three-fourths of the sixth grade students in the standardization group. The percentile rank in each subject for Tom's scores would be 96.

Why does the grade equivalent vary so much, while all of Tom's percentile ranks would be 96? When curricular patterns are considered, the reason becomes clear. A student may make progress in reading and language by the type of outside work and study he does at home. In arithmetic, the progress is much more dependent upon what has been taught. Normally, a student will not be able to solve division of fractions problems until they have been taught and studied in school; the same student will be able to interpret readings above his grade level if he does quite a bit of reading at home.

Standard scores.[6]   Most standardized tests allow for an interpretation of the results as a "standard" or "transformed" score. A standard score is one converted from a raw score. It can be expressed on a uniform standard scale without seriously altering its relationship to the other scores of the group.

REPORTING TO PARENTS

Classroom progress

Methods of reporting vary from school system to school system. Therefore the form of the written report card will be dependent upon the local school system. However, one of the most valuable means of reporting progress in mathematics to parents is through parent–teacher conferences. The teacher should be prepared to give a short overall evaluation of progress in mathematics and to examine with the parent the pupil's arithmetic folder. If a student is having difficulties, the parent will often appreciate suggestions for helping the pupil at home. In addition, the teacher may effectively use this time to explain the goals of her mathematics program and to clear up any parental confusion concerning the goals and methods of modern mathematics.

[6] The scope of this book does not allow for a thorough discussion of standard scores. A better understanding may be obtained by consulting one of the books on educational measurement listed at the end of the chapter.

Results of standardized tests

There are varying policies on reporting the results of standardized tests to parents. If handled in the context of a parent–teacher conference, there is little reason why the parent should not know the results of his child's tests. A few suggestions designed to give the parent a true picture of test results follow.

1. Normally the parent can most easily understand results if reported in percentile ranks. The teacher can make a statement such as "Bill scored at the 55 percentile. This means that he scored better than about 55 percent of the group on which the test was standardized. He's just at about the middle of the group. While he is at this point in national averages, he doesn't rank at the same place in his class. Our class is above average, so Bill ranks at the 45 percentile in our class."

2. If grade equivalent scores are reported, extreme care should be exerted by the teacher. The parent should not be led to believe that because his sixth grader scored at 8.5 on the test that he could be successful in eighth-grade work. A statement such as the following one can be made by the teacher: "Ann's grade equivalent in problem solving was 8.5. This means that she answered the same number of questions correctly as the average person at the middle of the eighth grade. It doesn't mean she could do eighth-grade work, but she is doing very well." If the parent thinks in terms of "double promotion" because of the test results, ask, "Would you rather have a girl who is near the top of her class in sixth grade or one who is near the middle of the class in eighth grade? Which would be better, an A sixth grader or a C eighth grader?" Also, the parent should be made aware of the fact that very high or very low grade equivalents are quite unreliable. They only give an indication of a very good or a very poor score on the test.

FINAL NOTE

Evaluation of pupil progress in elementary school mathematics is a difficult and time-consuming process. When the dividends to be derived from a good measurement program are assessed, there can be little doubt of its value. However, not only does the teacher measure the achievement of a pupil, but in the process she also carefully thinks through her educational objectives, focuses attention on an individual pupil's strengths and weaknesses, and studies the effectiveness of a particular teaching strategy.

STANDARDIZED TESTS IN ELEMENTARY SCHOOL MATHEMATICS

Acorn Publishing Co., Inc., Rockville Centre, Long Island, New York.
    a. Arithmetic Test (Fundamentals of Reasoning)

A Subtest of Municipal Battery
  Covers: Computation; number comparisons; comparisons; problems;
      and problem analysis
  Level: Grades 3–6, Grades 6–8
b. Arithmetic Test: National Achievement Tests
  Covers: Arithmetic fundamentals (speed, number comparisons, fun-
      damental skills); arithmetic reasoning (comparisons, prob-
      lem analysis, finding problem key, problems)
  Level: Grades 3–8

Bureau of Educational Measurements, Kansas State Teachers College, Emporia,
  Kansas.
  a. Arithmetic: Every Pupil Scholarship Test
    Measures two levels (not listed)
    Level: Grades 4–6
  b. Kansas Arithmetic Test
    Covers: Computation; problem solving
    Level: Grades 3–5, Grades 6–8
  c. Kansas Primary Arithmetic Test
    Covers: Addition and subtraction; multiplication and division; mis-
        cellaneous problems; basic number concepts; simple reason-
        ing problems
    Level: Grades 1–3
  d. Primary Arithmetic: Every Pupil Scholarship Test
    Measures two levels
    Level: Grades 1–3
  e. Schrammel-Otterstrom Arithmetic Test
    Covers: Computation; comprehension; problems
    Level: Grades 4–6

California Test Bureau, 5916 Hollywood Boulevard, Hollywood, California.
  a. California Arithmetic Test, 1957 Edition, WXYZ Series, 1963 Norms
    Covers: Arithmetic reasoning; arithmetic fundamentals
    Level: Lower Primary, Grades 1–2; Upper Primary Grades H2–L4;
        Elementary, Grades 4–6
    Also see sections of California Achievement Test, 1957 Ed.
  b. Diagnostic Tests and Self-Helps in Arithmetic
    Consists of four screening tests and twenty-three diagnostic tests cover-
    ing all phases of arithmetic through the eighth grade
    Level: Grades 3–12
  c. Los Angeles Diagnostic Tests: Fundamentals of Arithmetic
    Designed to measure achievement in the four fundamental operations
    Level: Grades 2–8
  d. Los Angeles Diagnostic Tests: Reasoning in Arithmetic
    Designed to measure pupil accomplishment in relation to one-step,

two-step, denominate numbers, percentages and processes
Level: Grades 3–9
e. Number Fact Check Sheet
Level: Grades 5–8

Educational Records Bureau, 21 Audubon Avenue, New York 32, New York.
a. A Brief Survey of Arithmetic Skills, Revised Edition
Covers: Computation; reasoning
Level: Grades 5–12

Educational Test Bureau, 120 Washington Avenue, Minneapolis, Minnesota.
a. Analytical Scales of Attainment: Arithmetic
Covers: Quantitative relationships; problems; arithmetic vocabulary; fundamental operations
Level: Grades 3–4, Grades 5–6
b. Coordinated Scales of Attainment: Arithmetic
Covers: Computation; problem solving
Level: Grades 4–6

Educational Testing Service, Princeton, New Jersey.
a. Cooperative Sequential Tests of Educational Progress. Forms 4A, 4B
Covers: Broad understanding of general mathematical concepts
Level: Grades 4–6
b. Cooperative School and College Ability Tests. Forms 5A, 5B
Covers: Numerical computation; problem solving. Designed to evaluate the student's capacity to perform academic tasks

Harcourt, Brace & World, 757 Third Avenue, New York 17, New York.
a. Metropolitan Arithmetic Tests
Covers: Arithmetic computation; problem solving and concepts
Level: Elementary, Grades 3–4; Intermediate, Grades 5–6
b. New York Test of Arithmetical Meanings
Covers: Premeasurement and numerical concepts
Level: One, Grades 1.9–3.1; Two, Grades 2.9–3.1
c. Otis Arithmetic Reasoning Test
Level: Grades 4–12
d. Stanford Achievement Test, Forms W, X, Y, Z
Covers: Primary I Battery, Arithmetic; Primary II Battery Arithmetic Computation, Arithmetic Concepts; Intermediate I Battery and Intermediate II Battery, Arithmetic Computation, Arithmetic Concepts; Arithmetic Applications
Level: Primary I, Grade 1; Primary II, Grades 2–3; Intermediate I, Grade 4; Intermediate II, Grades 5–6
e. Stanford Arithmetic Tests, Forms J, K, L, M
Covers: Arithmetic problem solving; arithmetic concepts; arithmetic computation

    Level: Elementary, Grades 3–4; Intermediate, Grades 5–6
  f. Stanford Tests in Preparation—December, 1965
      1. Diagnostic tests in arithmetic—for assessing specific areas of arithmetic difficulty
      2. Modern mathematics test—supplementary measure for schools following a modern arithmetic curriculum

Holt, Rinehart and Winston, 383 Madison Avenue, New York, New York.
  a. Readiness and Achievement in Arithmetic
    Level: Grades 1–2

Houghton Mifflin, 2 Park Street, Boston, Massachusetts.
  a. Iowa Tests of Basic Skills, Forms 3 and 4
    Covers: Arithmetic concepts; arithmetic problem solving
    Level: Grades 3–5, Grades 5–9

Public School Publishing Company, 345 Calhoun Street, Cincinnati 19, Ohio.
  a. American School Achievement Tests: Arithmetic Readiness
    Level: Kindergarten and Grade 1
  b. American School Achievement Tests: Part 2 Arithmetic
    Covers: Computation; problems
    Level: Grades 4–6
  c. Arithmetic Computation: Public School Achievement Tests
    Level: Grades 3–8
  d. Arithmetic Reasoning: Public School Achievement Tests
    Level: Grades 3–8
  e. Diagnostic Chart for Fundamental Processes in Arithmetic
    Covers: Four fundamental operations
    Level: Grades 2–8

Ridge Manor Publishing Company, Ridge Manor, Florida.
  a. The Wilson General Survey Tests in Arithmetic
    Level: Grades 5–10
  b. The Wilson Inventory and Diagnostic Tests in Arithmetic
    Level: Grades 3–9

Scholastic Testing Service, Inc., 3774 West Devon Avenue, Chicago, Illinois.
  a. Scholastic Achievement Series: Arithmetic
    Covers: Computation; reasoning
    Level: Grades 2–3, Grades 4–6
    For Catholic schools

Science Research Associates, Inc., 259 E. Erie Street, Chicago, Illinois.
  a. SRA Achievement Series, Forms C and D
    Covers: Arithmetic reasoning; arithmetic concepts; arithmetic computation

Level: Grades 1–9

Arithmetic subtests are a part of the complete test batteries.

Scott, Foresman & Company, 433 E. Erie Street, Chicago, Illinois.

    a. Seeing Through Arithmetic Tests

        Covers: Problem Solving; computation; selecting equations; solving equations; information; concepts

        Level: Grades 4–6

Steck Company, Austin 1, Texas.

    a. Arithmetic Essentials Test

        Covers: Seven levels (not listed)

        Level: Grades 3–6

University of California, Los Angeles, California.

Wilbur H. Dutton, Department of Education

    a. Arithmetic Comprehension Test

        Covers: Basic arithmetical concepts; emphasizes understanding with the inclusion of some modern math

        Level: Form III No. 1, Grade 3; Form 1B, Grade 4; Form 1A, Grade 5; Form 1C, Grade 6

STUDY SUGGESTIONS

1. Read the examiner's manual for two of the standardized arithmetic tests listed in the chapter. Then, take each arithmetic test. How do the tests compare in terms of objectives and types of items?
2. Develop an inventory test for the beginning of the grade you teach or plan to teach.
3. Making use of the content contained in an elementary school mathematics textbook, write several items of each type considered in the chapter.
4. Write an arithmetic theme on a phase of mathematics in which you feel you are weak.
5. Study an arithmetic readiness test. Why do you think that arithmetic readiness tests have not been as widely used as reading readiness tests?
6. Develop a list of items that should be included in a pupil's arithmetic folder.
7. Make a list of the advantages and uses of the following procedures: teacher observation, teacher-made tests, standardized tests.
8. Examine a current experimental curriculum in elementary school mathematics. Compare the content and purposes of this program with a current standardized test.

SUGGESTED REFERENCES

Buros, O. K., ed., *The Sixth Mental Measurements Yearbook* (Highland Park, New Jersey: The Gryphon Press, 1965).

DeVault, M. Vere, ed., *Improving Mathematics Programs, Trends and Issues in the Elementary Schools* (Columbus, Ohio: Charles E. Merrill, 1961), Chap. 8.

Ebel, Robert L., *Measuring Educational Achievement* (Englewood Cliffs, New Jersey: Prentice-Hall, 1965).

Lindquist, E. F., ed., *Educational Measurement* (Washington, D. C.: American Council on Education, 1951).

National Council of Teachers of Mathematics, *Evaluation in Mathematics,* Twenty-sixth Yearbook (Washington, D. C.: The Council, 1961).

————, *Instruction in Arithmetic,* Twenty-fifth Yearbook (Washington, D. C.: The Council, 1960), Chap. 7 and 8.

Thorndike, Robert L., and Hagen, Elizabeth, *Measurement and Evaluation in Psychology and Education,* 2nd ed. (New York: Wiley, 1961), Chap. 17.

Thorpe, Cleata B., *Teaching Elementary Arithmetic* (New York: Harper & Row, 1962), Chap. 25.

USE OF SUGGESTED REFERENCES

1. Obtain two standardized tests in elementary school mathematics. Make notes on these tests. Compare your comments with those given by a reviewer in *Mental Measurements Yearbook.* Also, read several reviews. What weaknesses of mathematics tests are mentioned most?

2. Ebel is an excellent guide to the construction of good teacher-made tests. Develop several test items and compare your results with Ebel's suggestions for writing test items.

3. Read the appropriate sections in *Educational Measurement* and then develop a set of criteria for selection of a standardized test in elementary school mathematics.

4. Study Glennon's article in *Improving Mathematics Programs.* Use ideas from this chapter to develop several test questions designed to measure mathematical meaning.

5. Compare the suggestions in *Evaluation in Mathematics* with those in this chapter.

6. Use chapters 7 and 8 in *Instruction in Arithmetic* to develop guidelines for evaluation and guidance in elementary school mathematics.

7. From the suggestion in Thorndike and Hagen and other sources, answer the question: What is the best way to report mathematical achievement to parents?

8. Read Thorpe's suggestions on the correction of tests and the use of test results. What procedures can be used to make a test an effective learning situation?

16

Instructional media for teaching elementary school mathematics

This chapter contains suggestions for various instructional tools that are useful and necessary to the teaching of elementary school mathematics. Space does not permit an exhaustive treatment of each phase of media. Therefore, suggested references of standard works in the field are included.

THE TEXTBOOK

The role of the textbook

The textbook is an indispensable item in the operation of a successful elementary school mathematics program. However, too often it becomes the only instruction material used in the mathematics program. This is unfortunate and may happen because the teacher lacks a clear-cut philosophy concerning the use of materials. The following suggestions for the use of materials are in keeping with the approach to the teaching of elementary school mathematics developed in this book.

1. Normally an introduction to a new topic should involve a pre-text development that allows for pupil thinking and discovery. Suggestions for this type of introduction have been detailed in previous chapters. For introductory lessons the text serves as a reference "to check to see if the book agrees with our statements." It also provides extension material for further development of the topic.

2. Textbook materials normally contain fewer errors and ambiguities than teacher-prepared duplicated exercises. Therefore, they provide the single best source for practice material, once the basic understanding of a mathematical idea has been developed. In addition to the textbook used by all of the pupils, the teacher should have special exercises for below average and above average pupils. Well-developed, teacher-made exercises are of great importance.

3. The majority of current superior textbooks provide a teacher's manual

with suggestions for appropriate instructional equipment, reference books, games, and other activities. These suggestions should aid the teacher in presenting a varied mathematics program. The teacher should make a careful evaluation of the merits of various suggestions because many books provide more suggestions for materials than are appropriate for a single day's study of mathematics. Also, some of the suggestions are of dubious value.

4. If the sequence of topics in the adopted textbook is in keeping with the curriculum of a school, it is normally best to follow that sequence. This does not mean that every page needs to be studied by the class. Most books provide more practice material than is necessary for the average student. The teacher is responsible for using discretion in selecting how much of the material on a given topic will be of value to her class.

5. The early chapters of many texts are a review of the previous year's mathematics program. In situations where this is the case, the teacher should devise a variety of pre-text reintroductions to improve the motivation of the topic and avoid the feeling that children may have that "we're doing the same old thing."

6. In the intermediate grades, where pupils can readily read the material, the textbook is usually of greater value than in the primary grades. The teacher of primary-grade pupils will have, at best, a mediocre program if only the textbook is used.

7. Textbooks vary in quality and approach. Often an adopted series has many superior materials and some that are not of high caliber. The teacher can often receive valuable ideas for classroom instruction from the teacher's manuals of several other series.

8. While the textbook plays a very important part in the elementary school mathematics program, it is only one source of needed materials. A superior mathematics program will use many others.

Selection of the textbook

The textbook selected for a school system should be in accord with the philosophy, curriculum, and goals of the elementary school mathematics program. Because teachers use the adopted textbook series extensively, great care should be taken in its selection. The vignette that follows presents a possible plan for textbook selection.

The superintendent called together the administrative personnel who worked with elementary school mathematics—principals, supervisors, and curriculum consultants. He charged the mathematics consultant (or an elementary principal interested in mathematics) with the responsibility of setting up a committee to select an elementary school mathematics textbook series. In addition, the superintendent provided each of the participants with a policy statement concerning ethics in textbook adoptions. The remainder of the meeting was turned over to the consultant, who was to act as the coordinator for the textbook selection. The coordinator asked that principals recommend teachers who were interested in mathematics curriculum improvement.

From the list of interested teachers, five teachers were appointed to the committee. They represented the early primary, primary, and intermediate grades. The high school mathematics chairman was available for consultation concerning coordination (K-12). The selection committee chairman wrote to each textbook publisher who published elementary school mathematics textbooks. The list of publishers was obtained from the American Textbook Publishers Institute, 1 Madison Avenue, New York. He also obtained copies of the current professional books concerned with the teaching of elementary school mathematics.

When the textbooks and professional books arrived, the chairman called a meeting of the committee. At this meeting the committee members were informed that (1) a total of ten half-days would be made available for study meetings and other work (substitute teachers would be hired to free the committee members), (2) clerical help needed for typing and duplication was being made available, (3) the entire staff of teachers was being informed concerning the membership of the committee and was being asked to make suggestions and to consult with the committee (the committee was free to use the other teachers as advisors), (4) the selection was to be made in six months, and (5) the new course of study was to be considered as a guide to help in textbook selection.

Because almost twenty textbook series were submitted for consideration, the committee agreed that the first efforts should be devoted to eliminating those series which did not fit the goals of the school district and hopefully to narrowing the field to six. To accomplish this task each member was asked to review the textbooks at the grade level at which she taught and to select the six she thought merited further consideration. The chairman selected a grade level that was not represented by committee members for his study.

The committee members were given the district policy statement concerning textbooks and the following tips on textbook selection.

What a good textbook should do.

1. Provide teacher direction and guidance, not dictation and limitation.
2. Provide basic material for study and review.
3. Be interestingly written and well organized.
4. Be free from mathematical inaccuracies.
5. Reflect the latest research in teaching methods and use an exploratory-discovery approach to teaching.*
6. Provide a common frame of reference.
7. Show careful development of mathematical principles and generalizations.
8. Provide gradation of topics according to difficulty.
9. Provide appropriate diagrams, charts, and illustrations.

* In keeping with the course of study for the school district.

10. Provide a spiral arrangement of topics that promotes continuity from grade to grade.*

11. Provide good problem situations and material emphasizing the usefulness of mathematics.*

12. Provide variation in content to meet individual needs.*

13. Provide interesting and challenging practice exercises to develop basic skills.*

Errors to be avoided.

1. Don't let a single error prejudice you against the entire series.

2. In final textbook selection, keep in mind all grades, not just your own.

3. Consider only the materials that are available.

4. Don't let minor conflicts between a series and the course of study (particularly in grade placement) rule out a series. It may be necessary to use only portions of the adopted series, or it may be necessary to change the course of study.

5. Take care in using textbook selection guides provided by a publisher of mathematics textbooks. These are often slanted toward that particular series.

Format and content considerations to be kept in mind.

Format. Cover design, style of type, size of type, layout of pages, consistent placement of page numbers, use of color, eye appeal, binding, glossary, table of contents, index, appendix, illustrations.

Content. Development of meaning of mathematical operations and of number systems (whole numbers, rational numbers, integers), problems, tests, study suggestions, exercises.

Two weeks later the committee met and each member submitted the names of the six textbooks that he felt would best fit the needs of the school's mathematics program. From those lists, six text series were suggested for further consideration. Committee members then went about rating the series using the specific topics suggested above. Less weight was given to format than to content. Specifically, the committee members were asked to rate each item on a 5-point scale from 1 (included but poor) to 5 (superior). For example, the textbook series might rate 3 on verbal problems and 1 on tests.

When this rating was completed, the six textbook publishers were asked to send in representatives who were to give a presentation to the committee concerning specific topics. The representatives were to be ready to answer questions submitted by the committee. After meeting with all of the representatives, the committee compiled rating points and selected a textbook series.

After the selection of the series, a plan was formulated to educate the teachers in the use of the series. Also, plans were laid to evaluate the series after a year of use.

---

* In keeping with the course of study for the school district.

MANIPULATIVE MATERIALS

In previous sections of this book, reference was made to various types of manipulative materials. There are numerous commercial devices and many useful materials developed for the teacher. A partial listing of possible devices follows. A list of commercial agencies that produce devices, films, and filmstrips is presented at the end of the chapter.

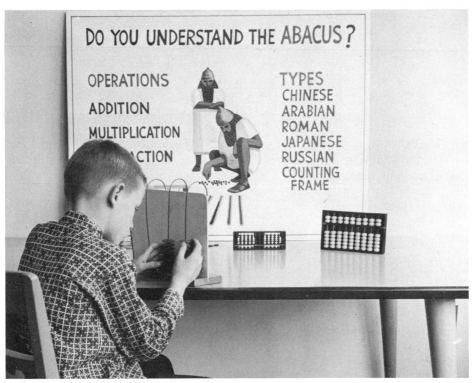

Source: Still Photo Services U. D. I. S., Pennsylvania State University.

Devices such as the abacus can be used to develop a deeper understanding of the number system.

Devices for understanding the number system

1. Number lines (positive and negative integers, rationals, reals). Teachers can use marked number lines, or they may wish only to mark off with points. This allows for use of number lines with all types of situations such as fractions, negatives, or the beginning of a sequence 456, etc.

2. Popsicle sticks, tickets, blocks of tens and ones, or strips of paper to use in grouping and regrouping.

3. Various types of abacuses for grouping-regrouping situations, place value, and rationalizing computation.

4. Cutouts of geometric forms to develop geometric ideas. Also, fractional parts of geometric forms to develop meaning in fractional study.

5. The flannel board (many uses).

6. Fractional equivalent board.

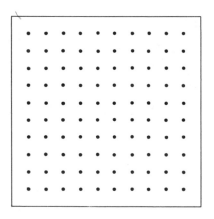

7. Pegboard, ceiling tile, or cards with 100 or 1,000 squares. These can be used for achieving an understanding of decimals, percent, array multiplication ideas, and fractions.

8. Rods of varying length for showing number relationships such as "different names for the same number" and for developing computational meanings.

9. Place-value charts for understanding place value and grouping-regrouping situations.

hundreds	tens	ones

10. Various colored marbles to be used to illustrate part of a set relation of fractions, counting, set development, problem solving, and work with probability.

11. One-inch building blocks for arrays, geometric forms, area, volume, and counting.

12. Flash cards for practice.

13. Dominoes for addition, subtraction, array patterns, multiplication, division, and probability.

14. Dice for addition, subtraction, and probability.

15. Various geometric shapes, plane and solid, for the development of geometric concepts.

16. Geometric boards made from hardboard for various geometric concepts.

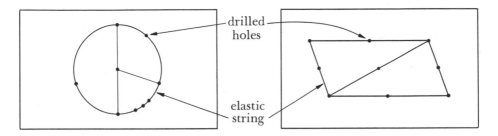

17. Multiplication-division board for multiplication and division relationships.

	1	2	3	4	5	6	7	8	9
1	1	2	3	4	5	6	7	8	9
2	2	4	6	8	10	12	14	16	18
3	3	6	9	12	15	18	21	24	27
4	4	8	12	16	20	24	28	32	36
5	5	10	15	20	25	30	35	40	45
6	6	12	18	24	30	36	42	48	54
7	7	14	21	28	35	42	49	56	63
8	8	16	24	32	40	48	56	64	72
9	9	18	27	36	45	54	63	72	81

18. 100 board for number relationships and counting.

1	2	3	4	5	6	7	8	9	10
11	12	13	14	15	16	17	18	19	20
21	22	23	24	25	26	27	28	29	30
31	32	33	34	35	36	37	38	39	40
41	42	43	44	45	46	47	48	49	50
51	52	53	54	55	56	57	58	59	60
61	62	63	64	65	66	67	68	69	70
71	72	73	74	75	76	77	78	79	80
81	82	83	84	85	86	87	88	89	90
91	92	93	94	95	96	97	98	99	100

or

	1	2	3	4	5	6	7	8	9
10	11	12	13	14	15	16	17	18	19
20	21	22	23	24	25	26	27	28	29
30	31	32	33	34	35	36	37	38	39
40	41	42	43	44	45	46	47	48	49
50	51	52	53	54	55	56	57	58	59
60	61	62	63	64	65	66	67	68	69
70	71	72	73	74	75	76	77	78	79
80	81	82	83	84	85	86	87	88	89
90	91	92	93	94	95	96	97	98	99
100									

19. Counting materials: buttons, cubes, etc.

20. Egg cartons for array patterns, fundamental operations.

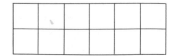

The above list is by no means exhaustive. It is presented principally to create a setting in which the reader can think of other possible devices.

PROGRAMMED INSTRUCTION

Because of its sequential nature, the field of mathematics has been one of the first areas to feel the impact of programmed instruction. The advantages purported for this type of instruction are that (1) individual differences are recognized, (2) the learning is active, (3) the student is given immediate knowledge of results, (4) the organized nature of knowledge is emphasized, (5) spaced review is provided, and (6) anxiety is reduced because the learner is not threatened by the task.[1]

Illustrative programs were provided in chapter 4; therefore, the material that follows is designed to list briefly uses of programmed materials in elementary school mathematics teaching and to give a brief guide to the development of programs by teachers.

Use of programmed materials

Programmed instruction may be used effectively in the following ways:

1. Programmed materials using very small steps can be used effectively as remedial materials. The small-step instruction allows the slow student maximum success and the opportunity to move along at a reasonable pace.

2. Programs presenting enrichment materials can be developed for above average students. The materials for the above average should be based on an inductive approach and presented in the same manner in which a superior teacher would question a child to elicit his thinking. The traditional small-step program often bores the bright pupil.

3. Simple programs can be used to provide practice materials in which pupils are able to check their own answers for correctness before proceeding on to the next exercise.

4. Programmed materials can be helpful for pupils who are absent from

[1] Ernest R. Hilgard, "What Support from the Psychology of Learning," N.E.A. Journal, Vol. 50, No. 8 (November 1961), pp. 20–21.

school for long periods of time and miss the development of one or more new topics.

As is the case for any instructional aid, programmed materials are not the major answer to improved instruction. They are but one type of material that can be used effectively in the elementary school mathematics class.

Developing programmed materials

The quality of programmed materials varies greatly, and many programs have been developed that follow a rather rote learning approach to elementary school mathematics instruction. Therefore, it is suggested that teachers experiment with the development of programmed materials for their own classroom use.

Early in the programmed instruction movement a number of hard and fast principles were thought necessary for proper programming. Later, research revealed that some of the most strongly recommended programming procedures were not essential for superior results. Thus, the only necessities for success are that the program should teach the desired content effectively and be of interest to the pupil. The following suggestions may prove helpful to teachers who are attempting to develop programmed materials.

1. Start out slowly. Don't attempt to program an entire remedial sixth-grade arithmetic program. A reasonable attempt might be to develop materials to help pupils experiencing difficulty in understanding how reciprocals work in the division of fractions.

2. Begin by writing the type of question you would ask a student to teach him a concept.

3. Use a very methodical presentation in preparing remedial materials. For example, use many simple questions that will lead to the formation of a concept. Use more difficult questions in developing enrichment programs. A rule to follow might be to try to ask questions which the pupils can answer correctly if they *exert effort.*

4. Sit down with one of the pupils for whom you intend the materials. See how he reacts. Then revise the materials in the light of his comments.

5. Try the materials with other pupils. If necessary, revise again. The materials needn't be perfect. If the pupils learn the desired mathematical concepts and have a good attitude toward the materials, you have succeeded.

OTHER INSTRUCTIONAL MEDIA

Films and filmstrips

A rather large number of motion-picture films have been produced for use in elementary mathematics classes. In general, the films have not been widely used. This may be because it is difficult to develop a mathematical topic in the content of a 15- to 30-minute film. In addition, often the equivalent of one or two weeks of instructional time is packed into a single 30-minute film. This type of film is actually useful only for review purposes. Probably the best type of film for elementary school mathematics classes is that which depicts some phase of mathematical history, such as the history of measurement or early notational systems.

Filmstrips are helpful in the elementary school classroom because they allow for flexibility in use. Topics in sets, geometry, and measurement are particularly suited to filmstrips. Also, while the motion picture allows for no pupil discovery, the filmstrip can be used to raise questions and to draw conclusions during the course of the strip. For example, before looking at a frame, pupils can compare their ideas with those presented in the filmstrip.

Supplementary books

In recent years many attractive and worthwhile trade books on mathematics have been written for use as supplementary and reference materials. Each elementary school classroom should be equipped with an appropriate mathematical dictionary and reference books that can be used for study in depth of the topics for the grade. Bibliographies of appropriate books can be found by consulting state courses of study, the books received, and book review sections of *The Arithmetic Teacher, School Science and Mathematics, The AAAS Science Book List for Children,*[2] and *The Elementary and Junior High School Mathematics Library.*[3] Also, the teacher's editions of many textbook series have a number of suggested references.

The bulletin board

Attractive and interesting science and social studies bulletin boards are found in most modern elementary school classrooms. However, a visitor to an elementary school classroom today would not be as likely to see one on mathematics. A mathematics bulletin board properly handled can do much to add interest to the program and to challenge pupils' thinking. Several "idea books" are listed at the end of this chapter. Specific suggestions for bulletin boards are given below.

1. Use mathematics bulletin boards to stimulate interest, to introduce a new topic, for enrichment, as a summary of a unit, to display mathematics themes, to elicit pupil discussion, and to illustrate number or geometric ideas.

2. Many mathematics bulletin boards should be handled by the teacher; others should be handled by pupils. It is suggested that the teacher handle bulletin boards that are used to motivate a mathematics unit and that pupils

---

[2] Hilary J. Deason, *The AAAS Science Book List for Children* (Washington, D. C.: American Association for the Advancement of Science). (Purchase current edition.)
[3] Clarence Ethel Hardgrove, *The Elementary and Junior High School Mathematics Library* (Washington, D. C.: The National Council of Teachers of Mathematics, 1960).

take care of the boards that explain or summarize. When the teacher holds herself to high standards in bulletin board construction, her pupils will do the same. It is rather easy to get an idea of the caliber of bulletin boards constructed by the teacher by looking at those of the pupils.

3. A wide variety of materials can be used for bulletin boards and the boards can be used in various ways. For example, actually mount measuring instruments; use cloth or burlap for backing; connect a bulletin board to the mathematics table with yarn or arrows.

4. Use captions that ASK QUESTIONS. A question is much more of an attention-getter than a statement. A question also forces the reader to do some thinking. For example, compare *Equivalent Fractions,* with *What Are Equivalent Fractions?* or *Points* with *What Do You Know About Points?*

5. Bulletin board material can be filed for future use. The teacher can make an "easy to use" file by sketching a picture of the board on a large manila envelope and then putting the materials in the envelope when they have been removed from the board.

The tape recorder

Several possible uses of the tape recorder in the mathematics classes have been mentioned in previous chapters. The following suggestions are a review of possible tape recorder uses. (1) The teacher can prerecord verbal problems and exercises to be used by a small group. (2) Pupils can record their thinking on various mathematical processes; other class members can play over the material and the teacher can use it for analysis. (3) Practice material of a timed nature may be tape recorded effectively and used when needed. (4) The tape recorder makes a very effective control device in presenting text material. Pupils listen carefully, knowing that the tape recorder will not repeat itself. (5) Material can be presented to one group of pupils via a tape recording while the teacher works with another group.

The overhead projector

The overhead projector is a "natural" for use in mathematics classes. (1) The teacher can use the overhead projector in the same manner as the chalkboard. However, with the overhead device the teacher faces the class, and she can return to an earlier example or drawing. (2) Overhead transparencies of array patterns, number lines, and geometric shapes can save a great deal of time in class discussion. Instead of waiting for the teacher to draw an 8 by 12 array, a previously prepared array can be used. (3) The overhead equipment can be extremely effective in introductory work. Each pupil is provided with a sheet of plastic and is asked to work the problem on the plastic using a china marking pencil or crayon. The teacher then asks the pupils to put their solutions on the overhead projector and to discuss the methods that they used. This procedure has two advantages: (a) it saves the time that is needed to write each procedure on the chalkboard from the tablet and (b) it allows the teacher to have the pupils expain their methods in a sequence from the most concrete to the most abstract presentation. (4) Introductory problems can be projected. (5) Illustrations and pictures that are appropriate to primary-grade problem situations can be projected.

Television

Television has been used for both pupil and teacher education. At present it is difficult to predict the future role of TV in elementary school mathematics education. The teacher should be aware of the difficulty of using exploratory approaches to teaching over television. There is the danger that an elementary mathematics course on TV is only a "show and tell" lecture. Television series of the enrichment type, such as that featuring Bill Baird[4] and his puppets, are examples of effective uses of TV in elementary school mathematics instruction.

PERSPECTIVES

Educational media can greatly aid the teaching of elementary school mathematics. The teacher who does not use a wide variety of instructional materials will miss many opportunities to clarify mathematical concepts. On the other hand, care must be taken that educational media are not used in a "tail wagging the dog" fashion. It is not necessary or even good practice to become so engrossed in media that the question becomes "How can I best use media to teach mathematics?" rather than "How can I best teach mathematics? Will media help?" Educational media is no panacea for the mathematics curriculum, but such materials can be valuable tools for instruction.

[4] *Adventures in Number and Space,* Westinghouse Broadcasting Company, New York, New York.

General references on media

Berger, Emil J., and Johnson, Donovan A., *A Guide to the Use and Procurement of Teaching Aids for Mathematics* (Washington, D. C.: The National Council of Teachers of Mathematics, 1959).

Briggs, Janet, and others, *Implementing Mathematics Programs in California* (Menlo Park, California: Pacific Coast Publishers).

Brown, J. W., Lewis, R. B., and Harcleroad, K. F., *A-V Instruction,* 2nd ed. (New York: McGraw-Hill, 1964).

Burgert, Robert H., and Meadows, Elinor S., *Appealing Bulletin Board Ideas* (Danville, New York: F. A. Owen Publishing Company. 1960).

Dale, E. A., *Audio-Visual Method of Teaching* (New York: Holt, Rinehart and Winston, 1954).

DeVault, M. Vere, *Improving Mathematics Programs* (Columbus, Ohio: Charles E. Merrill Books, 1961), Chaps. 9 and 10.

Grossnickle, Foster E., and Brueckner, Leo J., *Discovering Meanings in Elementary School Mathematics* (New York: Holt, Rinehart and Winston, 1963), Chaps. 17 and 19.

Grossnickle, Foster E., Junge, Charlotte, and Metzner, William, "Instructional Materials for Teaching Arithmetic," *The Teaching of Arithmetic,* Fiftieth Yearbook, National Society for the Study of Education (Chicago: The University of Chicago Press, 1951), Part II, Chap. IX.

Hardgrove, Clarence Ethel, *The Elementary and Junior High School Mathematics Library* (Washington, D. C.; The National Council of Teachers of Mathematics, 1960).

Hardgrove, Clarence Ethel, and Sueltz, A., "Instructional Material," *Instruction in Arithmetic,* Twenty-Fifth Yearbook of the National Council of Teachers of Mathematics (Washington, D. C.: The Council, 1960), Chap. 10.

Marks, John, Purdy, C. Richard, and Kinney, Lucien B., *Teaching Elementary School Mathematics for Understanding* (New York: McGraw-Hill, 1965), Chap. 14.

Thomas, R. M., and Swartout, S. J., *Integrated Teaching Materials* (New York: McKay, 1963).

Bulletin boards

Johnson, Donovan A., "How to Use Your Bulletin Board," *How to Do It Series,* No. 1 (Washington, D. C.: National Council of Teachers of Mathematics, 1955).

Koskey, Arthur, *Baited Bulletin Boards* (San Francisco: Fearon Publishers, 1954).

Producers and distributors of manipulative materials, films, filmstrips, and records

Bailey Films Inc., 6509 De Longpre Avenue, Hollywood 28, California.

Beckley-Cardy Company, 1900 N. Narragansett, Chicago 39, Illinois.

Milton Bradley Company, 74 Park Street, Springfield 2, Massachusetts.

Bremmer Records, Wilmette, Illinois.

Coronet Films, Dept. RT-961, Coronet Building, Chicago 1, Illinois.

Creative Playthings, Inc., 316 North Michigan Avenue, Chicago, Illinois.

Cuisenaire Company of America, 9 Elm Avenue, Mt. Vernon, New York.

Denoyer-Geppert Company, 5235 Ravenswood Avenue, Chicago 40, Illinois.

The Educational Film Guide, H. W. Wilson Company, 950 University Avenue, New York 53, New York.

Enrichment Teaching Materials, 246 Fifth Avenue, New York 1, New York.

Eye Gate House, Inc., 2716 41st Avenue, Long Island City 1, New York.

The Filmstrip House, 347 Madison Avenue, New York 17, New York.

Garrard Press, 510 North Hickory Street, Champaign, Illinois.

Ginn & Company, 205 West Wacker Drive, Chicago 6, Illinois; 72 Fifth Avenue, New York 11, New York.

Holiday House, 8 West 13 Street, New York 11, New York.

Houghton Mifflin Company, 2 Park Street, Boston 7, Massachusetts.

Ideal School Supply Company, 8316 South Birkhoff Street, Chicago, Illinois.

Jam Handy Organization, 2821 East Grand Boulevard, Detroit 11, Michigan.

Johnson-Hunt Productions, 6509 De Longpre Avenue, Hollywood 28, California.

Knowledge Builders, Visual Education Building, Floral Park, New York.

F. A. Owen Publishing Company, Dansville, New York.

Popular Science Film Strips, McGraw-Hill Book Company, 330 West 42nd Street, New York 36, New York.

Science Research Associates, Inc., 259 E. Erie Street, Chicago 11, Illinois.

Silver Burdett Company, Morristown, New Jersey.

Society for Visual Education, Inc., Subsidiary of Graflex, Inc., 1345 Diversey Pkwy, Chicago 14, Illinois.

The Strathmore Company, Aurora, Illinois.

Visual Education Consultants, Inc., 2066 Helena Street, Madison 4, Wisconsin.

J. Weston Walch, Box 1075, Portland, Maine.

Webster Publishing Company, Division of McGraw-Hill, 1154 Reco Avenue, St. Louis 26, Missouri.

Young America Films, McGraw-Hill Book Company, 330 West 42nd St., New
York 36, New York.

Free and inexpensive materials

A number of commercial agencies have free materials for use in elementary
school mathematics. The list of available materials is constantly changing.
The sources listed below, which are up-dated regularly, provide a quick means
of identifying possibly free materials.

Educators Guide to Free Teaching Aids (Randolph, Wisconsin: Educators
Progress Service).
Salisbury, Gordon, and Sheridan, Robert, *Catalog of Free Teaching Aids,* San
Francisco: Fearon Publishing, Inc.).
Free and Inexpensive Learning Materials (Nashville, Tennessee: George Pea-
body College for Teachers, Division of Surveys and Field Services).

Organizations developing programs and publications

Madison Project—Robert B. Davis, Mathematics Project Office, Webster Col-
lege, Webster Groves 19, Missouri.
Minnemath Center Reports—Minnesota School Mathematics Center, Univer-
sity of Minnesota, Minneapolis 55, Minnesota.
National Council of Teachers of Mathematics, 1201 Sixteenth Street, N. W.,
Washington 6, D. C.
National Science Foundation, 1951 Constitution Avenue, N. W., Washington,
D. C.
School Mathematics Study Group, Stanford University, Stanford, California,
and Yale University Press, 92A Yale Station, New Haven, Connecticut.
Sets and Numbers Project—Patrick Suppes, Director, Sets and Numbers Project,
Stanford University, Stanford, California.
University of Illinois Arithmetic Project, 1207 West Stoughton, University of
Illinois, Urbana, Illinois.
University of Maryland Mathematics Project—Mathematics Project, College
of Education, University of Maryland, College Park, Maryland.

Paperbound materials

Anchor Books, Doubleday and Company, Inc., 575 Madison Avenue, New
York 22, New York.
Apollo Editions, Inc., 425 Park Avenue South, New York 16, New York.
Barnes and Noble, Inc., 105 Fifth Avenue, New York 3, New York.
Compass Books, 625 Madison Avenue, New York 22, New York.
Cornerstone Library, Inc., 630 Fifth Avenue, New York 20, New York.
Dell Publishing Company, Inc., 750 Third Avenue, New York 17, New York.

Dover Publications, Inc., 180 Varick Street, New York 14, New York.

Encyclopaedia Britannica Press, 425 North Michigan Avenue, Chicago 11, Illinois.

Fawcett Publications, Inc., 67 West 44th Street, New York 36, New York.

W. H. Freeman and Company Publishers, 660 Market Street, San Francisco 4, California.

Ginn and Company, Statler Building, Back Bay P. O. 191, Boston 17, Massachusetts.

D. C. Heath and Company, 285 Columbus Avenue, Boston 16, Massachusetts.

Holt, Rinehart and Winston, 383 Madison Avenue, New York 17, New York.

New American Library of World Literature, Inc., 501 Madison Avenue, New York 22, New York.

Penguin Books, Inc., 3300 Clipper Mill Road, Baltimore 11, Maryland.

Science Research Associates, Inc., 259 East Erie Street, Chicago 11, Illinois.

L. W. Singer and Company, Inc., 249–259 West Erie Boulevard, Syracuse 2, New York.

Webster Publishing Company, 1154 Reco Avenue, St. Louis 26, Missouri.

Periodicals

Arithmetic Teacher, National Council of Teachers of Mathematics, 1201 Sixteenth Street, N. W., Washington, D. C. 20036.

Mathematics Teacher, National Council of Teachers of Mathematics, 1201 Sixteenth Street, N. W., Washington, D. C. 20036.

Mathematics Student Journal, National Council of Teachers of Mathematics, 1201 Sixteenth Street, N. W., Washington, D. C. 20036.

School Mathematics Study Group Newsletter, Stanford University, School of Education, Stanford, California.

School Science and Mathematics, Central Association of Science and Mathematics Teachers, Inc., 535 Kendall Avenue, Kalamazoo, Michigan.

Science and Math Weekly, American Education Publications, 1205 Fairwood Avenue, Columbus, Ohio.

Mathematical terms

Gundlach, Bernard H., *The Laidlaw Glossary of Arithmetical-Mathematical Terms* (River Forest, Illinois: Laidlaw, 1961).

Quinn, Daniel C., *A Guide to Modern Mathematics* (Chicago: Science Research Associates, Inc., 1964).

Publishers of elementary school mathematics textbooks

Addison-Wesley Publishing Company, Inc., Reading, Massachusetts.

Allyn and Bacon, Inc., 150 Tremont Street, Boston, Massachusetts.

American Book Company, 55 Fifth Avenue, New York 3, New York.

Encyclopaedia Britannica, Educational Department, 425 North Michigan Avenue, Chicago 11, Illinois.

Ginn & Company, 205 West Wacker Drive, Chicago 6, Illinois; 72 Fifth Avenue, New York 11, New York.

Harcourt, Brace & World, Inc., 757 Third Avenue, New York, New York.

Harper & Row, Publishers, 49 East 33 Street, New York 16, New York.

D. C. Heath & Company, 285 Columbus Avenue, Boston 16, Massachusetts.

Holt, Rinehart and Winston, Inc., 383 Madison Avenue, New York 17, New York.

Iroquois Publishing Company, Inc., 1300 Alum Creek Drive, Columbus 16, Ohio.

Laidlaw Brothers, Thatcher & Madison, River Forest, Illinois.

Macmillan Company, The, 60 Fifth Avenue, New York 11, New York.

McCormick-Mathers Publishing Company, Inc., 1440 East English Street, Wichita, Kansas.

McGraw-Hill Book Company, Inc., 330 West 42nd Street, New York 36, New York.

Charles E. Merrill Books, Inc., 1300 Alum Creek Drive, Columbus 16, Ohio.

Noble & Noble, Publishers, Inc., 67 Irving Place, New York 3, New York.

Prentice-Hall, Inc., Englewood Cliffs, New Jersey.

Science Research Associates, Inc., 259 E. Erie Street, Chicago 11, Illinois.

Scott, Foresman & Company, 433 East Erie Street, Chicago 11, Illinois.

Charles Scribner's Sons, 597 Fifth Avenue, New York 17, New York.

Silver Burdett Company, Morristown, New Jersey.

L. W. Singer Company, Inc., A Division of Random House, 249 West Erie Boulevard, Syracuse 2, New York.

Webster Publishing Company, A Division of McGraw-Hill, 1154 Reco Avenue, St. Louis 26, Missouri.

Yale University Press, New Haven, Connecticut.

17

Questions on improving
elementary school mathematics

The previous chapters have dealt with specific suggestions for teaching elementary school mathematics. In this chapter several more general questions often asked by teachers are considered.

How can a teacher bring herself up-to-date and/or keep up-to-date? Keeping up-to-date in any area of the curriculum requires first a desire on the part of the teacher to keep up-to-date. Like the proverbial horse being lead to water, only the teacher who has a real desire to improve her competence in mathematics and the teaching of mathematics will do so. The suggestions that follow are offered as an aid to teachers and administrators who wish to up-date their knowledge and wish to keep up-to-date.

1. Read periodicals such as *The Arithmetic Teacher, The Mathematics Teacher, School Science and Mathematics, The Grade Teacher,* and *The Instructor,* which contain monthly articles concerned with the teaching of elementary school mathematics. *The Arithmetic Teacher* is of particular help since it contains book reviews and reviews of new materials. Since it is not feasible for every teacher to belong to the National Council of Teachers of Mathematics (although it would be very helpful if all elementary teachers were members), it is suggested either that the principal obtain *The Arithmetic Teacher* for the teachers' reading room or that several teachers pool their resources in joining professional organizations. For example, each of five teachers can join a different organization, and all can share the magazines they receive. In this way each has easy access to journals on mathematics, language arts, reading, social studies, and science.

2. Attend credit and noncredit courses offered for the improvement of elementary teachers' mathematics background. Increasingly, educational television stations are providing programs on mathematics for teachers; universities are offering extension work in mathematics; and elementary schools are providing resource persons to offer in-service classes. Also, federal agencies sponsor summer institutes and in-service institutes for the development of leadership personnel for in-service work.

3. Form small discussion groups, pick a topic, and share information.

4. Obtain and work with materials for improving mathematics content and materials for improving the teaching of elementary school mathematics, such as those listed in the Selected Bibliography.

5. Try new ideas in the classroom. Probably the best way to stay up-to-date is to get involved in change. Try out new materials as they are published and try out "experimental" suggestions given in *The Arithmetic Teacher*.

6. The administrator can

    a. Provide released time for in-service mathematics courses.

    b. Provide materials for independent study.

    c. Obtain films designated for in-service work.

    d. Seek assistance from the state department of education.

    e. Consult nearby colleges and universities.

    f. Study needs, wants, and background of teachers.

    g. Provide new materials for teacher evaluation.

    h. Disseminate information concerning courses, National Science Foundation Institutes, workshops, and meetings that are available to teachers.

    i. Plan cooperatively with nearby schools to bring in consultants and speakers on topics in mathematics.

    j. Set up mathematics laboratories to be used for in-service education.

    k. Keep parents informed of curriculum developments in mathematics.

    l. Provide for representation from the school district at national meetings concerned with mathematics education.

    m. Provide for reports from national meetings on mathematics education.

There is a great deal of discussion about fostering creativity through school subjects. Does mathematics lend itself to creative thinking? Normally the layman does not think of mathematics as an area that lends itself well to the development of creative thinking. However, a discussion with a research mathematician might lead one to believe that all of mathematics centers around developing thought patterns that lead to creativity.

In the past, the methods used to teach mathematics were of a variety that did little to encourage creative thinking. In fact, they may well have discouraged most high-level thought processes. Typically the teacher would say, "Your answer is wrong because you have not worked the problem in the way I taught in class." Today there is ever-increasing attention to the development of creative mathematical thinking, and with it, greater numbers of pupils are finding mathematics to be an interesting and rewarding field of intellectual endeavor. Projects in which pupils develop their own notational system, mathematical models for physical world situations, "magic squares" and similar pattern arrangements, and mathematical systems can be used to foster creativity.

How well do pupils like mathematics as compared to the other subjects in the curriculum? Contrary to the subjective judgment of most laymen, in surveys of pupil preference of subjects, mathematics usually rates number one.[1]

Teaching procedures that use a guided discovery approach take much longer to develop new topics. Doesn't it take longer to teach mathematics in this manner? While the "idea developing" phases take much longer in a guided discovery approach than in an explanatory approach, the better understanding of mathematical principles developed using the guided discovery approach reduces the time necessary for practice or drill. Thus, the time taken for either approach is about the same. Also, two recent studies support the contention that for maximum achievement, more than half of mathematics class time should be devoted to developmental-meaningful activities.[2]

What can I do with intermediate-grade level pupils who move into our "modern math" program from another school using traditional content and traditional teaching procedures? Transfer pupils pose a real problem. The following ideas have proved useful in bringing a pupil up-to-date.

1. Programmed materials such as *Mathematics Enrichment, A, B, C, and D,* published by Harcourt, Brace & World, offer modern content in a format of small-step programmed materials. Pupils can up-date themselves with these materials.

2. If the pupil is willing, it is often a useful thing for the teacher to provide the pupil with the text for the grade level below and to suggest selected exercises that will help in up-dating the pupil.

3. The problem is not as acute as it appears on the surface to be, since the majority of mathematics teaching materials follows a spiral approach to mathematical topics. Thus, topics from previous years' work are reviewed. During the review periods the teacher should devote extra time to pupils who are new to the system.

4. A few publishers provide paperback workbooks that contain portions of the content from previous years. The selection is directed to pupils who have been using a more traditional program.

There is an emphasis upon correct vocabulary today. How much vocabulary should be developed? Should correct vocabulary always be used? The number of technical mathematical terms taught in the elementary school is increasing. An example of this increase can be noted by examining the materials developed by the School Mathematics Study Group.[3] In the beginning one-third of the first-grade program the following terms occur: set, set member, collection, subset, review set, empty set, joining sets, union of sets, remove, remainder set, shape, round, face, edge, corner, inside, outside, surface, circle, rectangle, triangle, circular region, rectangular region, triangular region, pair,

[1] Claire E. Faust, "A Study of The Relationship Between Attitude and Achievement in Selected Elementary School Subjects" (Unpublished Ph.D. dissertation, State University of Iowa, 1962).

[2] Donald E. Shipp and George H. Deer, "The Use of Class Time in Arithmetic," *The Arithmetic Teacher,* Vol. 7, No. 3 (March 1960), pp. 117–121; and Albert H. Shuster and Fred L. Pigge, "Retention Efficiency of Meaningful Teaching," *The Arithmetic Teacher,* Vol. 12, No. 1 (January 1965).

[3] School Mathematics Study Group, *Mathematics for the Elementary School,* preliminary ed. (Stanford, California: Leland Stanford Junior College, 1963).

equivalent, as many as, more than, fewer than, and partition. Each of these terms is used in a mathematical manner.

In addition to the acquisition of new terms, there is an emphasis upon "cleaning up" the present vocabulary of elementary school mathematics. Terms such as "cancellation" may be quite misleading. Other words such as "borrow," "carry," and "goes into" should probably be replaced by more precise terms.

Most elementary school pupils are interested in learning new terms, and there is little reason to begin with an incorrect term. For maximum success in vocabulary development, the following suggestions are offered:

1. Give pupils an opportunity to familiarize themselves with a mathematical concept before learning the name. Thus, pupils should have wide experience using the commutative property of addition before naming it.

2. Avoid the "matching type" of vocabulary drill exercises. Concentrate on correct use of vocabulary in situations in which correct vocabulary helps a discussion.

3. Remember the mathematical idea is more important than the name.

How can "meaning" be maintained? Often teachers introduce new topics in mathematics with an emphasis upon understanding and then quickly proceed to efficient computational processing without a review of meaning. It is strongly suggested that periodically the teacher ask questions such as "I noted that you all renamed in this subtraction situation without writing any changes in the numerals. Can you tell me what the basic principles of this process are?" "You've been inverting and multiplying when you divide fractions. Why does this work? What mathematical principles are involved?" "You multiplied the measure of the length by the measure of the width to find the area of this rectangle. Why?"

Very little mention has been made of money in this book. Isn't the use of money in teaching elementary school mathematics important? The use of money in teaching elementary school mathematics is quite important. However, the author feels that money situations should follow the mathematical understanding of a topic. If money situations are used in introductory work, the mathematical ideas are often clouded. For example, with money pupils think of ones (pennies), tens (dimes), and then ones again (dollars). Also the use of nickels and quarters often detracts from the development of tens and ones. If money is used in subtracting, 43¢ − 27¢ for example, pupils will subtract 2 dimes, 1 nickel and 2 pennies.

43¢	3 dimes	2 nickels	3 pennies
− 27¢	2 dimes	1 nickel	2 pennies
	1 dime	1 nickel	1 penny

After each new topic is developed, it is *very* worthwhile to use money situations in problem solving.

Should I allow pupils to use "crutches" such as counting on their fingers? Many "crutches" are good examples of correct mathematical thinking. They may be immature methods of computing, but they often illustrate basic mathematical principles. Pupils will normally discard the practice of finger counting, for example, when they find more economical ways of thinking.[4]

McConnell's statement made in 1941 still has much merit today. He said:[5]

Repeating the final form of a response from the very beginning may actually encourage the habituation of immature procedures and seriously impede necessary growth.

Intermediate steps such as the use of the "crutch" in subtraction, aid the learner both to understand the process and to compute accurately. With proper guidance, these temporary reactions may be expected to give way to more direct responses in later stages of learning.

How much time per day should be devoted to mathematical instruction? This is a difficult question to answer. The importance of mathematics in the world today is greatly increasing. Also, there is evidence that an increase in the mathematics time allotment does increase achievement.[6] If class discussion and time for pupil work are considered, a valid argument can be made for a time allotment of approximately forty minutes per day in grades one and two and at least sixty minutes per day in grades three through six.

I believe that it is important for average and bright pupils to understand mathematical processes, but isn't it better for slow pupils to learn their mathematics by practicing without understanding? This is a commonly held belief and, on the surface, appears to have some merit. But, a strong case can and should be made for slow learners being taught to understand mathematics. If the slow learner is only taught that $5 \times 7 = 35$ and then forgets this multiplication fact, there are no means for him to obtain an answer. If, on the other hand, the multiplication fact has been developed through the understanding of multiplication as a series of equal additions and as forming a 7 by 5 array pattern, the pupil can go back to these forms to find an answer. Having this understanding is important for the slow learner since he normally possesses a poor memory.

Teachers often ask children to "prove" their answer. Is proof in the mathematical sense used in the elementary school? In the primary grades when a teacher asks a pupil to prove that his answer is correct, she is using prove as a synonym for verify. The teacher wishes the pupil to give several other similar examples in which the property or idea holds true. This is not proof in the mathematical sense, but it is a good learning procedure for primary school pupils. Also, opportunities should be given to children to discover that just because something works once or twice doesn't mean it will always work.

As the pupil moves up the educational ladder, he should have the opportunity to study some simple mathematical proofs. The use of a modular system

[4] John R. Clark, "The Use of Crutches in Teaching Arithmetic," *The Arithmetic Teacher*, Vol. 1, No. 1 (October 1954), pp. 6–10.

[5] T. R. McConnell, "Recent Trends in Learning Theory," *Arithmetic in General Education*, Sixteenth Yearbook, National Council of Teachers of Mathematics (New York: Bureau of Publications, Teachers College, Columbia University, 1941), p. 279.

[6] Oscar T. Jarvis, "Time Allotment Relationships to Pupils Achievement in Arithmetic," *The Arithmetic Teacher*, Vol. 10, No. 5 (May 1963), pp. 248–250.

such as the one illustrated in chapter 1 gives pupils an opportunity to prove a mathematical property by testing all possible cases. Pupils may also be presented with situations in which they can use direct proof. The example below illustrates such a procedure.

Given: Commutative property, associate property, basic addition facts, place value[7]

Find: $23 + 45 = N$

$(20 + 3) + (40 + 5) = (20 + 3) + (5 + 40)$	commutative property
$= 20 + 3 + (5 + 40)$	associative property
$= 20 + (3 + 5) + 40$	associative property
$= 20 + 8 + 40$	addition fact
$= 20 + 40 + 8$	commutative property
$= (20 + 40) + 8$	associative property
$= 60 + 8$	addition of $20 + 40$
$= 68$	addition of $60 + 8$

The opportunities to use mathematical proof should become more frequent as a pupil progresses in his mathematical maturity. Yet, extreme care should be taken to prevent elementary school mathematics from becoming highly abstract. If the pupils involved are at the third-grade level, the use of tens and ones blocks to verify that $23 + 45 = 68$ is to be preferred to a long listing of commutative property, associative property, place value, etc.

Should pupils memorize number facts? A few people working in the field of mathematics education have suggested that it is not necessary for pupils to learn the basic addition, subtraction, multiplication, and division facts "by heart." Even with the large number of automatic computers available today and with future increases in the number of easily portable computers, the citizen of tomorrow will still be required to use many basic number facts in his everyday activities. A great deal of time is saved if persons "just know" the basic number facts. However, the study for mastery should occur after pupils understand the basic ideas.

What about homework? Mathematics has traditionally been the elementary school subject most used for homework assignments. Yet the value of mathematical homework assignments is questionable. Some of the best mathematics teaching occurs when pupils are working on assignments and the teacher is observing, questioning, and helping. It is suggested that the majority of homework assignments in mathematics occurs at the end of units when pupils are practicing and fixing concepts, not when concepts are being developed.

I have trouble with parents when I give homework. They often use different procedures and make confusing suggestions to pupils. What can be done to alleviate this difficulty? Parents should be informed concerning recent

[7] Note: at a higher level properties of exponent would be used.

changes in mathematics curriculum. Many school systems have offered courses in modern mathematics for parents, with outstanding success. In many small communities attendance at these meetings has numbered over one hundred. In larger communities several sections of classes for parents are offered each semester. In addition, several books on modern mathematics for parents have been written, and individual teachers and groups of teachers may well prepare periodic letters explaining the attack used on a particular topic.

Source: Publishers Newspaper Syndicate.

If new programs are to be effective, parents must understand their goals.

If several teachers at a grade level work together in preparing these letters, it is quite possible to provide the parents with a math bulletin every two weeks. One letter written by a fourth-grade teacher is presented below.

Dear Mr. and Mrs. Martin:

Recently a parent asked me, "Why do you ask the children to think or figure out things for themselves? You're supposed to teach them." This was a very legitimate question, and I believe you might be interested in my answer.

What is the purpose of teaching mathematics? Is there just one purpose—to teach the basic facts of the four operations? Or are there multiple purposes—teaching the basic facts, developing imagination, developing an understanding of math as a whole, and developing a good attitude toward mathematics?

Our children are growing up in a very complex world. Today, it is more important than ever to have the ability to think for ourselves. We have decisions to make every day. When a child goes shopping, he needs to think and reason. In everyday situations reasoning for ourselves is very important. Problems arise where we need not just add, subtract, multiply, and divide, but where we must decide which process to use before we can do the computation.

As for reasoning and discovery—do you think this is something new? The answer is, no. The Egyptian scribe Ahmes left this challenge: to find ten ways to solve one problem rather than one way to solve ten problems. . . . This is what we as teachers are trying to accomplish today.

If you have been following educational development, you will see that discovery is important not only in mathematics but also in science and other subjects. How do scientists solve a problem for which there is no present answer? Yes, they experiment and try to DISCOVER their answer.

There have been many controlled experiments in using the "thinking" method versus the "tell to" method when teaching mathematics. These experiments show us that discovery gives true knowledge that stays with the child.

Answer this question for yourself, and it should give you the answer to your inquiry. Which do you remember longer—a fact or statement that someone tells you or one which you must discover, compute, figure out, or look up for yourself?

Obviously, each of the pupils cannot "discover" every new concept in mathematics for himself. But, I like to give him the opportunity before "telling him."

Sincerely,

Mrs. M. Campbell

In addition to periodic letters and parent conferences, the school may stock several copies of books designed to up-date parents in modern mathematics. Several paperback books can be made available to parents or suggested to them.[8]

[8] For example, Francis J. Mueller, *Understanding the New Elementary School Mathematics* (Belmont, California: The Dickenson Publishing Co., 1965); Ralph T. Heimer, and Miriam S. Newman, *The New Mathematics for Parents* (New York: Holt, Rinehart and Winston, 1965); and Evelyn Sharp, *A Parent's Guide to the New Mathematics* (New York: Dutton, 1964).

SELECTED REFERENCES FOR TEACHING MATHEMATICS
IN THE ELEMENTARY SCHOOL

Banks, J. H., *Learning and Teaching Arithmetic* (Boston: Allyn and Bacon, 1964).

Brooks, E., *The Philosophy of Arithmetic* (Philadelphia: Normal Publishing Co., 1880).

Clark, J. R., and Eads, L. K., *Guiding Arithmetic Learning* (New York: Harcourt, Brace & World, 1954).

Copeland, Richard W., *Mathematics and the Elementary Teacher* (Philadelphia: Saunders, 1966).

Corle, C. G., *Teaching Mathematics in the Elementary School* (New York: Ronald, 1964).

Deans, E., *Elementary School Mathematics: New Directions,* U.S. Department of Health, Education, and Welfare (Washington, D.C.: GPO, 1963).

DeVault, M. Vere, ed., *Improving Mathematics Programs: Trends and Issues in the Elementary School* (Columbus, Ohio: Charles E. Merrill Books, Inc., 1961).

Dienes, Z. P., *Building Up Mathematics* (London: Hutchinson Educational Ltd., 1960).

Dutton, W. H., *Evaluating Pupils' Understanding of Arithmetic* (Englewood Cliffs, New Jersey: Prentice-Hall, 1964).

Dutton, W. H., and Adams, L. J., *Arithmetic For Teachers* (Englewood Cliffs, New Jersey: Prentice-Hall, 1961).

Dwight, Leslie A., *Modern Mathematics for the Elementary Teacher* (New York; Holt, Rinehart and Winston, 1966).

Educational Research Council of Greater Cleveland, *Key Topics in Mathematics for the Primary Teacher* (Chicago: Science Research Associates, 1962).

————, *Key Topics in Mathematics for the Intermediate Teacher* (Chicago: Science Research Associates, 1965).

Flournoy, M. Frances, *Elementary School Mathematics,* The Center for Applied Research in Education, Inc. (Englewood Cliffs, New Jersey: Prentice-Hall, 1964).

Grossnickle, F. E., and Brueckner, L. J., *Discovering Meanings in Elementary School Mathematics* (New York: Holt, Rinehart and Winston, 1963).

Hartung, M. L., Van Engen, H., Knowles, L., and Gibb, E. G., *Charting The Course for Arithmetic* (Chicago: Scott, Foresman, 1960).

Heddon, James W., *Today's Mathematics* (Chicago: Science Research Associates, 1964).

Heimer, R. T., and Newman, M. S., *The New Mathematics for Parents* (New York: Holt, Rinehart and Winston, 1965).

Hollister, and Gunderson, *Teaching Arithmetic in the Primary Grades* (Boston: Heath, 1964).

Howard, Charles F., and Dumas, Enoch, *Teaching Contemporary Mathematics in the Elementary School* (New York: Harper & Row, 1966).

————, *Basic Procedures in Teaching Arithmetic* (Boston: Heath, 1963).

Kramer, K., *The Teaching of Elementary-School Mathematics* (Boston: Allyn and Bacon, 1966).

McSwain, E. T., and Cooke, R. J., *Understanding and Teaching Arithmetic in the Elementary School* (New York: Holt, Rinehart and Winston, 1958).

Marks, J. L., Purdy, C. R., and Kinney, L. B., *Teaching Elementary School Mathematics for Understanding*, 2nd ed. (New York: McGraw-Hill, 1964).

Morrisett, L. N., and Vinsonhaler, J., *Mathematical Learning*, Monographs of the Society for Research in Child Development (Chicago: University of Chicago Press, 1965), Vol. 30, No. 1.

Morton, R. L., *Teaching Children Arithmetic* (New York: Silver Burdett, 1953).

National Council of Teachers of Mathematics, *Arithmetic in General Education*, Sixteenth Yearbook (Washington, D.C.: The Council, 1941).

————, *Insight into Modern Mathematics*, Twenty-third Yearbook (Washington, D.C.: The Council, 1957).

————, *Growth of Mathematical Ideas*, Twenty-fourth Yearbook (Washington, D.C.: The Council, 1958).

————, *Instruction In Arithmetic*, Twenty-fifth Yearbook (Washington, D.C.: The Council, 1960).

————, *Enrichment Mathematics for the Grades*, Twenty-seventh Yearbook (Washington, D.C.: The Council, 1963).

————, *Topics in Mathematics for Elementary School Teachers*, Twenty-ninth Yearbook (Washington, D.C.: The Council, 1964).

National Society for the Study of Education, *The Teaching of Arithmetic*, Fiftieth Yearbook, Part II (Chicago: University of Chicago Press, 1951).

Overman, J. R., *The Teaching of Arithmetic* (Chicago: Lyons and Carnahan, 1961).

Piaget, Jean, *The Child's Conception of Number* (New York: Humanities, 1952).

Piaget, J., Inhilder, B., and Szeminska, A., *The Child's Conception of Geometry* (New York: Basic Books, Inc., 1960).

Rappaport, David, *Understanding and Teaching Elementary School Mathematics* (New York: Wiley, 1966).

Shipp, D. E., and Adams, S., *Developing Arithmetic Content and Skills*, (Englewood Cliffs, New Jersey: Prentice-Hall, 1964).

Smith, David E., *The Teaching of Arithmetic* (Boston: Ginn, 1909).

Spencer, Peter L., and Brydegaard, Marguerite, *Building Mathematical Competence in the Elementary School* (New York: Holt, Rinehart and Winston, 1966).

Spitzer, Herbert F., *Enrichment of Arithmetic* (New York: McGraw-Hill 1964).

————, *The Teaching of Arithmetic*, 3rd ed. (Boston: Houghton Mifflin, 1961).

Spross, Patricia M., *Elementary Arithmetic and Learning Aids* (Washington, D.C.: GPO, 1965).

Stern, C., *Children Discover Arithmetic: An Introduction to Structural Arithmetic* (New York: Harper & Row, 1949).

Stokes, C. N., *Teaching the Meanings of Arithmetic* (New York: Appleton-Century-Crofts, 1951).

Swenson, E. J., *Teaching Arithmetic to Children* (New York: Macmillan, 1964).

Thorpe, C. B., *Teaching Elementary Arithmetic* (New York: Harper & Row, 1962).

Vopel, Marvin C., *Concepts and Method of Arithmetic* (New York: Dover, 1964).

Wheat, H. G., *How to Teach Arithmetic* (New York: Harper & Row, 1961).

HISTORICAL BOOKS

Bell, E. T., *Men of Mathematics* (New York: Simon and Schuster, 1937).

Danzig, Tobias, *Number, The Language of Science* (Garden City, New York: Doubleday, 1954).

Eves, H., *An Introduction to the History of Mathematics* (New York: Holt, Rinehart and Winston, 1964).

Kline, M., *Mathematics in Western Culture* (New York: Oxford University Press, 1953).

Midonick, Henrietta O., ed., *The Treasury of Mathematics* (New York: Philosophical Library, Inc., 1965).

Newman, James R., ed., *The World of Mathematics: A Small Library of the Literature of Mathematics*, 4 Vols. (New York: Simon and Schuster, 1956).

Sanford, Vera., *A Short History of Mathematics* (Boston: Houghton Mifflin, 1930).

Smith, David E., *History of Mathematics*, Vol. II (New York: Dover, 1958).

RESEARCH REFERENCES

These references should be helpful to the student who wishes to explore the research of elementary school mathematics.

Beatty, Leslie S., "Re-orienting to the Teaching of Arithmetic," *Childhood Education,* 26:272–278 (February 1950).

Bernstein, Allen L., "Library Research—A Study in Remedial Arithmetic," *School Science and Mathematics,* 59:185–195 (March 1959).

Brown, Kenneth E., *Analysis of Research in the Teaching of Mathematics,* U.S. Department of Health, Education, and Welfare, Office of Education (Washington, D.C.: GPO), for years 1955 and 1956, Bulletin No. 4, 1958, 73 pp.; for years 1957 and 1958, Bulletin No. 8, 1960, 50 pp.; for years 1959 and 1960, Bulletin No. 12, 1963, 69 pp.

Brownell, William A., "Teaching of Mathematics in Grades I Through VI," *Review of Educational Research,* 15:276–288 (October 1945).

Brownell, William A., and Grossnickle, Foster E., "Teaching of Mathematics in Grades I Through VI," *Review of Educational Research,* 12:386–404 (October 1942).

Brownell, William A., and others, *Arithmetic in Grades I and II,* Duke University Research Studies in Education, No. 6 (Durham: Duke University Press, 1941).

Brueckner, Leo J., "Arithmetic," *Review of Educational Research* 4:140–143, 215–217 (April 1934); 7:453–463, 545–547 (December 1937).

Burch, Robert L., and Moser, Harold E., "The Teaching of Mathematics in Grades I through VIII," *Review of Educational Research,* 21: 290–304 (October 1951).

Burns, Paul C., "Arithmetic Research That Has Made a Difference," *Elementary School Journal,* 65: 386–392 (April 1965).

Burns, Paul C., and Dessart, Donald J., "A Summary of Investigations Relating to Mathematics in Elementary Education: 1964" *School Science and Mathematics,* 65: 779–790 (December 1965).

Buros, Oscar K., ed., *Mental Measurements Yearbook* (New Brunswick, New Jersey: Rutgers University Press, First Yearbook, 1938; Third Yearbook, 1949). (Highland Park, New Jersey: Gryphon Press, Second Yearbook, 1940; Fourth Yearbook, 1953; Fifth Yearbook, 1959; Sixth Yearbook, 1965).

Buswell, Guy T., "Arithmetic," in Chester W. Harris, ed., *Encyclopedia of Educational Research* (New York: MacMillan, 1960), pp. 63–74.

————, "A Critical Survey of Previous Research in Arithmetic," *Report of the Society's Committee on Arithmetic,* Twenty-ninth Yearbook, National Society for the Study of Education (Bloomington, Illinois: Public School Publishing Co., 1930), pp. 445–470.

_____, "Summary of Arithmetic Investigations," *Elementary School Journal,* 1926 through 1932.

_____, "Selected References on Elementary School Instruction—Arithmetic," *Elementary School Journal,* 1933 through 1947.

Buswell, Guy T., and Judd, Charles H., *Summary of Educational Investigations Relating to Arithmetic* (Chicago: University of Chicago Press, 1925).

Dawson, Dan T., and Ruddell, Arden K., "The Case for the Meaning Theory in Teaching Arithmetic," *Elementary School Journal,* 55: 393–399 (March 1955).

Dutton, Wilbur H., *Evaluating Pupils' Understanding of Arithmetic* (Englewood Cliffs, New Jersey: Prentice-Hall, 1964).

Dyer, Henry S., Kalin, Robert, and Lord, Frederick M., *Problems in Mathematical Education* (Princeton: Educational Testing Service, 1956).

Fehr, Howard F., "Present Research in the Teaching of Arithmetic," *Teachers College Record,* 52: 11–23 (October 1950).

Gibb, E. Glenadine, "A Review of a Decade of Experimental Studies Which Compared Methods of Teaching Arithmetic," *Journal of Educational Research,* 46: 603–608 (April 1953).

_____, "A Selected Bibliography of Research in the Teaching of Arithmetic," *Arithmetic Teacher,* 1: 20–22 (April 1954).

Gibb, E. Glenadine, and Van Engen, H., "Mathematics in the Elementary Grades," *Review of Educational Research,* 27: 329–342 (October 1957).

Glennon, Vincent J., and Hunnicutt, C. W., *What Does Research Say About Arithmetic?* (Washington, D. C.: Association for Supervision and Curriculum Development, National Education Association, 1958).

Hartung, Maurice L., "Estimating the Quotient in Division," *Arithmetic Teacher,* 4: 100–111 (April 1957).

_____, "Selected References on Elementary School Instruction—Arithmetic," *Elementary School Journal,* 1948 to present.

Hightower, H. W., "Effect of Instructional Procedures on Achievement in Fundamental Operations in Arithmetic," *Educational Administrative Supervision,* 40: 336–348 (October 1954).

Howell, Henry Budd, *A Foundational Study in the Pedagogy of Arithmetic* (New York: Macmillan, 1914).

Hunnicutt, C. W., and Iverson, William J., *Research in the Three R's* (New York: Harper & Row, 1958), pp. 347–429.

Johnson, Harry C., "Problem-Solving in Arithmetic: A Review of the Literature," *Elementary School Journal,* 44:396–403 (March 1944); 44:476–482 (April 1944).

Knipp, Minnie B., "An Investigation of Experimental Studies Which Compare Methods of Teaching Arithmetic," *Journal of Experimental Education,* 13:23–30 (September 1944).

Lumsdaine, A. A., and Glaser, Robert, *Teaching Machines and Programmed*

Learning (Washington, D.C.: Department of Audio-Visual Instruction, National Education Association, 1960).

Monroe, Walter S., and Englehart, Max D., *A Critical Summary of Research Relating to the Teaching of Arithmetic* (Urbana: University of Illinois, 1931).

Morton, R. L., "What Research Says to the Teacher," *Teaching Arithmetic,* No. 2 (Washington, D.C.: NEA, 1953).

Moser, Harold E., and others, "Aims and Purposes in the Teaching of Mathematics," *Review of Educational Research,* 18:315–322 (October 1948).

Pikal, Frances, "Review of Research Related to the Teaching of Arithmetic in the Upper Elementary Grades," *School Science and Mathematics,* 57:41–47 January 1957).

Riess, Anita, *Number Readiness in Research (A Survey of the Literature)* (Chicago: Scott, Foresman, 1947).

Ruch, G. M., and Mead, Cyrus D., "A Review of Experiments on Subtraction," in Twenty-ninth Yearbook, N.S.S.E. (Bloomington, Illinois: Public School Publishing Co., 1930), pp. 671–678.

Schaaf, William L., "Selected Annotated Bibliography," *Instruction in Arithmetic,* Twenty-fifth Yearbook, N.C.T.M. (Washington, D.C., 1960), pp. 320–354.

Sherer, L., "Some Implications from Research in Arithmetic," *Childhood Education,* 29:320–324 (March 1953).

Smith, David Eugene, "Arithmetic"; "Mathematics," in Paul Monroe, ed., *Cyclopedia of Education* (New York: Macmillan, 1918), Vol. 1, pp. 203–207; Vol. 2, pp. 159–160.

Spitzer, Herbert F., *What Research Says About Teaching Arithmetic,* Department of Classroom Teachers, American Educational Research Association of the NEA (Washington, D.C.: 1962).

Spitzer, Herbert F., and Burch, Robert, "Methods and Materials in the Teaching of Mathematics," *Review of Educational Research,* 18:337–349 (October 1948).

Spitzer, Herbert F., and Burns, Paul C., "Mathematics in the Elementary School," *Review of Educational Research,* 31:248–249 (June 1961).

Stretch, Lorena B., "One Hundred Selected Research Studies," *Arithmetic in General Education,* Sixteenth Yearbook of the National Council of Teachers of Mathematics (Washington, D.C.: The Council, 1941), pp. 318–327.

Summers, Edward G., "A Bibliography of Doctoral Dissertations Completed in Elementary and Secondary Mathematics from 1918–1952," *School Science and Mathematics,* 61:323–335 (May 1961). Up-dated periodically.

————, "Elementary and Secondary Science and Mathematics Dissertations Reported in 1962," *School Science and Mathematics,* 63:733–738 (December 1963).

Summers, Edward G., and Stochl, James E., "A Bibliography of Doctoral Dissertations in Elementary and Secondary Mathematics from 1950–1960," *School Science and Mathematics,* 61:431–439 (June 1961).

Summers, Edward G., and Hubrig, Billie, "Doctoral Dissertation Research in

Mathematics Reported for 1963," *School Science and Mathematics,* 65:505–528 (June 1965).

Van Engen, Henry, "A Selected List of References on Elementary School Arithmetic," *Mathematics Teacher,* 43:168–171 (April 1950).

————, "A Summary of Research and Investigations and Their Implications for the Organization and Learning of Arithmetic" *Mathematics Teacher,* 41:260–265 (October 1948).

Weaver, J. Fred, "A Bibliography of Selected Summaries and Critical Discussions of Research in Elementary School Mathematics," *Arithmetic Teacher,* 7:364–366 (November 1960).

————, "Six Years of Research on Arithmetic Instruction: 1951–56," *Arithmetic Teacher,* 4:88–99 (April 1957).

————, "Research on Arithmetic Instruction," *Arithmetic Teacher,* 5:109–118 (April 1958); 6:121–132 (April 1959); 7:253–265 (May 1960); 8:255–260, 301–306 (May and October 1961); 9:287–290 (May 1962); 10:297–300 (May 1963); 11:273–275 (April 1964); 12:382–387 (May 1965).

————, "Whither Research on Compound Subtraction?" *Arithmetic Teacher,* 3:17–20 (February 1956).

Weaver, J. Fred, and Gibb, E. Glenadine, "Mathematics in the Elementary School," *Review of Educational Research,* 34:273–285 (June 1964).

Wilson, Guy M., "Arithmetic," in W. S. Monroe, ed., *Encyclopedia of Educational Research* (New York: Macmillan, 1941), pp. 42–58.

————, "The Social Utility Theory as Applied to Arithmetic: Its Research Basis, and Some of Its Implications," *Journal of Educational Research,* 41:321–337 (January 1948).

Woody, Clifford, "Arithmetic, Fine Arts, Physical and Health Education, and Industrial Arts," *Review of Educational Research,* 1:261–267, 307–310 (October 1931); "Arithmetic," 5:14–30, 93–97 (October 1935).

Wrightstone, J. Wayne, "Influence of Research on Instruction in Arithmetic," *Mathematics Teacher,* 45:187–192 (March 1952).

CONTENT BACKGROUND BOOKS FOR ELEMENTARY SCHOOL TEACHERS

Anderson, R. D., and others, *Concepts of Informal Geometry,* School Mathematics Study Group, Studies in Mathematics, Vol. V (New Haven: Yale University Press, 1960).

Bell, C., Hammond, C. D., and Herrara, R. B., *Fundamentals of Arithmetic for Teachers* (New York: Wiley, 1962).

Bell, M. S., Chinn, W. G., McDermott, M., Pieters, R. S., and Willerding, M.,

A Brief Course in Mathematics for Elementary School Teachers, School Mathematics Study Group, Studies in Mathematics, Vol. IX (Stanford: Stanford University Press, 1963).

Brumfiel, C. F., Eicholz, R. E., Shanks, M. E., *Fundamental Concepts of Elementary Mathematics* (Reading, Massachusetts: Addison-Wesley, 1962).

Brumfiel, C. F., Eicholz, R. E., Shanks, M. E., and O'Daffer, P. G., *Principles of Arithmetic* (Reading, Massachusetts: Addison-Wesley, 1963).

Crouch, R., Baldwin, G., and Wisner, R. J., *Preparatory Mathematics for Elementary Teachers* (New York: Wiley, 1965).

Educational Research Council of Greater Cleveland, *Key Topics in Mathematics for the Primary Teacher* (Chicago: Science Research Associates, 1962).

Evenson, A. B., *Modern Mathematics: Introductory Concepts and Their Implications* (Chicago: Scott, Foresman, 1962).

Fehr, Howard F., and Hill, Thomas J., *Contemporary Mathematics for Elementary Teachers* (Boston: Heath, 1966).

Glicksman, A. M., *Vectors in Three Dimensional Geometry* (Washington, D.C.: National Council of Teachers of Mathematics, 1961).

Haag, V. H., *Structure of Elementary Algebra,* School Mathematics Study Group, Studies in Mathematics, Vol. 111 (New Haven: Yale University Press, 1960).

_____, *Structure of Algebra* (Reading, Massachusetts: Addison-Wesley, 1964).

Hacker, G., Barnes, W. E., and Long, C. T., *Fundamental Concepts of Arithmetic* (Englewood Cliffs, New Jersey: Prentice-Hall, 1963).

Hafstrom, J. E., *Basic Concepts in Modern Mathematics* (Reading, Massachusetts: Addison-Wesley, 1961).

Hamilton, N. T., and Landin, J., *Set Theory and the Structure of Arithmetic* (Boston: Allyn and Bacon, 1961).

Henkin, L., Smith, W. N., Varineau, V. J., and Walsh, M. J., *Retracing Elementary Mathematics* (New York: Macmillan, 1962).

Keedy, Mervin L., *A Modern Introduction to Basic Mathematics* (Reading, Massachusetts: Addison-Wesley, 1963).

_____, *Number Systems: A Modern Introduction* (Reading, Massachusetts: Addison-Wesley, 1965).

Keedy, M. L., and Nelson, C. W., *Geometry: A Modern Introduction* (Reading, Massachusetts: Addison-Wesley, 1965).

Kingston, J. Maurice, *Mathematics for Teachers of the Middle Grades* (New York: Wiley, 1966).

Larsen, H. D., and Ludlow, H., *Arithmetic for Colleges,* 3rd ed. (New York: Macmillan, 1963).

Lay, L. C., *Arithmetic: An Introduction to Mathematics* (New York: Macmillan, 1961).

Leveque, W. J., *Elementary Theory of Numbers* (Reading, Massachusetts: Addison-Wesley, 1962).

McFarland, Dora, and Lewis, Eunice M., *Introduction to Modern Mathematics for Elementary Teachers* (Boston: Heath, 1966).

Mitchell, B. E., and Cohen, H., *A New Look at Elementary Mathematics* (Englewood Cliffs, New Jersey: Prentice-Hall, 1965).

Moise, E. E., *Elementary Geometry from an Advanced Standpoint* (Reading, Massachusetts: Addison-Wesley, 1963).

Mosteller, F., Rourke, R. E., and Thomas, G. B., *Probability and Statistics* (Reading, Massachusetts: Addison-Wesley, 1961).

Mueller, F. J., *Arithmetic: Its Structure and Concepts,* 2nd ed. (Englewood Cliffs, New Jersey: Prentice-Hall, 1964).

National Council of Teachers of Mathematics, *Topics in Mathematics for Elementary School Teachers,* Twenty-ninth Yearbook (Washington, D. C.: The Council, 1964).

————, *Insights into Modern Mathematics,* Twenty-third Yearbook (Washington, D. C.: The Council, 1957).

Ohmer, M. M., Aucoin, C. V., and Cortez, M. J., *Elementary Contemporary Mathematics* (Waltham, Mass.: Blaisdell Publishing Company, 1964).

Osborn, R., DeVault, M. V., Boyd, C. C., and Houston, W. R., *Extending Mathematics Understanding* (Columbus, Ohio: Charles E. Merrill Books, Inc., 1961).

Peterson, J. A., and Hashisaki, J., *Theory of Arithmetic* (New York: Wiley, 1963).

Schaaf, W. L., *Basic Concepts of Elementary Mathematics,* 2nd ed. (New York: Wiley, 1965).

Scheid, F. S., *Elements of Finite Mathematics* (Reading, Massachusetts: Addison-Wesley, 1963).

School Mathematics Study Group, *Concepts of Algebra,* Studies in Mathematics, Vol. VIII (New Haven: Yale University Press, 1961).

————, *Intuitive Geometry,* Studies in Mathematics, Vol. VII (New Haven: Yale University Press, 1961).

————, *Number Systems,* Studies in Mathematics, Vol. VI (New Haven: Yale University Press, 1961).

Swain, R. L., and Nichols, E. D., *Understanding Arithmetic* (New York: Holt, Rinehart and Winston, 1965).

University of Maryland Mathematics Project, *Mathematics for Elementary School Teachers,* Book I and Book II (College Park: University of Maryland Mathematics Project, 1964).

Van Engen, Henry, Hartung, Maurice L., and Stochl, James E., *Foundations of Elementary School Arithmetic* (Chicago: Scott, Foresman, 1965).

Wade, T. L., and Taylor, H. E., *Fundamental Mathematics* (New York: McGraw-Hill, 1961).

Ward, M., and Hardgrove, C. E., *Modern Elementary Mathematics* (Reading, Massachusetts: Addison-Wesley, 1964).

Webber, G. C., and Brown, J. A., *Basic Concepts of Mathematics* (Reading, Massachusetts: Addison-Wesley, 1963).

Whitesitt, J. E., *Principles of Modern Algebra* (Reading, Massachusetts: Addison-Wesley, 1964).

Wren, F. L., *Basic Mathematical Concepts* (New York: McGraw-Hill, 1965).

Young, F. H., *Essentials of Algebra and Trigonometry* (Reading, Massachusetts: Addison-Wesley, 1964).

Youse, B. K., *Arithmetic: A Modern Approach* (Englewood Cliffs, New Jersey: Prentice-Hall, 1963).

APPENDIX A

Goals for school mathematics [1]

CURRICULUM FOR ELEMENTARY SCHOOL (K-6)

As we have indicated above, the objective for mathematics instruction in the elementary grades is familiarity with the real number system and the main ideas of geometry. Familiarity requires in addition acquaintance with some of the principal applications of real numbers and geometry. We outline here in some detail several topics which may be suitable. We have divided the elementary school roughly in two parts comprising grades K through 2 and grades 3 through 6, but it must be understood that this is only to give an indication of the kind of performance we expect from very young children.

The brevity of the present discussion derives from a respect for the reader's time. The authors request that this brevity should not be mistaken either for dogmatism or for oversimplification. The evolutionary future of mathematics instruction in American schools is a complex matter indeed, which involves many uncertainties, difficulties, compromises, and points of disagreement. The present discussion is, we hope, a first approximation to an intelligent plan for guiding this evolution in a generally wise direction.

In particular, nothing in this report is intended to exclude any better ideas that may arise elsewhere. Where ideas are concerned, it seems clear that the evolution of the curriculum should be inclusive and receptive, rather than exclusive and dogmatic.

The topics below are organized along mathematical lines; it is not intended that they should necessarily be taken up in the order indicated.

---

[1] The report of the Cambridge Conference on School Mathematics. Copyright 1963 by Educational Services, Inc. The curriculum so presented was intended by the authors as a guide for planners of the future rather than as a model for present-day administrators.

The earliest grades, K through 2

The real number system. The child usually learns quite early and easily how to count. As soon as he is able to count, he can begin to get experience with the number line. This line can be regarded from the first as a representation for all real numbers, even though the child will not be immediately able to give sophisticated names for most of these numbers. Nonetheless, he *can* speak of "a little more than three" and "a little less than five," and he can give a temporary name like ☆, to any number.

Early experiences in studying numbers should be designed to give insight into the mathematical properties of the real number system. *They probably should not focus on the learning of algorithms,* which will come considerably later in the curriculum.

Experiences with numbers using concrete objects which can be counted, measured, and arranged in various ways should have a prominent place in the first years of school.

These early experiences can be surprisingly creative, can involve the child actively, and can deal with matters of honest mathematical merit. All of the following appear to be possible very early in the child's career:

1. Experiences with "grouping" that will establish the idea of place-value numerals to various bases, including base 10.

2. Extensive use of zero as a number, not merely as a symbol.

3. The idea of inequalities, and the symbols $<$ and $>$.

4. The idea of transitivity of $<$. (This can be built into game situations where the child is asked to guess a "secret" number from a set of carefully devised clues, and so on.)

5. The number line, including negatives from the beginning.

6. Use of rulers with 0 at the center.

7. Use of the number line in the "transitivity" games mentioned above.

8. Use of fractions with small denominators to name additional points on the number line.

9. Use of the idea of "the neighborhood of a point" on the number line; relation to inequalities.

10. Use of the number line to introduce decimals by change of scale.

11. The use of "crossed" number lines to form Cartesian coordinates; various games of strategy using Cartesian coordinates.

12. Use of an additive slide rule, including both positive and negative numbers.

13. Physical interpretations of addition and multiplication, including original interpretations made up by the children themselves (such as 2×4 represented by 4 washers on each of 2 pegs, or 2 stacks of 4 washers each, or a 2×4 rectangular array of washers [or dots, or pebbles, etc.], of 2 washers of each of 4 different colors, 4 washers of each of 2 different colors, and so on).

14. Questions that lead the children to "discover" the commutative nature of addition and multiplication.

15. Multiplication of a number "a little bit more than three" by a number "a little bit less than five."

16. Division with remainder using, for example, the pattern: "$20 \div 8$" means

"If we have 20 dots, how many rows of 8 will there be?"

```
.  .  .  .  .  .  .
.  .  .  .  .  .  .
.  .  .  .
```

Answer: "2 whole rows and 4 left over."

17. Division with fractional answers. $20 \div 8 = 2\frac{1}{2}$

18. Recognition of inverse operations.

19. Use of $\square$ as a variable in simple algebraic problems.

20. Experience with Cartesian coordinates, including both discrete and continuous cases, graphs of linear functions, graphs of functions obtained empirically, simple extrapolation ("When will the plant be seven inches tall?"), and so on. Various games of strategy played on Cartesian coordinates, etc. Graph of $\square + \triangle = 10$, in connection with learning "addition facts," etc.

Geometry. Geometry is to be studied together with arithmetic and algebra from kindergarten on. Some of the aims of this study are to develop the planar and spatial intuition of the pupil, to afford a source of visualization for arithmetic and algebra, and to serve as a model for that branch of natural science which investigates physical space by mathematical methods. The geometric portion of the curriculum seems to be the most difficult to design. Therefore the geometry discussed here for grades K, 1, and 2 represents a far more tentative groping than was the case for the work in real numbers described earlier.

The earliest grades should include topics and experiences like these:

1. Identifying and naming various geometric configurations.

2. Visualization, such as cutting out cardboard to construct 3-dimensional figures, where the child is shown the 3-dimensional figure and asked to find his own way to cut the 2-dimensional paper or cardboard.

3. The additive property of area, closely integrated with the operation of multiplication.

4. Symmetry and other transformations leaving geometrical figures invariant. The fact that a line or circle can be slid into itself. The symmetries of squares and rectangles, circles, ellipses, etc., and solid figures like spheres, cubes, tetrahedra, etc. This study could be facilitated with mirrors, paper folding, etc.

5. Possibly the explicit recognition of the group property in the preceding.

6. Use of straightedge and compass to do the standard geometric constructions such as comparing segments or angles, bisecting a segment or angle, etc.

7. Similar figures, both plane and solid, starting from small and enlarged photography, etc.

Logic and set theory: function. The logic of everyday life is often appallingly sloppy. While nothing approaching formal logic is presently recommended for the earliest grades, it does seem likely that general use of good logic by teachers will pay dividends in terms of the logic subsequently used by the children.

The idea of *set* and *function* should be introduced as soon as possible. In the earliest grades:

1. Number as a property of finite sets.

2. The comparison of cardinals of finite sets with emphasis on the fact that the result is independent of which mapping function is used.

3. Numerical functions determined by very simple formulas.

4. The use of logical statements to determine certain sets. For example, games like *Twenty Questions* in which the set of possibilities is successively narrowed through the answers to yes-no questions.

5. Familiarity with both true and false statements as a source of information.

Applications. The work with real numbers, described above, can be closely related to work in "science" and "applications," such as:

1. Measurement and units, in cases of length, area, volume, weight, time, money, temperature, etc.

2. Use of various measuring instruments, such as rulers, calipers, scales, etc.

3. Physical interpretations of $\frac{1}{2}$, $\frac{1}{4}$, $\frac{1}{3}$, $\frac{2}{3}$.

4. Physical interpretations of negative numbers in relation to an arbitrary reference point (as $0°$ Centigrade, or altitude at sea level, or the lobby floor for an elevator, etc.).

5. Physical embodiments of inequalities in length, weight, etc., again using games where the child must use the transitive property, or the fact that $a > c$ implies $a + b > c + b$.

6. Estimating orders of magnitude, with applications related to physics, economics, history, sociology, etc.

7. Visual display of data on Cartesian coordinates, such as recording growth of seedlings by daily measurement of height, or graph of temperature vs. time for hourly readings of a thermometer.

General remarks

The concepts described above are uneven in difficulty. Some of them can probably be introduced in nursery school, and no doubt should be. Others may prove to be impossible by second grade, either because of their intrinsic difficulty, or because of the large amount of material to be covered.

In nursery school, K-2, and, indeed, at all elementary school levels, the present suggestions assume a general pattern of pre-mathematics to introduce each new topic, to be followed later by as much formal study as may be appropriate. The pre-mathematics at each level will serve to provide a background of experiences, and to help develop clear concepts for the work of the following months or following years. Nearly all the preceding suggestions for K-2 fall under the general heading of "pre-mathematics." (Probably "pre-mathematics" and "formal mathematical study" are not dichotomous categories, but extremes on a continuous interval, with increasingly detailed "informal" study leading gradually into "formal" study.)

A comment might be made on the role of *physical equipment* in the earliest grades. Whether one thinks in terms of the pre-mathematical experiences that are embodied in the manipulation of physical materials, whether one regards these physical objects as aids to effective communication between teacher and child, or whether one regards them as attractive objects that increase motivation, the conclusion is inescapable that children can study mathematics more satisfactorily when each child has abundant opportunity to manipulate suitable physical objects. Possible candidates include blocks of appropriate sizes, plastic washers and pegboards, rulers, compasses, French curves, circles divided into equal sections, graph paper, paper ruled into columns to help the child line up digits in column addition, geometric shapes cut out of wood or heavy cardboard, pebbles for counting, numerals cut out of wood or cardboard, circular protractors, and so on.

One important general principle appears to be this: wherever possible, the child should have some intrinsic criterion for deciding the correctness of answers, without requiring recourse to authority. In the present work, this bed-rock foundation is generally provided by the fundamental operation of *counting*. The child's slogan might well be: when in doubt, *count!*

In more advanced work in later grades, solving problems by several different methods, recognition of patterns, and even the use of simple logic will play the role of a foundation for deciding correctness without recourse to authority. Physical interpretations also help fill this role.

Clearly, *counting* and *guessing* both have important roles to play, and should be neither excluded from the curriculum nor unduly restricted. Rather, they should be put in their proper place. Counting, at this stage, should probably have a fundamental place. The place for guessing is more confined, but not nonexistent.

In the general area of problem solving, the primary emphasis should be on *understanding the problem,* with secondary emphasis on carrying out the calculations to get the "answer." For example, after the concept of multiplication has been studied, it is appropriate to consider problems involving multiplication of large numbers, even though the actual computations appearing are beyond the algorithmic skill of the pupil. (They would, presumably, be carried out by the teacher or with the aid of a desk calculator.) When computing machines of all sizes are widely available, surely it is more important to know when to multiply than how to multiply.

Grades 3 through 6

In these four grades we should continue pursuit of the main objective, familiarity with the real number system and geometry. At the same time we must start pre-mathematical experiences aiming towards the more sophisticated work in high school.

The real number system.

1. Commutative, associative, and distributive laws. The multiplicative property of 1. The additive and multiplicative properties of 0.

2. Arithmetic of signed numbers.

3. For comparison purposes

   a. Modular arithmetic, based on primes and on nonprimes.

   b. Finite fields.

   c. Study of 2×2 matrices; comparison with real numbers; isomorphism of a subset of 2×2 matrices with real numbers; divisors of zero; identities for matrices; simple matrix inverses (particularly in relation to the idea of inverse operations and the nonexistence of a multiplicative inverse for zero). Possible use of matrices to introduce complex numbers.

4. Prime numbers and factoring. Euclidean algorithm, greatest common divisor.

5. Elementary Diophantine problems.

6. Integral exponents, both positive and negative.

7. The arithmetic of inequalities.

8. Absolute value.

9. Explicit study of the decimal system of notation including comparison with other bases and mixed bases (e.g. miles, yards, feet, inches).

10. Study of algorithms for adding, subtracting, multiplying, and dividing both integers and rational numbers, including "original" algorithms made up by the children themselves.

11. Methods for checking and verifying correctness of answers without recourse to the teacher.

12. Familiarity with certain "short cut" calculations that serve to illustrate basic properties of numbers or of numerals.

13. The use of desk calculators, slide rules, and tables.

14. Interpolation.

15. Considerable experience in approximations, estimates, "scientific notation," and orders of magnitude.

16. Effect of "round-off" and significant figures.

17. Knowledge of the distinction between rational and irrational numbers.

18. Study of decimals, for rational and irrational numbers.

19. Square roots, inequalities such as $1.41 < \sqrt{2} < 1.42$.

20. The Archimedean property and the density of the rational numbers including terminating decimals.

21. Nested intervals.

22. Computation with numbers given approximately. (e.g. find π^2 given π.)

23. Simple algebraic equations and inequalities.

Perhaps no area of discussion brought out more viewpoints than the question of how the multiplication of signed numbers should be introduced. The simple route via the distributive law was considered, but a closely related approach was more popular. One observes that the definition of multiplication is ours to make but only one definition will have desirable properties. Others favored an experimental approach involving negative weights on balance boards, etc. Still others favored the "negative debt" approach. Even the immediate introduction of signed area was proposed. It seems quite likely that all approaches should be tried, since there will probably be much variation from student to student concerning what is convincing. The question is evidently not mathematical; it is purely pedagogic. The problem is to convey the "inner reasonableness" of $(-1) \times (-1) = +1$.

Geometry. In the later grades of elementary school, relatively little pure geometry would be introduced, but more experience with the topics from K-2 would be built up. The pictorial representation of sets with Venn diagrams and the graphing of elementary functions using Cartesian coordinates would be continued. In addition, there is much of value in the suggestions put forward by educators in Holland, and described by Freudenthal in an article in the *Mathematics Student* (1956, pp. 82–97), in which many geometrical questions are motivated by problems concerning solid bodies and the ways they fit together. New topics might include:

1. Mensuration formulas for familiar figures.
2. Approximate determination of π by measuring circles.
3. Conic sections.
4. Equation determining a straight line.
5. Cartesian coordinates in 3 dimensions.
6. Polar coordinates.
7. Latitude and longitude.
8. Symmetry of more sophisticated figures (e.g. wallpaper).
9. Similar figures interpreted as scale models and problems of indirect measurement.
10. Vectors, possibly including some statics and linear kinematics.
11. Symmetry argument for the congruence of the base angles of an isosceles triangle.

Logic and foundations.
1. The vocabulary of elementary logic: true, false, implication, double implication, contradiction.
2. Truth tables for simplest connectives.
3. The common schemes of inference:

$$\frac{P \to Q \text{ and } P}{Q} \qquad \frac{P \to Q \text{ and } \sim Q}{\sim P}$$

4. Simple uses of mathematical induction.

5. Preliminary recognition of the roles of axioms and theorems in relation to the real number system.

6. Simple uses of logical implication or "derivations" in studying algorithms, more complicated identities, etc.

7. Elements of flow charting.

8. Simple uses of indirect proof, in studying inequalities, proving $\sqrt{2}$ irrational, and so on.

9. Study of sets, relations, and functions. Graphs of relations and functions, both discrete and continuous. Graphs of empirically determined functions.

10. Explicit study of the relation of open sentences and their truth sets.

11. The concepts of isomorphism and transformation.

The common practice of traditional 9th-grade algebra has been to ignore truth values and questions of implication. True statements, false statements, and statements of unknown truth value are jumbled together on pages of writing, related by implication in an unspecified way. The authors apparently hoped that sooner or later something good would happen. As algebraic notions enter the elementary grades, truth values should be explicitly discussed.

As the child grows, he learns more and more fully what constitutes a mathematical proof. Specious proofs presented to him early in his education may tend to block his progress toward understanding what a proof really is. This must be avoided. If a discussion is *not* a proof, it should not masquerade under false colors.

On the other hand, experience in making honest proofs can and probably should begin in the elementary grades, especially in algebraic situations. While extensive formal study of logic in the elementary grades is not favored by most mathematicians, it is hardly possible to do anything in the direction of mathematical proofs without the vocabulary of logic and explicit recognition of the inference schemes. The feasibility of such study has already been demonstrated by classroom experimentation.

Work towards indirect proof will build on the experience with false statements started in the early grades. The study of inequalities can be particularly useful here. Exciting experience with implication, uniqueness, contradiction, etc., can be built into games that can be played in the classroom. Children in elementary school may be able to achieve some comprehension of mathematical induction, especially in relatively simple forms, such as the calculation of explicit terms of a sequence defined by recursion.

Theory of real functions.

1. Intuitive consideration of infinite sequences of real numbers.

2. The logarithm function, built up by interpolation, from approximate equalities like $2^{10} \sim 10^3$ (see Appendix B of Cambridge Report).

3. Trigonometric functions.

4. Partial and linear orderings, with applications.

5. Linearity and convexity.

We have in mind an informal, experimental approach to the trigonometric functions similar to the approach to logarithms. We imagine defining the functions on the whole line using the intuitive concept of a point moving uniformly on the unit circle. We could then study many of the qualitative aspects of the functions, such as maxima, minima, and periods. We can relate them to problems in harmonic motion and the oscillation of pendulums, possibly even to wave motion if suitable equipment is available. Approximate values of the functions for acute angles could be obtained by measuring carefully-drawn right triangles. These tables could be extended by symmetry, periodicity, and interpolation (either by linear calculation or by applying a French curve to the graph). Applications to the usual problems in indirect measurement are immediate. The appropriate depth of penetration and level of sophistication for elementary school experiences with trigonometric functions is probably a matter to be determined on the basis of actual teaching experience.

The treatment of trigonometric functions sketched here and the treatment of logarithms outlined in more detail in Appendix B (of Cambridge Report) was motivated by several considerations. Tables of these functions will be much more meaningful to a student who has worked hard to build his own table, even if the latter goes only to two decimals. The process of making the table will concentrate much attention on the definition of the functions. Moreover, the student who does the job conscientiously will acquire a good intuitive grip on their qualitative properties. In particular, the table of logarithms involves a good deal of arithmetic; this will afford plenty of practice in a context which many students will regard as worthwhile. Finally, experience at this level in calculating tables can only heighten the student's appreciation of the easier methods that become available through Taylor's series later. The same remarks apply to the empirical determination of π.

Applications.   Because a good deal of science can, and probably will, be introduced into primary school, more applications of mathematics will be possible in the upper grades.

Some of the most important applications involve probability and statistics, which we conceive as purely empirical subjects at this level. The study should begin with

1. Empirical investigation of many-times-repeated random events.

2. Arithmetic study of how the ultimate stabilization of observed relative frequency occurs through "swamping."

These investigations should be applied to the problems of measurement in connection with all science experiments.

There will be many applications of geometry to problems of indirect measurement and to areas and volumes. The use of graphs, interpolation, and extrapolation should lead to the idea of rate of change. Scientific notation becomes a great convenience when dealing with the very large and the very small numbers which occur in astronomy or the atomic realm.

Even in these grades it seems desirable to emphasize the notion of a "model" which captures only a part, even an approximate part, of the real situation.

Longer projects for students.   In addition to all the explicit topics mentioned above, it is important that each child get some experience with the more extended aspects of discussion. As the student progresses in mathematics, he will come increasingly to encounter long protracted discussions or solutions of problems. At some point in the future he will meet problems that take hours, days, or weeks for complete discussion, sometimes requiring a long sequence of lemmas or partial solutions. It is not clear *a priori* how one can best prepare for this at the elementary school level, but whatever preparation can be made would be worthwhile.

One possibility is that there be short topics to be studied entirely independently. These should probably be organized at the appropriate level and written up as pamphlets. In many respects, these pamphlets would be like enrichment material for the particularly able student, but every student should do some independent work requiring more extensive effort than the usual assigned problems. If a variety of topics were available, then students could have a choice of project; this in itself would probably increase the level of interest.

APPENDIX B

Sets

Some mathematical terms are so basic that there are no simpler terms to use for their definitions. These terms are said to be undefined terms. *Set* is one of the undefined terms in mathematics. Although undefined, set can be intuitively thought of as being used in the same sense as the words *collection* or *group*. "Things" that form a set can be real or imaginative, related or unrelated. The members of a set are referred to as *elements*. Thus, Nancy and Fred could be considered to be elements or members of the set of fourth graders in Washington School.

A nearly standard form of notation is used to denote sets. Curly brackets { } are normally used to enclose a listing of the elements that make up a set. In the early elementary grades a circle is often used in place of the curly brackets. A capital letter is normally used to designate a set and a lower case letter to designate an element of a set. The notation $x \in Y$ means that object (x) is a member of set (Y).

Before setting up the qualifications for membership in a given set, it is important to know the entire universe from which a set is drawn. For example, all of the pupils in Kennedy Elementary School might be the *universe* or *universal set (U)* for a problem. From this universal set the set of all fourth graders, the set of all fifth graders, etc. could be drawn.

Members within a set can be grouped in various ways. In dealing with a set of fourth graders it may be important to refer to only the girls in the fourth grade. The girls in fourth grade would be a *subset* of the entire set of fourth graders. Two schemes for referring to subsets are shown below.

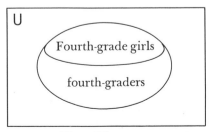

Venn Diagram
$U = $ pupils in Kennedy School

{Fourth grade girls} $\subset$ {Fourth graders}
$\subset$ is read: "is a subset of"

Subsets may be *proper* or *improper*. A proper subset is one in which every element of the subset is contained in the set, but not every element of the set is contained in the subset. Thus, the fourth grade girls (in a school enrolling both boys and girls) are a proper subset of fourth graders. Fourth graders are a subset of fourth graders, but not a proper subset since every element of the set is contained in the subset.

The *empty set* (∅), null set, or void set is a subset of every set. For example, if from the set of fifth graders in a given room one is asked to identify the subset containing the pupils who can correctly spell "ornithorhynchus" one may find that the subset is the empty set.

SETS AND NUMBER

A set of objects will have a number property. That is, the members of a set can be matched in one-to-one correspondence with the number scale $\left(\underset{|\quad|\quad|\quad|}{0\ 1\ 2\ 3}\right)$.

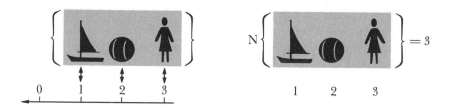

The number we associate with this set is 3.

OPERATIONS WITH SETS

There are several mathematical operations involving sets which are of importance to elementary school mathematics programs. Problems with solutions and the appropriate notation for the set operations are presented below.

Set Union

A kindergarten boy has an apple and a pear. He buys an orange and a banana. What is the set of all of the fruit he has? The union (∪) of the set {apple, pear} and the set {orange, banana} is formed to solve the problem.

{apple, pear} ∪ {orange, banana} = {apple, pear, orange, banana}

Addition of whole numbers {0, 1, 2, 3, . . .} can be developed from the union of sets which have *no elements in common*. Such sets are called *disjoint sets*. Thus,

$$\{apple, pear\} \cup \{orange, banana\} = \{apple, pear, orange, banana\}$$

$$N\{apple, pear\} + N\{orange, banana\} = N\{apple, pear, orange, banana\}[1]$$
$$2 + 2 = 4$$

Properties of set union.   The following properties of union of sets can be verified by substituting given sets for the capital letters.

$A \cup B = B \cup A$ Commutative Property
$(A \cup B) \cup C = A \cup (B \cup C)$ Associative Property
$A \cup \emptyset = A$ Property of the Identity Element

Set intersection

Every pupil in Miss Jones' room has a different first name. A committee for the bulletin board is composed of Gary, Bill, and Alice. A committee for the mathematics table is composed of Mary, George, and Gary. Which pupils are members of both committees? The intersection ($\cap$) of the sets is

Bulletin Board   Mathematics Table

{Gary, Bill, Alice} ∩ {Mary, George, Gary} = Gary

If two sets are *disjoint* (have no elements in common) their intersection is $\emptyset$, the empty set.

Properties of set intersection.
$A \cap B = B \cap A$ Commutative Property
$(A \cap B) \cap C = A \cap (B \cap C)$ Associative Property

---

[1] Note: $N\{apple, pear\}$ is read; the number we associate with a set containing an apple and a pear.

Set complement

If the universal set is composed of the sixth graders, a set of this class is composed of the pupils who are absent. The *complement* of the set of absent pupils is the set of pupils present. If the universal set is the set of all mammals, and one set is the set of dogs, the complement of the set of dogs is all other mammals. If we designate the set of dogs as A, then the complement of this set is designated A'.

Cartesian product of sets

Kitty has three hats; $A = $ {blue, red, white} and two coats $B = $ {grey, blue}. What are the different hat-coat outfits she can form from these? The Cartesian product of these sets is illustrated below.

A x B

$\times$	grey	blue
blue	blue, grey	blue, blue
red	red, grey	red, blue
white	white, grey	white, blue

{blue, red, white}

{grey, blue}

Multiplication of numbers can be developed from the cross-product (Cartesian product) of sets.

$$N\{\text{blue, red, white}\} \times N\{\text{grey, blue}\} = $$

$$N\{(\text{blue, grey}) (\text{blue, blue}) (\text{red, grey}) (\text{red, blue}) (\text{white, grey}) (\text{white, blue})\}$$

$$3 \times 2 = 6$$

INDEX

Swenson, Esther J., 45, 107, 283
Syage, K. J., 73
Szeminska, A., 354

Team learning
  in classroom, 59
  help for slower pupils, 70
Temperature, measure of, 370
Tests, *see* Evaluation
Textbooks
  publishers of, 448
  role of, 433
  selection of, 434-436
Thiele, C. L., 15
Thomas, R. M., 445
Thompson, James B., 286
Thorndike, Edward, 14
Thorndike, Robert L., 422, 432
Thorpe, Cleata B., 432
Time, measure of, 365-370
Topology, 343-348
Torrance, Paul E., 68
Tosti, D. T., 74
Tracy, Neal H., 52
Tredway, D. C., 299

Van Engen, Henry, 169, 202, 234, 286, 303
Volume, measure of, 362

Weaver, J. Fred, 50, 68, 76, 137, 405
Welch, Ronald C., 306
Welmers, Everett T., 22
Wheat, Harry G., 380
White, Helen M., 306
Wilkinson, Jack D., 401
Wilson, Guy, 14, 15, 373
Wirtz, Robert W., 71, 148
World calendar, 369

Young, Robert V., 308

Zero
  associated with empty set, 36
  in basic facts, 81
  in division, 180
  exponent, 266
  fractions, rationals, 205
  identity element for addition, 86
  identity element for subtraction, 116
  in modular arithmetic, 3, 6
  in multiplication, 146
Zweng, Marilyn J., 175